Electronics and Nuclear Physics

By the same author

Practical Modern Physics

Exploring Physics, Books 1 to 5

Advanced Physics: Materials and Mechanics
Fields, Waves and Atoms

Physics for Today and Tomorrow

Electronics and Nuclear Physics

T. DUNCAN B Sc M Inst P

Senior Lecturer in Education, University of Liverpool. Formerly Senior Physics Master, King George V School, Southport

JOHN MURRAY · LONDON

First edition 1966
Reprinted (revised) 1967
Second edition 1969
Reprinted 1973, 1976, 1977

Printed and bound in Great Britain by
Redwood Burn Limited, Trowbridge & Esher

0 7195 3288 4

Preface

This book is intended to cover the modern physics sections of the various G.C.E. 'A' and 'S' level syllabuses and of the alternative physics syllabus of the Scottish Certificate of Education. The publication in 1961 of *Physics for Grammar Schools* by the Association for Science Education and in 1963 of the *Interim Report on the Teaching of Modern Physics* by the Modern Physical Sciences Committee of the same body in association with the Nuffield Foundation were notable events for school physics teaching. The contents and order of presentation of the topics adopted here follow the recommendations of these reports closely.

After an introductory survey in Chapter 1 of the growth of the atomic outlook, the electron and its properties are considered in Chapter 2. The traditional approach using gas discharge tube phenomena has been abandoned in favour of a study in which electrons are obtained by the simpler process of thermionic emission. One chapter is devoted to the cathode ray oscilloscope and some of its many applications. In considering the three basic operations of electronics, i.e., rectification, amplification and oscillation, a knowledge of a.c. theory is assumed.

Classical quantum theory ideas are introduced to explain the photoelectric effect and certain features of X-ray spectra. The constituents of the nucleus and radioactivity are treated in Chapters 9 and 10 and in Chapter 11 the principles involved in radioactivity measurements are outlined using sources and apparatus now available to schools.

The treatment of the structure of the atom in Chapter 12 is to some extent historical since it is felt that the development of ideas helps to illustrate the interplay between theory and experiment in science. The Bohr model is described and given a mathematical treatment which may, if desired, be omitted. The main emphasis in the latter part of this chapter is on the idea of energy levels. Wave mechanics is beyond the scope of a school physics course but an attempt has been made to indicate, by analogy, the implications for atomic structure. The present interpretation of the wave-particle duality of matter and radiation is also considered.

The last two chapters provide an introduction to two branches of physics, viz., nuclear physics and solid-state physics, where tremendous progress has been made during the last twenty years and further developments are promised.

Whilst the majority of schools still use the C.G.S. system of units, the needs of those working with M.K.S. units have not been neglected and in the worked examples both systems are employed.

In writing this book the works of many others have been consulted. Some of these are mentioned in the further reading list of Appendix 3 but the author wishes to acknowledge his debt to them all. Dr P. J. Hayman, Lecturer in Physics in the University of Liverpool, very generously assisted with proof reading and discussions with him produced many improvements in the text. Whilst every effort has been made to eliminate errors, any which remain are the responsibility of the author. Mr. I. Birchall, B.Sc., Radiation Protection Officer to the University of Liverpool, kindly gave advice on the section dealing with radiation hazards.

Permission to use questions from recent examinations was readily given by the different examining boards and acknowledgement is made after each question by the following abbreviations: *A.E.B.* (Associated Examining Board); *C* (Cambridge Local Examinations Syndicate); *J* (Joint Matriculation Board); *L* (University of London); *O* (Oxford Local Examinations); *O and C* (Oxford and Cambridge Schools Examination Board); *S* (Southern Universities Joint Board); *W* (Welsh Joint Education Committee). For permission to reproduce, or base drawings on, copyright material, grateful acknowledgement is made to the sources given in the text.

Finally, thanks are due to my wife who typed the manuscript, much of it several times, to my daughter Heather, who checked the answers to the numerical questions, and to the publishers whose courtesy and efficiency have lightened the task of publication.

T.D.

November 1965

PREFACE TO SECOND EDITION

Apart from some minor alterations and corrections, sections have been added on *Colour television* (p. 53), *Radioactivity and nuclear stability* (p. 165), *d.c. amplifier* (p. 175) and *Microelectronics: integrated circuits* (p. 270).

The recommendations of the A.S.E.'s Education (Research) Committee in their report *SI units, signs, symbols and abbreviations for use in school science* have on the whole been accepted. However, it is felt that the adoption of SI units should be tempered by common sense and convenience. For these reasons the electron-volt and the curie are retained.

The numerical questions at the end of each chapter are now in SI units (or their approved multiples or sub-multiples) and for effecting this I am indebted to Mr B. L. N. Kennett, B.A. and my daughter Heather. Thanks are also due to the examining boards for allowing the conversion.

To conform to the A.S.E.'s *1966 Report on the Teaching of Electricity*, only B and E are used.

Since the first edition was published several teachers have discussed the book with me or written about it and I am very grateful to them for their interest and helpful comments.

June 1969 T.D.

Plates

Contents

SI Units

Physical quantity	*Unit*	
	Name	*Symbol*
Length (l)	metre	m
Mass (m)	kilogram	kg
Time (t)	second	s
Velocity (v)	metre per second	m s^{-1}
Acceleration (a)	metre per second squared	m s^{-2}
Force (F)	newton	N
Energy (including heat)	joule	J
Power (P)	watt	W
Electric current (I)	ampere	A
Electric charge (Q)	coulomb	C
Potential difference (V)	volt	V
Resistance (R)	ohm	Ω
Capacitance (C)	farad	F
Inductance (L)	henry	H
Frequency (f)	hertz	Hz
Magnetic flux density (B)	tesla	T
Electric field strength (E)	volt per metre	V m^{-1}
	newton per coulomb	N C^{-1}
Amount of substance	mole	mol

In this book optical wavelengths are usually given in micrometres (1 μm = 10^{-6} m) and atomic measurements in nanometres (1 nm = 10^{-9} m).

1 Atomic nature of matter and electricity

One of the outstanding features of twentieth-century science has been the development of the atomic theory. The idea that matter consists of small, separate particles called atoms is now universally accepted, but it was not until the nineteenth century that the theory was placed on a sound basis. Subsequently the discovery of sub-atomic particles led to the internal structure of the atom itself being revealed and the close relationship between matter and electricity established.

Although atoms cannot be 'seen' in the usual sense, our belief in their existence is based on their ability to account for a wide range of phenomena which are difficult to explain in any other way.

Dalton's atomic theory

The modern atomic theory was proposed in 1803 by John Dalton, an English schoolmaster. He thought of atoms as tiny, indivisible balls, all the atoms of a given element being exactly alike and different from those of other elements in behaviour and mass. There were therefore as many kinds of atoms as elements.

According to Dalton, chemical reaction did not alter atoms but merely resulted in their rearrangement; furthermore, combination to form 'compound-atoms', as they were called, took place between simple whole number ratios of atoms. Thus, if elements

A and *B* combined they did so in the ratio of one atom of *A* to one atom of *B* or one of *A* to two of *B* and so on. With these assumptions he explained the laws of conservation of mass, constant composition and multiple proportions.

Dalton realized that the absolute masses of atoms were very small but he found their relative masses or atomic weights taking the hydrogen atom to have unit mass. His great contribution was to establish the theory on a quantitative basis and make the idea of atoms more definite.

One difficulty encountered by the theory was its inability to explain the volume relationships which exist between combining gases. In 1808 Gay-Lussac found that gases combine in simple proportions by volume. Thus, 1 volume of hydrogen + 1 volume of chlorine give 2 volumes of hydrogen chloride. It was felt that this simple number-volume relationship indicated a simple relationship between the numbers of atoms involved in the reaction. The most obvious assumption would be that equal volumes of gases contain equal numbers of atoms. It then follows that ultimately, 1 atom of hydrogen + 1 atom of chlorine give 2 compound-atoms of hydrogen chloride. Each hydrogen atom and each chlorine atom must therefore divide into two since two compound-atoms are formed. Atoms, however, are indivisible by chemical reaction and so the assumption that equal volumes of gases contain the same number of atoms cannot be true.

Dalton's theory had previously been concerned with combination by weight; it apparently was not sufficiently comprehensive to account for combination by volume without modification.

Atoms and molecules

In 1811 Amedeo Avogadro, an Italian scientist, reconciled the atomic theory with Gay-Lussac's law by introducing another basic particle, the molecule, consisting of a group of two or more atoms which could be separated by chemical means. Dalton's compound-atoms were clearly molecules but Avogadro's new entity was intended to embrace elements as well as compounds. Thus the atoms of hydrogen, chlorine and many other gases were considered to exist in pairs, forming diatomic molecules.

Avogadro's proposal was that equal volumes of gases existing under the same conditions of temperature and pressure contain equal numbers of molecules. Applying this to Gay-Lussac's law we have, 1 molecule of hydrogen + 1 molecule of chlorine give 2 molecules of hydrogen chloride. Each hydrogen chloride molecule receives one atom of hydrogen and one atom of chlorine and there is no question of an atom having to divide. Using chemical formulae the reaction may be written, $H_2 + Cl_2 = 2HCl$.

Two kinds of particle are therefore necessary. One is the *atom*, defined as the smallest part of an element which can participate in a chemical reaction, and the other is the *molecule*, defined as the smallest particle of an element or compound capable of existing independently. Some elements, like helium, have monatomic molecules consisting of a single atom; the atom and molecule are identical in such cases.

The significance of Avogadro's hypothesis was not appreciated until 1858 when his fellow-countryman, Cannizzaro, pointed out its value in determining molecular and atomic weights.

Kinetic theory of matter

The kinetic theory is an extension of the atomic theory. It assumes that molecules are in a state of rapid motion, continually colliding with each other but not losing kinetic energy at each collision because of their perfect elasticity. They are also considered to exert forces of attraction and repulsion on each other which become negligible when the molecules are far apart, as in a gas.

The theory explains in terms of molecules many of the properties of matter in bulk, such as the existence of three states, compressibility, surface tension, viscosity, etc. The explanation of the macroscopic in terms of the microscopic is one of the main aims of modern physics and the kinetic theory has been particularly successful in this respect with gases. If the laws of mechanics which hold for ordinary objects are applied to gas molecules, the laws of Boyle and Charles can be derived and temperature taken to be a measure of the mean kinetic energy of translation of the molecules. The quantitative development of the kinetic theory of gases occurred between 1850 and 1860 and was largely due to Clerk Maxwell in England and R. Clausius in Germany.

Brownian motion

A scientific theory, like a map, is a man-made representation of reality and as well as helping to provide an explanation of facts it should, if it is to be useful, lead to predictions which can be tested by experiment. The atomic and kinetic theories satisfied this requirement but at the end of the nineteenth century some scientists felt that more direct evidence was needed to justify the basic assumption that atoms and molecules really did exist.

In 1827 the botanist, Robert Brown, discovered that fine pollen grains suspended in water were in a state of constant movement, describing small, irregular, zig-zag paths but never stopping. The effect, which increases with temperature and has been observed with many kinds of small particles suspended in both liquids and gases, is now called Brownian motion. It remained unexplained until the turn of the century when it was realized that it was a direct manifestation of molecular motion caused by unequal bombardment of the suspended particles by molecules of the surrounding medium. Very small particles are essential for two reasons. First, the small kinetic energy of the molecules cannot impart a finite velocity to a large particle. Second, only if the particle is small will it suffer impacts with a few hundred molecules at any instant and be able to reveal the irregularities in the motion of the molecules; otherwise, the force due to encounters with the molecules on one side will balance that due to those on the other and there is no resultant force on the particle. The phenomenon can be observed in smoke in a small glass cell, which is illuminated strongly from one side and viewed from above with a low-power microscope, Fig. 1.1.

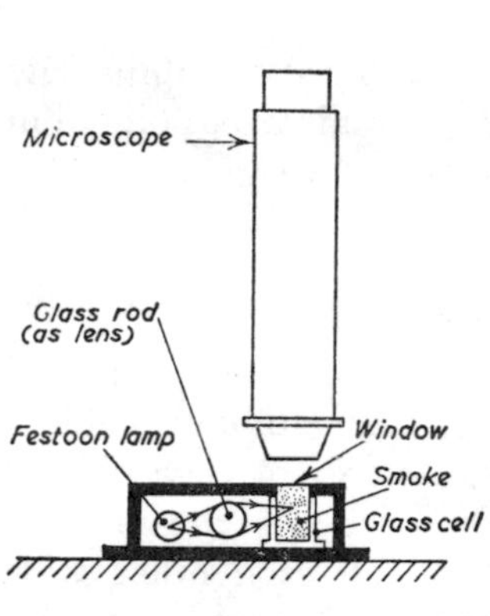

Fig. 1.1

Monolayers

An estimate for the size of a molecule may be obtained from experiments in which certain substances are spread out to form very thin films called *monolayers*. Thus, if a small quantity of stearic acid ($C_{17}H_{35}COOH$), a member of the fatty acid series, is dissolved in a volatile solvent such as benzene and some of the resulting solution diluted several times, a drop of the final solution will contain a very small amount of acid. When such a drop is placed in a large tray of clean water whose surface has been lightly sprinkled with lycopodium powder (a fine waterproof powder obtained from plants called club-mosses), the solution spreads out quickly to form a clear circular patch and the benzene evaporates leaving the stearic acid. Knowing the volume of acid in the drop (from the original mass of acid, its density and the dilution) and the area of the patch, we can calculate the thickness of the film; it is found to be about 20×10^{-10} m. If two drops are used the area of the circular patch is doubled but the thickness remains the same.

Monolayer experiments do not necessarily prove that matter is particulate but they suggest the existence of a limiting factor to the thinness of a film. In this case we can infer that if there are molecules of stearic acid, one dimension of the molecule has an optimum value of 20×10^{-10} m. Other investigations involving chemical and X-ray studies show that the stearic acid molecule consists of a long chain of carbon atoms surrounded by hydrogen atoms with an acid group at one end. The chain has a total length of about 20×10^{-10} m and a width of 5×10^{-10} m. In a monolayer of stearic acid the molecules must be standing on end with their lengths more or less perpendicular to the surface of the water.

The Avogadro constant : mass and diameter of an atom

A *mole* (abbreviated to mol) is defined as that amount of a substance which contains the same number of identical units (e.g. atoms, molecules or ions) as there are atoms in 12 grams of carbon 12. The identical units must be specified and carbon 12 is chosen for reasons given later (see pp. 147–150). Because of the way it is defined the molecular (and atomic) mass of every substance (in grams) contains the same number of molecules (or atoms). It should be noted that the mole is based on the gram and not the kilogram. The number of identical units in a mole is called the *Avogadro constant* and is denoted by N_A.

The first reliable determination of the Avogadro constant was made in 1912 by Jean Perrin, a French chemist. He found that gamboge particles (a gum resin derived from the bark of a tree found in Cambodia) suspended in water were distributed in the same way as the molecules in a column of gas; in effect the gamboge particles were behaving like large molecules. Using reasoning based on the kinetic theory he was able to obtain a value for N_A from measurements of the number of particles per unit volume at different heights in the water. Various other independent procedures all give results in excellent agreement; one accurate method involves the diffraction of X-rays using crystals (p. 130). The accepted value of the Avogadro constant is:

$$N_A = 6{\cdot}02 \times 10^{23} \text{ per mole}$$

A knowledge of the Avogadro constant enables the mass of an atom to be estimated. Consider hydrogen: if its molecular mass is taken as 2, then 2 g contain approximately 6×10^{23} molecules or $2 \times 6 \times 10^{23}$ atoms. Hence the mass of a hydrogen atom is $2/(2 \times 6 \times 10^{23})$, i.e., $1{\cdot}67 \times 10^{-24}$ g.

Molecular and atomic diameters may be computed from measurements such as the viscosity, diffusion or thermal conductivity of a gas. Expressions can be derived from the kinetic theory relating these properties to the size of the gas molecules and Avogadro's constant. In this way the diameters of the lighter atoms like hydrogen are found to be of the order 10^{-10} m, i.e., $0{\cdot}1 \times 10^{-9}$ m or 0·1 nm (1 nm = 1 nanometre = 10^{-9} m). A word of caution is necessary. Modern atomic theory no longer pictures the atom as having a hard, definite surface and there is therefore little point in trying to give atomic diameters too exact values.

Periodic table and atomic masses

With the passage of time the early nineteenth-century picture of an indivisible atom came to be doubted in the light of fresh information. During the 1860's chemical knowledge had increased sufficiently for it to be clear that there were elements with similar chemical properties. Moreover, the atomic masses of the elements were being established with greater certainty and attempts were made by various workers to relate the properties of the elements and their atomic masses.

The result of this work was summarized in 1869 by the Russian, Mendeleeff, who pointed out that there was a periodic variation of the properties of the elements if they were arranged in a table of increasing atomic masses. Thus the third and eleventh elements are the alkali metals lithium and sodium; the ninth and seventeenth are the halogens fluorine and chlorine. The first 18 elements of this arrangement, called the periodic table, are shown in Table 1.1.

TABLE 1.1

1 Hydrogen							2 Helium
3 Lithium	4 Beryllium	5 Boron	6 Carbon	7 Nitrogen	8 Oxygen	9 Fluorine	10 Neon
11 Sodium	12 Magnesium	13 Aluminium	14 Silicon	15 Phosphorus	16 Sulphur	17 Chlorine	18 Argon

The periodicity suggests that the elements are not completely independent but are somehow related. As early as 1816 William Prout had proposed that, in view of the near integral values of the few atomic masses then known, all elements were made by the union of hydrogen atoms. When fractional atomic masses, such as 35·5 for chlorine, were obtained, the idea lost support. The twentieth century has shown, however, that Prout's hypothesis was not so very far from the truth.

Electrolysis and the Faraday

During the latter half of the nineteenth century it was suggested that electricity, like matter, was atomic and that a natural unit of electric charge existed. The basis for this belief was Faraday's work on electrolysis (1831–34) which may be summarized by the statement—*a mole of monovalent ions of any substance is liberated by 96,500 coulombs*. This quantity of electricity is called the *Faraday constant* and is denoted by F.

Thus, the passage of 96,500 coulombs deposits 107·9 g of silver in a voltameter, but, since silver is monovalent and has atomic mass 107·9, this amount of substance contains approximately 6×10^{23} atoms. Assuming every atom of silver is associated with the same electrical charge during electrolysis it follows that each carries $96{,}500/6 \times 10^{23}$, i.e., $1{\cdot}60 \times 10^{-19}$ coulomb. Other atoms give the same value or an integral multiple of it and the natural unit of charge would appear to be $1{\cdot}60 \times 10^{-19}$ coulomb. The charged atoms responsible for conduction in an electrolyte are called ions and the number of units of charge associated with an ion equals its valency. For a monovalent ion

$$F = N_A e$$

where N_A is the Avogadro constant and e is the natural unit of charge.

It should be noted that the constancy of the Faraday only *suggests* that all monovalent ions carry the same charge. It could also be inferred that the charges on individual atoms vary but owing to the very large numbers involved the statistical average is always the same. The constancy of F would then indicate that the mean charge per monovalent ion is the same. There is, however, other evidence that all monovalent ions do carry the natural unit of charge.

Millikan's oil drop experiment

In 1909 R. A. Millikan started a series of experiments lasting many years which supplied evidence for the atomic nature of electricity and provided a value for the magnitude of the unit of electric charge. The principle of Millikan's method is to observe very small oil drops, charged either positively or negatively, falling in air under gravity and then either rising or being held stationary by an electric field.

The essential features of the apparatus are shown in Fig. 1.2. A spray of oil drops is formed above a tiny hole in the upper of two parallel metal plates and some find their way into the space between them. The drops are strongly illuminated and appear as bright specks on a dark background when viewed through a microscope.

With no electric field between the plates, one drop is selected and its velocity of fall found by timing it over a convenient number of divisions on a scale in the eyepiece of the microscope. (To find the actual distance fallen, the eyepiece scale is calibrated by viewing a millimetre scale through the microscope and comparing it with the eyepiece scale.) For a spherical drop of radius r, moving with uniform velocity v through a homogeneous medium having coefficient of viscosity η, Stokes' law states that the viscous force retarding its motion is $6\pi\eta rv$. In falling, the drop attains its terminal velocity almost at once because it is so small. The retarding force acting up then equals its weight,

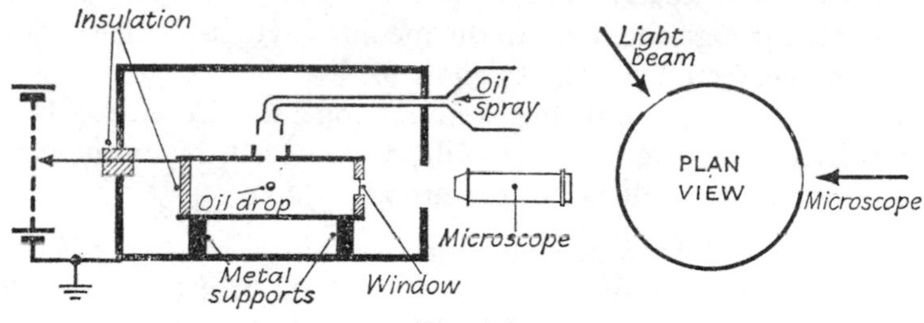

Fig. 1.2

given by $\frac{4}{3}\pi r^3 \rho g$, where ρ is the density of the oil and g the acceleration due to gravity. If v is the terminal velocity and the small upthrust of the air is neglected

$$6\pi\eta rv = \tfrac{4}{3}\pi r^3 \rho g \qquad (1)$$

From this the radius r of the drop can be found.

Some of the drops become charged either by friction in the process of spraying or from ions in the air. Suppose the drop under observation has a negative charge Q. When a potential difference is applied to the plates so that the top one is positive, an electric field is created which exerts an upward force on the drop. If V is the p.d. and E the intensity of the field required to keep the drop at rest, then the electric force experienced by it is EQ, since by definition E is the force on unit charge. The electric force on the drop then equals its weight and so

$$EQ = \tfrac{4}{3}\pi r^3 \rho g \qquad (2)$$

E equals the potential gradient V/d where d is the distance between the plates, r is known from equation (1) and hence Q can be calculated.

Certain measures were adopted by Millikan to ensure an accurate result:

(*a*) He used non-volatile oil to prevent evaporation altering the mass of a drop.

(*b*) Convection currents between the plates and variation of the viscosity of the air due to temperature change were eliminated by enclosing the apparatus in a constant-temperature oil bath.

(*c*) Stokes' law assumes fall in a homogeneous medium, the air consists of molecules and, as Millikan put it, very small drops 'fall freely through the holes in the medium'. He investigated this effect and corrected the law to allow for it.

(*d*) To simplify the theory we have considered the drop held at rest by the electric field but Millikan reversed the motion and found the upward velocity of the drop.

Millikan found that the charge on an oil drop, whether positive or negative, was always an integral multiple of a basic charge. Drops of glycerin and of mercury gave the same result. He studied drops having charges many times this natural unit and by using X-rays he was able to change the charge on a drop. The same minimum charge, now known as the *electronic charge*, e, was always involved. The value of the 'atom' of electric charge is

$$e = 1{\cdot}60 \times 10^{-19} \text{ coulomb}$$

It is the same as the charge on a monovalent ion.

Electricity and matter

The discovery of sub-atomic particles has shown that electricity and matter are closely related; in fact electricity in the form of electrons is part of the substance of the atoms of matter. For the present only a brief account of the atom will be given.

Atoms are made up from three types of particles: protons, neutrons and electrons. (Many other sub-atomic particles, such as positrons, mesons and antiprotons, are known but most are short-lived and are not primary components.) Protons and neutrons are packed together into a very small nucleus around which is distributed a number of electrons, usually called the extra-nuclear electrons. A proton carries a charge of $+e$, an electron of $-e$ and the neutron is uncharged. Normally the numbers of protons and electrons in an atom are equal, making it as a whole electrically neutral.

Whilst protons and neutrons generally remain in the nucleus, electrons can be detached from atoms and electrical conduction is explained in terms of their mobility. In a metal such as copper there are large numbers of loosely held electrons and when a p.d. is applied they drift under its influence, constituting an electric current. A current is conventionally considered to consist of positive charges moving round the circuit from the positive to the negative terminal of the source of p.d., but we now believe it to be a movement of negative charges (electrons) in the opposite direction. So far as external effects of the current are concerned the statements are equivalent, but in electronics the latter view is frequently adopted.

In electrolytes positive and negative ions are responsible for conduction. A positive ion is an atom or group of atoms which is deficient in one or more electrons, while a negative ion has one or more extra electrons. During electrolysis the positive ions travel to the cathode of the voltameter and each removes an electron from it to become neutral again. The negative ions go to the anode and give up their surplus electrons. The net effect is a transfer of electrons from cathode to anode, the ions acting as carriers.

Gases are ordinarily poor conductors but their molecules can be ionized by various agents and conduction then occurs. Gaseous conduction will be studied in Chapter 9.

Field ion microscope

No one is ever likely to 'see' an atom in the usual sense of the word but with the aid of the field ion microscope, invented by Professor Erwin Müller in 1955, it is possible to produce visible effects which can be interpreted as being directly due to the existence of individual atoms. In this respect atoms can be 'seen'. A field ion microscope is shown in Plate 1.

Details of the microscope tube are shown in Fig. 1.3. The

object is the tip of an extremely fine metal needle and the final image, which may be viewed directly or photographed, is obtained on a fluorescent screen. In operation the tube is highly evacuated and then a previously inserted helium ampoule is broken causing a slight increase of pressure due to the helium released. A high voltage (25 kV) is applied and creates an electric field between the tip and the screen. This field is extremely strong (400 million volts per cm) and it tears off electrons from helium atoms near the point. The positively charged helium ions so formed are accelerated by the field towards the screen where they cause it to fluoresce and produce a picture like the one shown in Plate 2 for a tungsten tip.

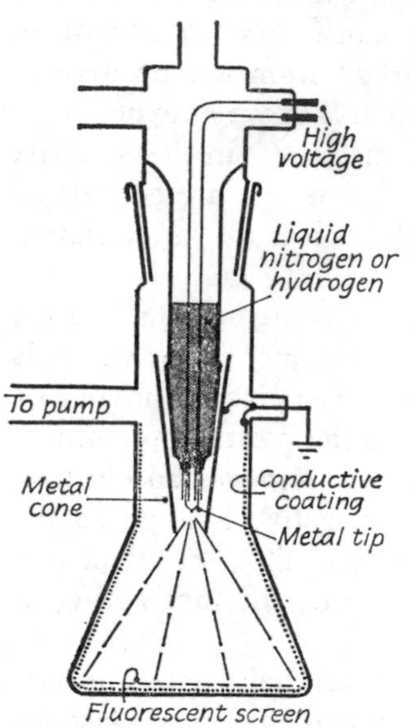

Fig. 1.3

What conclusions can be drawn about the structure of the needle tip from such pictures? If the needle is considered to be built from a pyramid-like structure consisting of layers of atoms one on top of the other, then the tip of the

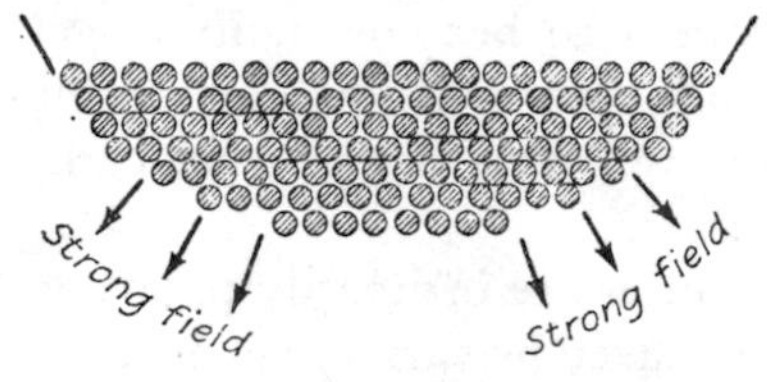

Fig. 1.4

needle would appear as in Fig. 1.4. The surface of the tip is 'most curved' at the edges of the various layers of atoms where one layer drops back to the next. The electric field emerging from these points is strongest and will produce and repel most helium ions. A bright spot on the screen is therefore interpreted as being due to an 'edge' atom on the perimeter of one of the many layers making up the needle tip. The flashes of light forming the picture do not prove the reality of atoms but their existence can be inferred from an understanding of the field ion microscope.

Plate 1 Field Ion Microscope developed by Dr Erwin W. Müller of Pennsylvania State University.

(*Courtesy: Cenco*)

Plate 2 Photo-micrograph of a nearly perfect tungsten crystal, taken with the Müller Field Ion Microscope

(*Courtesy: Cenco*)

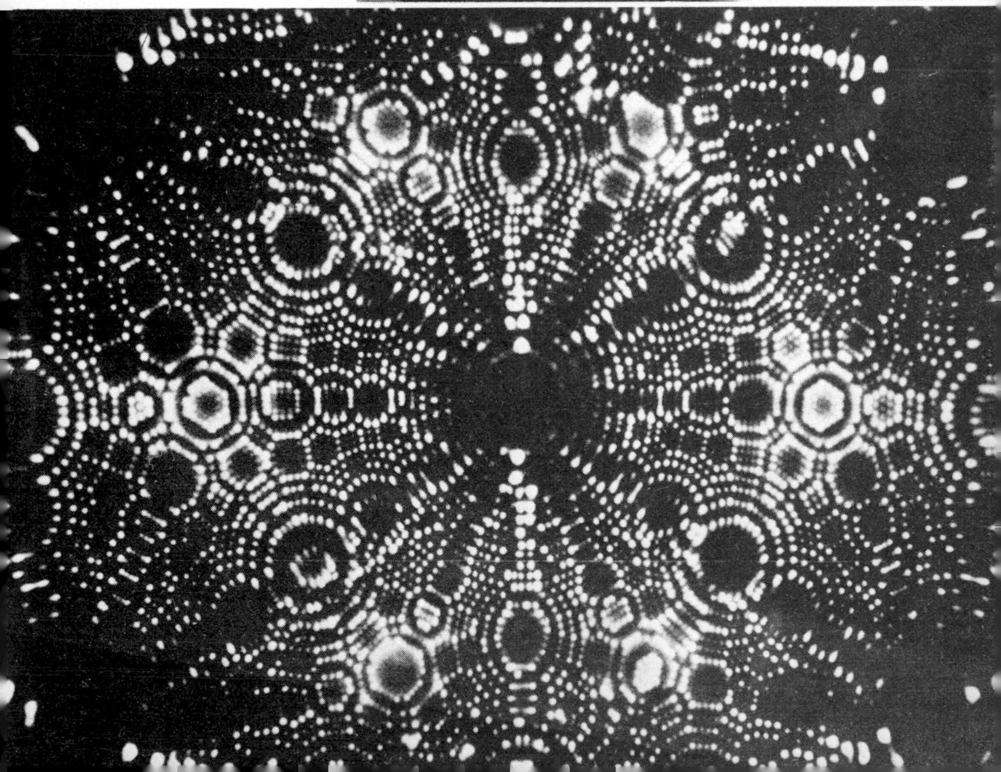

The metal tip has to be kept at a very low temperature, otherwise thermal motion of the atoms in the tip causes blurring and loss of resolution. Magnifications of about 2 million diameters are possible, compared with 100,000 for the electron microscope, which allows very large molecules to be 'seen', and 400 for the normal optical microscope.

The field ion microscope produces what amounts to a picture of the atomic structure of the surface of a metal and is an important research tool. Imperfections in metals can be detected leading to an understanding of failure or fatigue in metals subjected to high stress and temperature, such as occur in rockets and space vehicles. Other applications which can be studied include the effects of radiation on metals, an important aspect of nuclear engineering.

QUESTIONS

1. Discuss briefly the evidence for the view that matter is particulate.

2. In a monolayer experiment 1·0 cm^3 of oleic acid is added to 19 cm^3 of alcohol and 1·0 cm^3 of this solution diluted with 9 cm^3 more of alcohol. One drop of the solution on a water surface leaves a circular film of oleic acid of diameter 38 cm after the alcohol has evaporated. If the dropper gives 40 drops per cm^3 find the thickness of the film.

3. By counting scintillations it is found that 1 mg of polonium in decaying completely emits approximately $2{\cdot}9 \times 10^{18}$ alpha particles. If one particle is emitted by each atom and the atomic mass of polonium is 210, what is the Avogadro constant?

4. Estimate (*a*) the mass and (*b*) the diameter of the water molecule (assumed spherical) if water has molecular mass 18 and the Avogadro constant is 6×10^{23} per mole.

5. Smoke particles suspended in air, strongly illuminated and viewed through a microscope show small, random, irregular movements. What is the explanation of this phenomenon?

For what reasons would you conclude that it is not caused by convection, vibration of the apparatus, or the influence of the light beam?

How would the random movement be affected by (*i*) cooling the air to a low temperature, (*ii*) using smaller smoke particles? Give reasons for your answers. [*O. and C. part qn.*]

6. Outline briefly the evidence for the view that electricity is discontinuous in nature.

Explain the principles of a method by which the fundamental unit of electric charge (i.e., the charge on an electron) has been accurately measured, and show how the result is calculated from the observations made. [*S.*]

7. Give an account of a method by which the charge associated with an electron has been measured.

Taking this electronic charge to be $-1{\cdot}60 \times 10^{-19}$ C, calculate the potential difference in volts necessary to be maintained between two horizontal conducting plates, one 5×10^{-3} m above the other, so that a small oil drop, of mass $1{\cdot}31 \times 10^{-14}$ kg with two electrons attached to it, remains in equilibrium between them. Which plate would be at the positive potential?
(Earth's gravitational field strength $g = 9{\cdot}81$ N kg^{-1}) [*L.*]

8. An oil drop in air between two horizontal metal plates falls with a uniform velocity of $1{\cdot}90 \times 10^{-2}$ m s^{-1} when both plates are earthed. When a potential difference of 6920 V is maintained between the plates, which are separated by a distance of $1{\cdot}30 \times 10^{-2}$ m, the drop remains at rest. If the resistance to motion is given by the equation $F = 6\pi r\eta v$, where r is the radius of the drop, η the viscosity of the air and v is the velocity of the drop, calculate the radius of the drop and the charge carried by the drop. (Density of oil = 900 kg m^{-3}; viscosity of air = $1{\cdot}80 \times 10^{-5}$ Pa s; $g = 9{\cdot}81$ N kg^{-1})

Indicate how an experiment of this type enabled Millikan to measure the electronic charge. [*W. Schol.*]

9. A cloud of very small negatively charged water drops was produced in air in a closed vessel containing a pair of horizontal uncharged metal plates, $5{\cdot}0 \times 10^{-3}$ m apart, and the top of the cloud fell from the upper to the lower plate in 50 s. The top of a similar cloud fell over this distance in 28 s when the plates differed in potential by 1200 V. Obtain a value for the charge on a single drop, assuming the drops to be of equal size and to have equal charges.

Criticize this experiment as a method for determining the electronic charge. Describe briefly how Millikan modified and improved it.
(Take the viscosity of air as $1{\cdot}8 \times 10^{-5}$ Pa s; $g = 9{\cdot}81$ N kg^{-1}; density of water = 1000 kg m^{-3}) [*L. Schol.*]

10. Two plane parallel conducting plates $1{\cdot}50 \times 10^{-2}$ m apart are held horizontally, one above the other, in air. The upper plate is maintained at a positive potential of 1500 V while the lower plate is earthed. Calculate the number of electrons which must be attached to a small oil drop of mass $4{\cdot}90 \times 10^{-15}$ kg if it remains stationary in the air between the plates. (Assume that the density of air is negligible in comparison with that of oil.)

If the potential of the upper plate is suddenly changed to -1500 V what is the initial acceleration of the charged drop? Indicate, giving reasons, how the acceleration will change.
(The charge of an electron is $1{\cdot}60 \times 10^{-19}$ C and g is $9{\cdot}81$ N kg^{-1}.) [*J.*]

2 The electron

Electrons can escape from materials in various ways. The chief of these are:

(*i*) Thermionic emission.
(*ii*) Photoelectric emission.
(*iii*) Secondary emission.

The first method is most often used to obtain a supply of electrons and will now be considered. The other two methods will be dealt with in later chapters.

Thermionic emission

In this process electrons are made to leave the surface of a metal, or a metal coated with certain oxides, by the application of heat. The action may be considered to occur in the following way. The atoms in a metal are regularly spaced forming a rigid lattice structure, Fig. 2.1. Every atom has one or more loosely held electrons which, due to the close packing of atoms in a solid, are not attached to any particular atom but form an 'electron cloud' belonging to the metal as a whole. The atoms, being short of

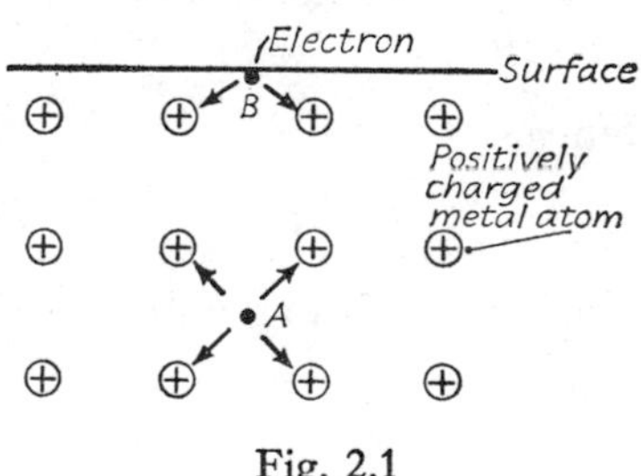

Fig. 2.1

electrons, are positively charged and exert attractive forces on the electrons in the inter-atomic spaces. At points like A inside the metal, the forces on an electron more or less balance; near the surface at B for example, an electron trying to escape experiences an inward pull due to the absence of atoms above it. The surface acts as a barrier which cannot be penetrated by an electron unless its kinetic energy is increased. If the metal is heated to a high temperature many of the inter-atomic electrons gain sufficient energy to break out.[1]

The energy required by an electron to enable it to escape from the surface of a metal is called the *work function* Φ and depends largely on the nature of the metal. Thermionic emission is analogous to 'boiling off' molecules from the surface of a liquid and the work function can be compared with the specific latent heat of vaporization.

The electron-volt

A charge Q (in coulombs) moving through a potential difference of V (in volts) gains energy QV (in joules, i.e. coulomb-volts). Thus for an electron accelerated through 1 volt, $Q = 1{\cdot}60 \times 10^{-19}$ coulomb, $V = 1$ volt and the energy gained equals $1{\cdot}60 \times 10^{-19} \times 1$ joule.

In many branches of modern physics the joule is often too large and another unit of energy, the *electron-volt*, is defined.

One electron-volt is the energy acquired by any singly charged particle, such as an electron, in falling through a potential difference of 1 volt.

Hence,

$$1 \text{ electron-volt } (1 \text{ eV}) = 1{\cdot}60 \times 10^{-19} \text{ joule}$$

A larger unit is one million electron-volts (1 MeV) which equals 10^6 electron-volts.

[1] It will be seen in Chapter 14 that modern solid-state theory views conditions in a metal from a slightly different standpoint, that of electronic energy levels; here the above picture is adequate.

Hot cathodes

In many electronic devices the cathode is heated and acts as the electron-emitter. Such devices are said to have thermionic or 'hot' cathodes. The smaller the work function of a metal the lower the temperature at which it releases electrons and, although any metal will give thermionic emission, in most cases the temperature has to be too near the melting point. Two emitting materials now used for hot cathodes are:

(*i*) TUNGSTEN. This metal has a work function of 4·5 eV and operates at the rather high temperature of 2200°C, i.e., white heat, but its melting point is about 3300°C. A large emission is possible and it is used chiefly in high-power radio transmitting valves.

(*ii*) OXIDE-COATED METALS. A mixture of the oxides of barium and strontium has a work function of approximately 1 eV and gives copious emission at 750°C, i.e., dull red heat. Most thermionic devices employ this type of emitter.

Hot cathodes are heated electrically either directly or indirectly. In direct heating a current is passed through the cathode itself which is in the form of a wire or filament made of tungsten or tungsten coated with oxide-mixture, Fig. 2.2*a*. Indirect heating is only possible with oxide-coated cathodes and is shown in Fig. 2.2*b*. Here the cathode consists of a thin hollow nickel tube on which the oxide is sprayed. The cathode is heated by passing a current through a fine tungsten wire, called the heater, inside the tube. The cathode and heater are separated by a material such as alumina (aluminium oxide) which is an electrical insulator. Indirect heating is most common since it allows a.c. to be used without the potential of the cathode continually varying. A typical heater supply for many thermionic devices is 6·3 volts a.c., 0·3 ampere.

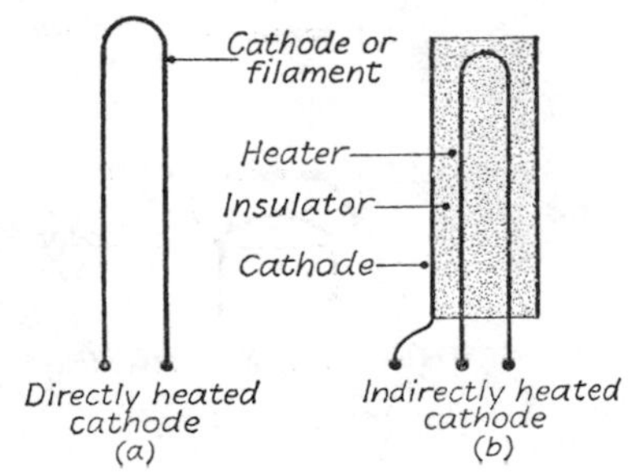

Fig. 2.2

Diode valve

The thermionic diode, introduced by J. A. Fleming in 1904, has a hot cathode and is surrounded by a metal anode, often in the

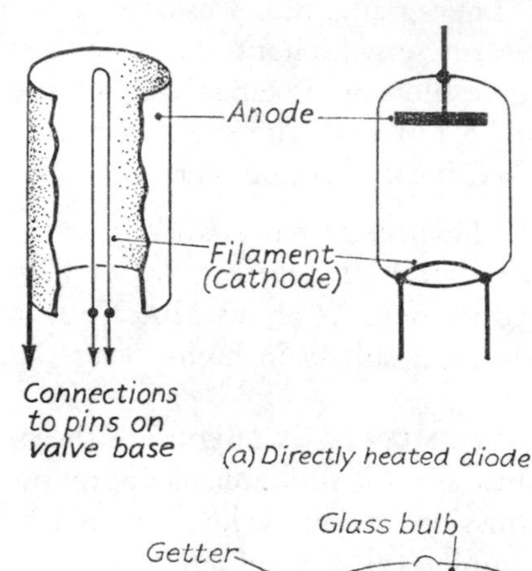

(a) Directly heated diode

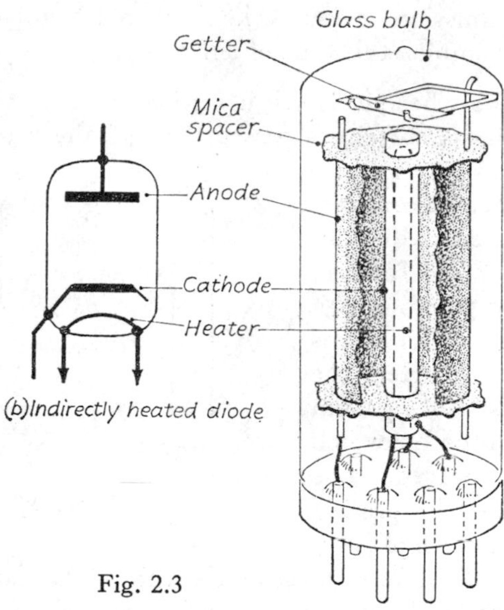

(b) Indirectly heated diode

Fig. 2.3

form of a nickel cylinder. The construction and symbols of directly and indirectly heated diodes are illustrated in Fig. 2.3.

To prevent air molecules interfering with the motion of the electrons the electrode assembly is enclosed in a highly evacuated glass bulb. The residual gas pressure is about 10^{-4} N m^{-2} but even so there are still a few thousand million molecules present in each cubic centimetre. Such a low pressure is obtained by a complex evacuation process culminating in the use of a 'getter'. This consists of a small amount of barium supported at the top of the valve, above the electrodes, as in Fig. 2.3. After the tube has been pumped out and sealed the getter is volatilized and the vapour combines with residual gas to reduce the pressure further. A black deposit is left on the inside of the top of the valve when the vapour condenses. The getter is heated by the action of high-frequency currents in coils surrounding the valve, the process being known as high-frequency induction heating. A new type of getter has recently been produced which is activated by heating but does not evaporate and leave a deposit. It has the further advantage of continuing to absorb residual gas after the manufacture of the valve.

When a battery is connected as in Fig. 2.4 so that the anode is at a positive potential with respect to the cathode, the electrons, being negatively charged, are attracted to the anode and form an electronic current, of the order of milliamperes, from cathode to anode. This can be regarded as a flow of conventional current in the opposite direction, i.e., from anode to cathode in the diode, and is called the anode current. The circuit is completed through the battery. If the battery connections are reversed so that the anode is negative with respect to the cathode, electrons are repelled by the anode and no current flows. The diode behaves like a mechanical valve allowing current in one direction only.

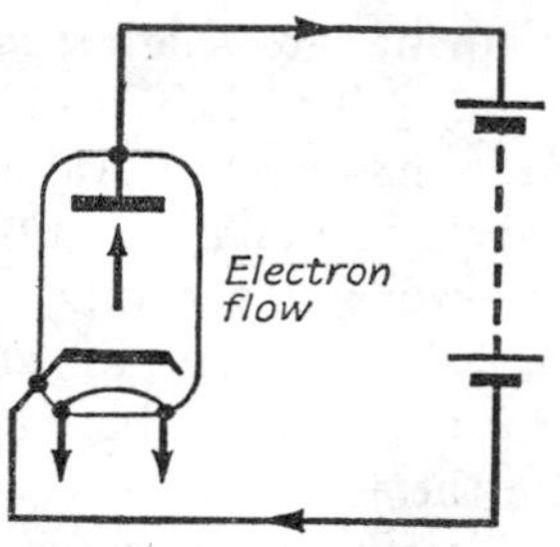

Fig. 2.4

The diode and other types of valves are being superseded by semiconductor devices in the most modern electronic equipment but much apparatus containing valves exists and there are some tasks which at present only valves can perform.

Characteristics of a diode valve

Characteristic curves show how the anode current depends on the anode voltage, i.e., the p.d. between anode and cathode, and

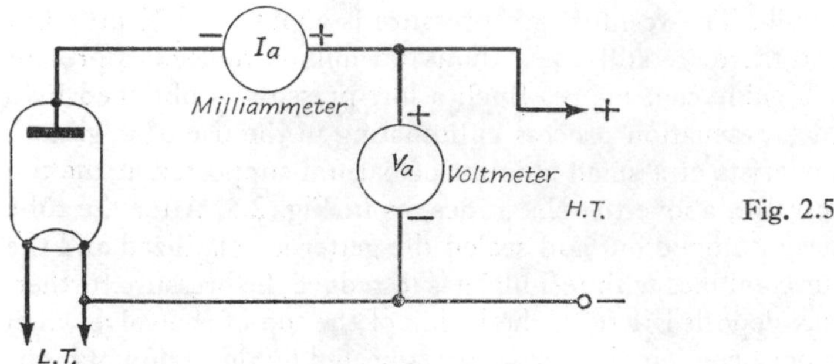

Fig. 2.5

may be determined experimentally for a directly heated diode using the circuit of Fig. 2.5.

As with most valve circuits two voltages are required—a low tension or L.T. supply to maintain heating current through the filament and a high tension or H.T. supply to provide the anode voltage. The L.T. can be a.c. or d.c. and varies from 1·4 volts for a battery-type valve to 6·3 volts or more for a mains-type valve. The H.T. must be d.c. and variable up to 100 or 200 volts according to the valve. The anode current I_a is measured by a milliammeter and the anode voltage V_a by a voltmeter. The filament is connected to H.T. negative to provide a complete circuit for the anode current.

To obtain the characteristic curve, V_a is increased by steps and the corresponding values of I_a recorded. If the results are plotted a curve is obtained similar to *OABC* in Fig. 2.6. It is explained as follows. When V_a is zero the electrons emitted by the filament

Fig. 2.6
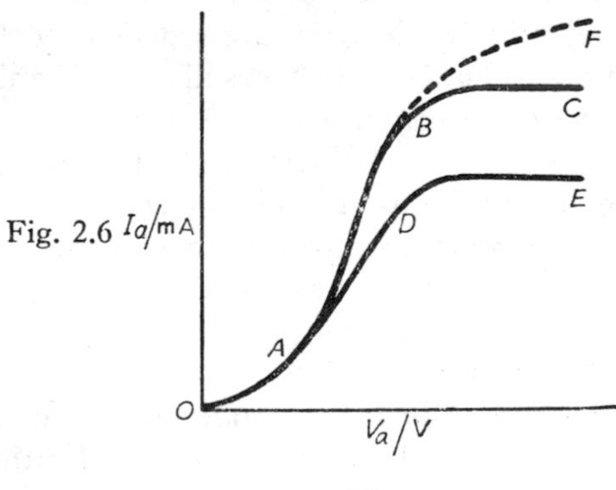

tend to cluster round it since their emission velocities are small. The negative charge of the electron cloud is called a *space charge* and it exerts a repulsive force on other electrons being emitted. Soon a condition of dynamic equilibrium is attained when the number of electrons returning to the filament per second equals the number emitted by it per second, Fig. 2.7*a*, so that the electron population of the space charge remains constant. Thus, no anode current is obtained. Along *OAB* when V_a has a positive value some of the outer electrons are attracted to the anode and current flows. The repulsive effect of the space charge is now smaller and the number of electrons returning to the filament becomes less than the number emitted, the anode current accounting for the difference, Fig. 2.7*b*. When V_a is sufficiently great the space charge is dispersed, all the electrons emitted go

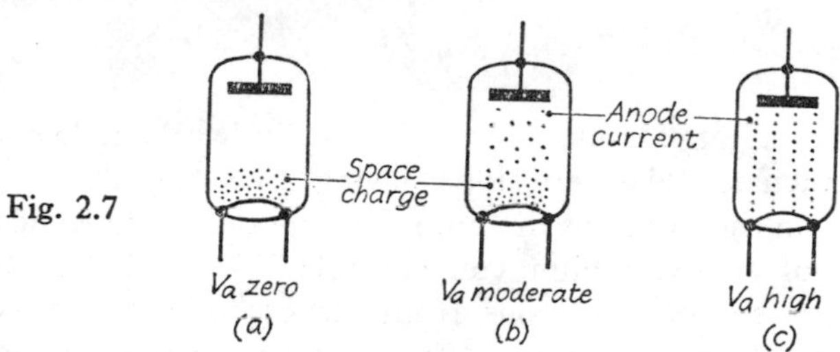

Fig. 2.7

straight across to the anode and I_a has its *saturation value* for that particular filament temperature, Fig. 2.7*c*. Along *BC* further increase of V_a has little effect on I_a for tungsten filament diodes.

The anode current is said to be *space charge limited* along *OAB*, and along *AB* it is given approximately by Child's three-halves power law

$$I_a = kV_a^{3/2}$$

where k is a constant. Ohm's law is clearly not obeyed. In practice diodes are usually operated in the space charge limited region.

At a lower filament current the emission temperature is smaller and the saturation current is less, as shown by *ODE* in Fig. 2.6. Oxide-coated valves saturate less abruptly due to the emission depending on the electric field at the cathode surface as well as on the cathode temperature. They follow a curve similar to *OF* in Fig. 2.6.

Cathode rays and the Maltese cross tube

Streams of electrons moving at high speed are called *cathode rays.* They exhibit several important and useful effects, some of which can be demonstrated with the Maltese cross tube of Fig. 2.8. It

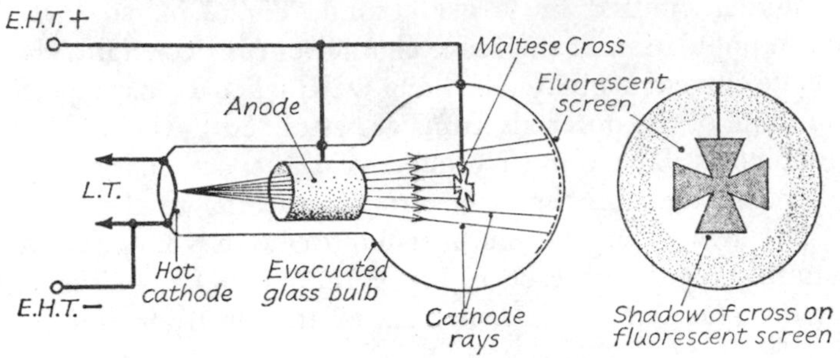

Fig. 2.8

consists of a hot cathode and a hollow cylindrical anode enclosed in an evacuated glass envelope having a coating of fluorescent material on the inside of the bulb. The anode is connected to the positive of an extra high voltage (E.H.T.) supply of 2000 or 3000 volts so that electrons from the cathode are accelerated along the tube in a divergent beam. Most by-pass the anode and a dark shadow of the cross appears on the screen against a fluorescent background, usually green or blue in colour. The formation of the shadow indicates that rays are travelling in straight lines from the cathode and those not intercepted by the cross cause the screen to fluoresce.

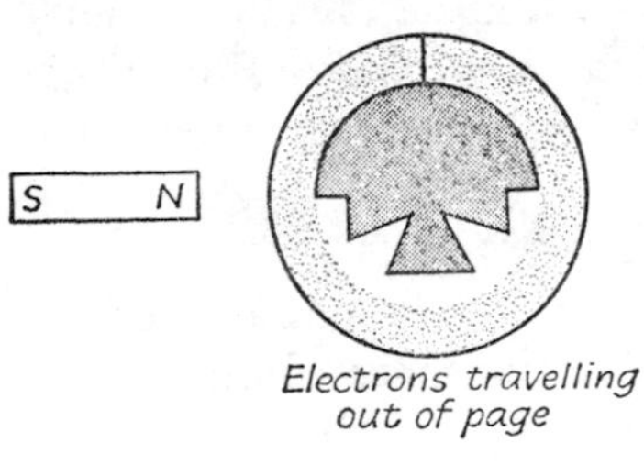

Fig. 2.9

When a magnet is brought near the side of the tube, level with the anode, the beam is deflected vertically and the shadow can be made partially or wholly to disappear, Fig. 2.9. Using Fleming's left-hand rule the direction of the deflection shows that the rays behave like a flow of negative charge, travelling in the direction cathode to anode.

If the tube has a directly heated tungsten filament operating at 'white heat' it also acts as a source of light and when the cathode rays are deflected by a magnetic field the light is not. A black shadow of the cross, normally masked by the fluorescent one, appears on the white background of the screen. This supports the view that cathode rays are streams of particles and are not electromagnetic radiation like light, as was once believed by some physicists.

The properties of cathode rays may be summarized as follows:

(*i*) They travel from the cathode in straight lines.

(*ii*) They cause certain substances to fluoresce.

(*iii*) They possess kinetic energy, most of which is changed to heat when they are brought to rest. (The anode of a valve gets hot.)

(*iv*) They can be deflected by a magnetic field.

(*v*) They can be deflected by an electric field.

(*vi*) They produce X-rays on striking matter (p. 126).

Discovery of the electron

The first evidence to establish the existence of the electron is usually considered to be provided by J. J. Thomson's experiment of 1897 in which he determined the charge to mass ratio (e/m) or specific charge of cathode rays. Although the specific charge could be measured even if cathode rays were, for example, a continuous fluid, it was generally supposed at the time that they were particles and the name 'electron' had been proposed. The value of e/m obtained by Thomson was always the same, whatever the source or method of production of the cathode rays. This suggested that electrons are all alike, universal constituents of matter, and by assuming that the charge carried was equal to that on a monovalent ion in electrolysis Thomson estimated the mass m of an electron, knowing e/m. Using modern values m is $9{\cdot}11 \times 10^{-31}$ kg, i.e., it is 1837 times smaller than the mass of the lightest atom, hydrogen. Other interpretations of the value of e/m are possible; it could be that the electron has the same mass as a hydrogen ion but a much greater charge. However, as a result of the work of Millikan and others there is now no doubt that an electron carries the fundamental unit of electric charge.

For most purposes the electron can be regarded as a sub-atomic particle having a negative charge of value e, the electronic charge, and a very small mass (since force is required to accelerate it). The value of the mass quoted above is known as the 'rest' mass. The term has arisen because it has been found that a particle accelerated to a velocity approaching that of light in a machine such as a cyclotron behaves as if its mass increases with velocity. Einstein predicted this result in his theory of relativity.

Ordinary particles are characterized by size and shape but such properties cannot be stated precisely for sub-atomic particles. To some extent the size of the electron depends on the method of determination and while some measurements indicate that it is a sphere of diameter 10^{-15} m, it is also satisfactory on occasions to consider it as a dimensionless point. By contrast its charge and mass can be uniquely specified. More will be said in Chapter 12 about the nature of the electron.

Before describing methods for the measurement of e/m the behaviour of cathode rays in electric and magnetic fields will be studied.

Velocity of cathode rays

The velocity of the electrons in a beam of cathode rays depends on the intensity of the electric field created by the accelerating voltage between anode and cathode. If the latter is known the velocity can be calculated.

An electron of charge e emitted from a hot cathode and accelerated by a potential difference V, gains energy eV. This amount of electrical energy is transferred from the electric field to kinetic energy of the electron as it accelerates. If it starts from the cathode with zero velocity and moves in a good vacuum then

$$eV = \tfrac{1}{2}mv^2$$

where m is the mass of the electron and v the velocity on reaching the anode. From this 'energy equation' it follows that

$$v = \sqrt{\frac{2eV}{m}}$$

Substitution of numerical values for e/m and V (in appropriate units) shows that the velocity attained is about $1{\cdot}9 \times 10^7$ m s^{-1} (i.e. one-sixteenth of the velocity of light) when $V = 1000$ volts.

Deflection of cathode rays by an electric field

If cathode rays are projected into an electric field acting at right angles to their direction of motion they are deflected from their original path. In Fig. 2.10 two deflecting plates P and Q apply

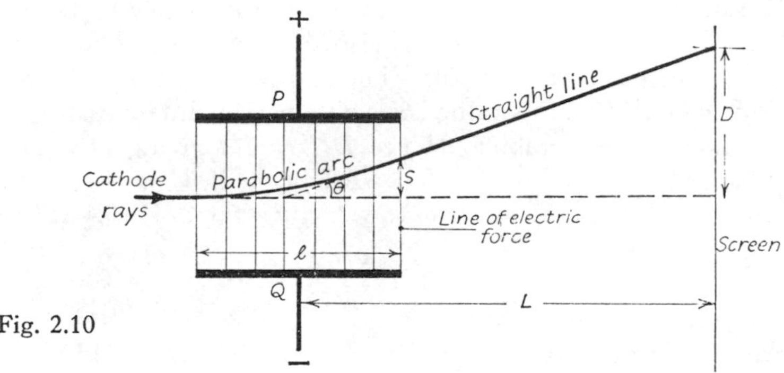

Fig. 2.10

a uniform field E, non-uniformities at the edge of the plates being ignored.

Consider an electron having charge e, mass m and horizontal velocity v on entering the field. If the upper plate is positive the electron experiences a force Ee and an acceleration Ee/m (from second law of motion) both acting vertically upwards. Since the field is uniform, the acceleration is uniform and combines with the initial horizontal velocity v, which the electron retains during the whole of its journey between the plates, to give a path which we shall show is a *parabola*, Fig. 2.11. The behaviour of the electron is similar to that of a projectile fired horizontally, its path (neglecting air resistance) is also a parabola, the resultant of a uniform horizontal velocity and the vertical acceleration due to gravity.

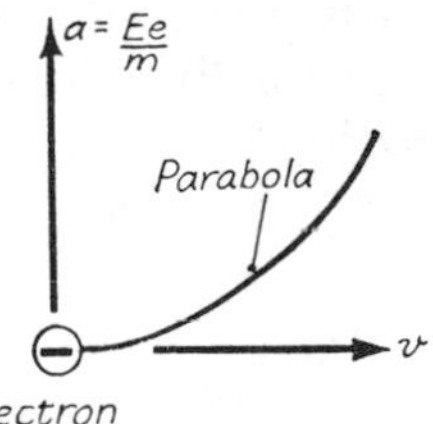

Fig. 2.11

If the electron is in the field for time t its vertical displacement

s is given by $s = \frac{1}{2}at^2$, where $a = Ee/m$. Since the horizontal velocity is uniform, $t = l/v$

$$\therefore\ s = \frac{1}{2}\cdot\frac{Ee}{m}\cdot\frac{l^2}{v^2}$$

$$= kl^2 \quad \text{where} \quad k = Ee/2mv^2.$$

This is the equation of a parabola since k is a constant.

After leaving the field the electron continues in a straight path. The deflection D on a screen is given approximately by $\tan\theta = D/L$ (Fig. 2.10), where $\tan\theta$ is also the slope of the tangent at the end of the parabolic path. The slope equals the differential coefficient ds/dl and its value $2kl$ is obtained by differentiating the equation of the parabola. Hence $D/L = 2kl$ giving $D = 2lLk$. Substituting for k we get $D = lLEe/mv^2$. If V is the voltage which accelerates the electron to velocity v then $eV = \frac{1}{2}mv^2$ and

$$D = \frac{ElL}{2V}$$

Thus D is proportional to the deflecting electric field E and inversely proportional to the accelerating voltage V. This result will be used later when considering the sensitivity of the cathode ray oscilloscope.

Deflection of cathode rays by a magnetic field

It is shown in textbooks on electricity that a conductor of length l, carrying a current I, in and at right angles to a uniform magnetic field of flux density (or magnetic induction) B, experiences a force BIl acting perpendicular to the field and to the conductor,

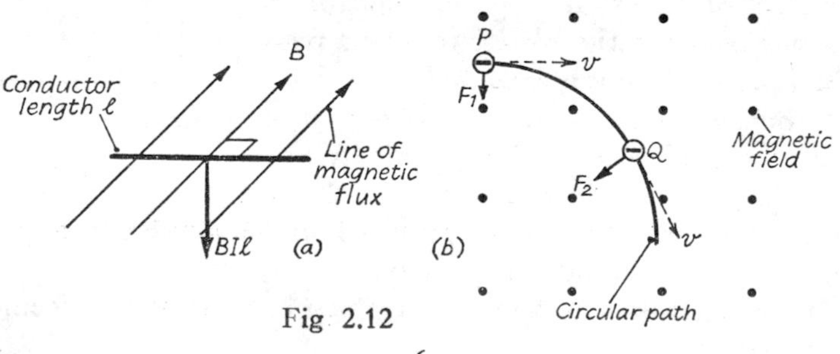

Fig 2.12

Fig. 2.12*a*. Moving electrons constitute an electric current and therefore cathode rays experience a force in a magnetic field. In Fig. 2.12*b* an electron of charge e and mass m is projected with velocity v at right angles to the uniform field B which is directed into and is normal to the paper. Under these conditions we shall see that the electron is subject to a constant force Bev and describes a *circular path.*

The magnitude of the force is deduced from the expression, force = BIl. Since current = charge/time, for a single electron travelling a distance l in time t, the equivalent current $I = e/t$. Hence, force = $BIl = B(e/t)l = Be(l/t) = Bev$ where $v = l/t$.

The direction of the force is given by Fleming's left-hand rule. At P, the force is represented by F_1 and acts at right angles to the field and to the direction of motion. The velocity v of the electron therefore remains unaltered (since F_1 is perpendicular to v) but the electron is deflected from its original path to, say, Q. Here the force F_2 acting on it still has the same value Bev and since the direction of motion and the field continue to be mutually perpendicular, F_2 is perpendicular to the new direction. The force is thus always at right angles to the electron path and only changes the direction of motion but not the speed. Consequently, the electron describes a circular arc of radius r and the constant radial force Bev supplies the centripetal force mv^2/r.

Hence,
$$Bev = \frac{mv^2}{r}$$

This equation describes the path of the cathode rays in the magnetic field.

Methods for the measurement of e/m

Three experiments with modern apparatus will be outlined. The accepted value of the charge to mass ratio of the electron is

$$e/m = 1{\cdot}76 \times 10^{11} \text{ coulombs per kilogram}$$

(*a*) *Cathode ray tube method using crossed fields*

This method is similar in principle to that developed by J. J. Thomson in which an electron beam is subjected to mutually perpendicular, i.e., crossed, electric and magnetic fields. Here, a vacuum-type cathode ray tube is used, Fig. 2.13, having a hot cathode C and an anode A with a horizontal collimating slit from which the electrons emerge in a flat beam. The beam produces a narrow luminous trace when it hits a vertical fluorescent screen S, marked in squares and set at an angle. S is supported by two parallel deflecting plates Y_1, Y_2, across which an electric field is applied. Two identical current-carrying coils X_1, X_2, mounted on opposite sides of the bulb create a magnetic field between the plates, at right angles to both the direction of travel of the electron beam and the electric field. The coils are separated by a distance equal to their radius and when connected in series, so that the current has the same direction in each, they give a magnetic field

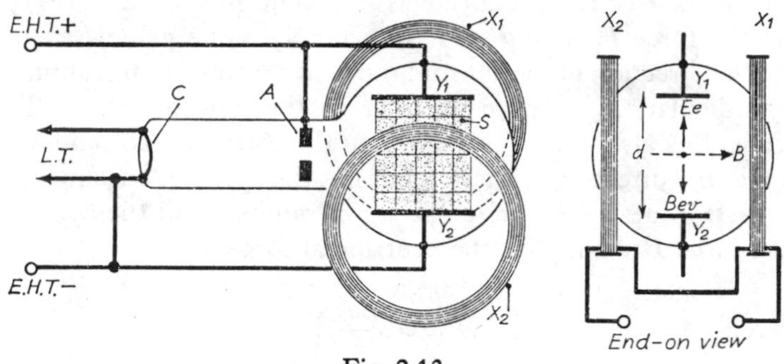

Fig. 2.13

of constant strength for a short distance along their common axis. When used in this way X_1 and X_2 are called Helmholtz coils.

Consider an electron of charge e and mass m which emerges from the anode having been accelerated to velocity v. Let E be the intensity of the electric field between Y_1 and Y_2 and B the magnetic flux density along the axis of X_1 and X_2. When the electron suffers no deflection, the electric force Ee on it must be equal and opposite to the magnetic force Bev. Hence,

$$Ee = Bev \qquad (1)$$

If the electron is emitted from the cathode with zero velocity and moves in a good vacuum, its kinetic energy $\frac{1}{2}mv^2$ is given by

$$\tfrac{1}{2}mv^2 = eV \qquad (2)$$

where V is the anode voltage. Eliminating v from (1) and (2)

$$\frac{e}{m} = \frac{E^2}{2B^2V}$$

If the voltage creating the electric field equals the anode voltage, $E = V/d$, where d is the distance between Y_1 and Y_2. Hence,

$$\frac{e}{m} = \frac{V}{2B^2d^2}$$

Thus, e/m can be found if V, B and d are known and expressed in appropriate units. B may be determined experimentally by removing the tube and investigating the region between the coils with a fluxmeter or it can be calculated from the appropriate formula.

(In SI units $B = 8\mu_0 nI/(5\sqrt{5}r)$ tesla where $\mu_0 = 4\pi \times 10^{-7}$ henry per metre for free space, n is the number of turns in one Helmholtz coil, I is the current in amperes in the coils and r is the radius of a coil in metres.)

In the above simple treatment the fields are assumed to be uniform and co-terminous, i.e., to extend over the same length of the electron beam. In practice such conditions are not achieved and this partly accounts for only an approximate value of e/m being obtained.

(*b*) *Magnetron method*[1]

The GRD7 diode valve is suitable for this method. It has a straight tungsten wire filament and a coaxial cylindrical anode with two guard rings, Fig. 2.14. This arrangement ensures a radial electric field, free from edge effects, between anode and filament. Normally when H.T. is applied the electrons emitted by the filament travel radially to the anode. However, if the valve is in a current-carrying solenoid whose magnetic field is parallel to the filament, the electrons are deflected into an approximately

[1] This method is mainly the work of the Mullard Educational Service and Messrs. Ferranti Ltd.

circular path whose radius depends on the strength of the field Fig. 2.15. At a given anode voltage there is a critical field for which the diameter of an electron orbit equals the radius of the anode cylinder. The electrons then just fail to reach the anode and are said to give the 'magnetron effect'. The anode current decreases sharply but for various reasons the 'cut-off' is not abrupt and the critical condition has to be estimated.

Since the electric field created by the anode voltage is much more intense around the filament than near the anode (due to the former being a wire and the latter a cylinder) we can assume that an electron is accelerated close to the filament and that for most

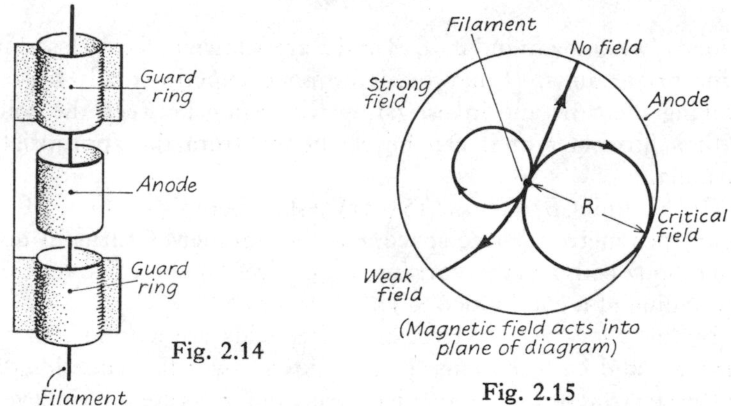

Fig. 2.14

Fig. 2.15

of its journey it has a nearly constant velocity v. If B is the magnetic flux density of the critical field for anode voltage V, an electron of charge e will experience a force Bev. The radius r of the circular orbit described by the electron is then given by the circular motion equation

$$Bev = \frac{mv^2}{r} \qquad (3)$$

where m is the mass of an electron. Assuming electrons are emitted from the filament with zero velocity the energy equation gives

$$\tfrac{1}{2}mv^2 = eV \qquad (4)$$

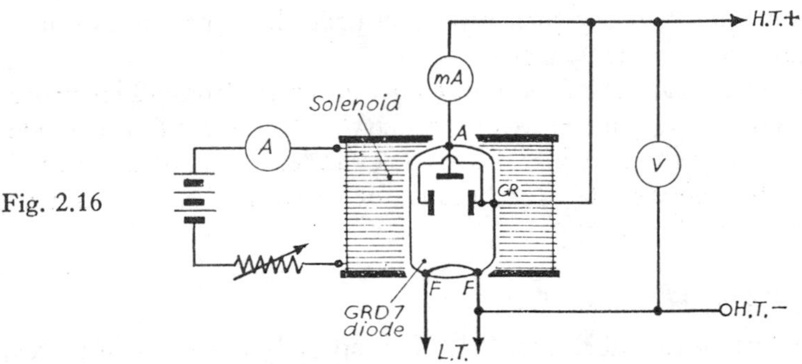

Fig. 2.16

Eliminating v from (3) and (4)

$$\frac{e}{m} = \frac{2V}{B^2r^2}$$

If R is the radius of the anode cylinder, $r = R/2$ and

$$\frac{e}{m} = \frac{8V}{B^2R^2}$$

When V, B and R are known, e/m can be calculated.

A convenient circuit is shown in Fig. 2.16; the magnetic field strength is varied by changing the solenoid current. For a given anode voltage the critical solenoid current I_c is estimated from a graph of anode current against solenoid current as shown in Fig. 2.17. The critical value of B corresponding to I_c is obtained experimentally or calculated using the expression for the field

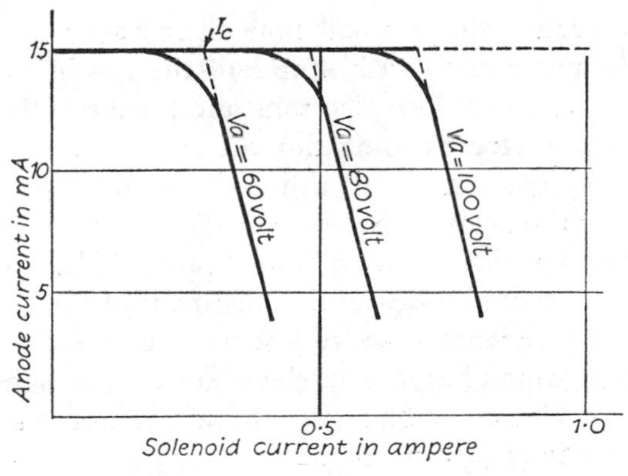

Fig. 2.17

inside a short, many-turn coil. The procedure may be repeated for different anode voltages.

The gradual cut-off of anode current arises from all electrons not having the same emission velocity and possibly to the anode not being in the centre of the anode cylinder, either on account of imperfect construction or because of expansion as the filament warms up.

(c) *Fine beam tube method*

The fine beam tube, Fig. 2.18, is a special type of cathode ray tube containing a small quantity of gas (often hydrogen) at a pressure of about 1 N m^{-2}. Electrons from a hot cathode

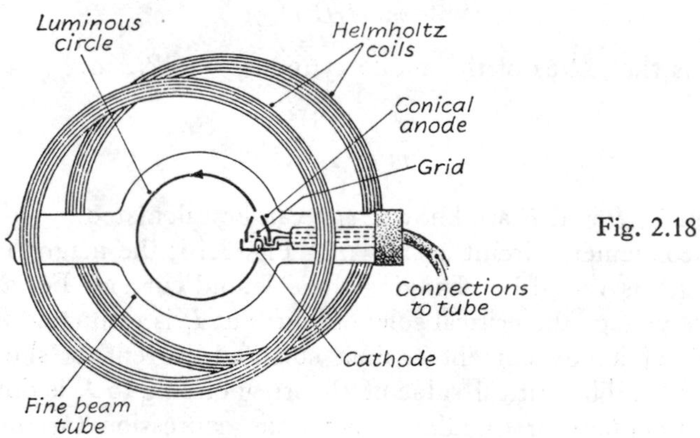

Fig. 2.18

emerge as a narrow beam from a small hole at the apex of a conical-shaped anode and collide with atoms of the gas in the tube. As a result, the latter may lose electrons and form positive gas ions. The electrons created by ionization are easily scattered but the relatively heavy gas ions form a line of positive space charge along the path of the beam which attracts the fast electrons from the anode, focusing them into a 'fine beam'. (The gas focusing action is only attained by careful adjustment of the gas pressure in the tube during manufacture.) It will be seen later (p. 204) that a gas atom which has lost an electron can emit light when it recaptures an electron. The gas, therefore, not only focuses the beam but also reveals its path.

Helmholtz coils are arranged one on each side of the tube and produce a magnetic field at right angles to the beam. If the field is sufficiently strong the electrons are deflected into a circular orbit and a luminous circle of low intensity appears when the tube is viewed in a darkened room. The diameter of the circle may be measured in various ways. Some tubes contain luminescent markers for adjusting the diameter to certain values; in other cases a large mirror with a scale is placed behind the tube so that the observer sees the circle, its image and the corresponding marks on the scale all in line. The circle diameter is altered by varying either the anode voltage or the current in the coils.

The theory of the method is similar to that of the magnetron method, the result being found from the expression

$$\frac{e}{m} = \frac{2V}{B^2 r^2}$$

where V is the anode voltage, B the magnetic flux density between the coils in the region of the tube and r the radius of the luminous circle. B is obtained experimentally or by calculation as before.

Formulae and units

In numerical examples the answer will automatically be obtained in the correct SI unit if the other quantities involved in the formula have been expressed in their basic SI units. Some useful expressions with their SI units are given below.

SI

Electric force Ee is in *newtons* if
E in volt metre^{-1} and
e in coulombs

Note: $E = V/d$, where V is in volts and d in metres

Magnetic force Bev is in *newtons* if
B in tesla
e in coulombs
v in metre s^{-1}
Note: Permeability of free space $\mu_0 = 4\pi \times 10^{-7}$ henry metre^{-1}

Centripetal force mv^2/r is in *newtons* if
m in kg
v in metre s^{-1}
r in metres

Energy $\frac{1}{2}mv^2$ is in *joules* if
m in kg
v in metre s^{-1}

Energy eV is in *joules* if
e in coulombs and
V in volts

Worked Example

(*a*) *An electron emitted from a hot cathode in an evacuated tube is accelerated by a p.d. of* 1000 *volts. Calculate the kinetic energy and velocity acquired by the electron.* ($e = 1{\cdot}60 \times 10^{-19}$ *coulomb*; $m = 9{\cdot}1 \times 10^{-31}$ *kg*.)

We have, kinetic energy = charge × p.d. = eV

$$V = 1000 \text{ volt}$$
$$e = 1{\cdot}60 \times 10^{-19} \text{ coulomb}$$
$$\therefore \text{ kinetic energy} = 1{\cdot}60 \times 10^{-19} \times 1000$$
$$= 1{\cdot}60 \times 10^{-16} \text{ joule}$$
But kinetic energy $= \frac{1}{2}mv^2$
$$\therefore \tfrac{1}{2}mv^2 = 1{\cdot}60 \times 10^{-16} \text{ joule}$$
$$m = 9{\cdot}1 \times 10^{-31} \text{ kg}$$
$$\therefore v = \sqrt{\frac{2 \times 1{\cdot}60 \times 10^{-16}}{9{\cdot}1 \times 10^{-31}}}$$
$$= 1{\cdot}8 \times 10^7 \text{ metre s}^{-1}$$

(*b*) *The electron now enters at right angles a uniform magnetic field of flux density* 1×10^{-3} *tesla. Determine its path.*

The magnetic force on the electron is Bev and this makes it describe a circular path of radius r given by the circular motion equation.

$$Bev = \frac{mv^2}{r}$$

Hence,
$$r = \frac{mv}{Be}$$

We have, $B = 10^{-3}$ tesla
From (*a*) $v = 1{\cdot}8 \times 10^7$ metre s^{-1}
From given values of e and m
$e/m = 1{\cdot}76 \times 10^{11}$ coulomb kg^{-1}

$$\therefore\ r = \frac{1{\cdot}8 \times 10^7}{10^{-3} \times 1{\cdot}76 \times 10^{11}}$$

$$= 0{\cdot}102 \text{ metre}$$

(*c*) *Find the intensity of the uniform electric field which, when applied perpendicular to the previous magnetic field so as to be co-terminous with it, compensates for the magnetic deflection. If the electric field plates are* $2{\cdot}0 \times 10^{-2}$ *m apart what p.d. exists between them?*

For the electric and magnetic forces to balance

$$Ee = Bev$$

Hence,
$$E = Bv$$

As before, $B = 10^{-3}$ tesla and
$v = 1{\cdot}8 \times 10^7$ metre s^{-1}
$\therefore\ E = 10^{-3} \times 1{\cdot}8 \times 10^7$
$= 1{\cdot}8 \times 10^4$ volt metres^{-1}
But $E = V_1/d$, where V_1 is the p.d. between the deflecting plates and d their separation
$d = 0{\cdot}02$ metre
$\therefore\ V_1 = Ed = 1{\cdot}8 \times 10^4 \times 0{\cdot}02$
$= 360$ volts

QUESTIONS

1. Explain the terms *thermionic emission* and *work function*.

Describe the structure of a thermionic diode valve.

Draw a diagram of the circuit which you would use to investigate the relation between the anode current and anode voltage for a diode valve. Sketch the graph you would expect to obtain and explain its chief features. The meaning of the terms 'space charge' and 'saturation current' should be made clear.

2. The current I through a diode valve is given in the following table for certain anode voltages V.

V in volts	0	80	150
I in mA	0	2	5

When the diode is connected in series with an anode resistor R to a 120-V d.c. supply, a current of 2 mA flows. Find (*a*) the value of R and (*b*) what the supply voltage must be to increase the current to 5 mA.

3. What is an *electron-volt*? Assuming that the charge on an electron is $-1{\cdot}60 \times 10^{-19}$ coulomb express one electron-volt in terms of another unit.

Calculate the kinetic energy and velocity of protons after being accelerated from rest through a potential difference of $2{\cdot}00 \times 10^5$ volts. (Assume that the mass of a proton $= 1{\cdot}67 \times 10^{-27}$ kg.) [*J.*]

4. How may cathode rays be produced? What are their chief properties?

An electron starts from rest and moves freely in an electric field whose intensity is $2{\cdot}4 \times 10^3$ V m^{-1}. Find (*a*) the force on the electron, (*b*) its acceleration and (*c*) the velocity acquired in moving through a potential difference of 90 V.
(The charge on an electron $= 1{\cdot}60 \times 10^{-19}$ C and the mass of an electron $= 9{\cdot}12 \times 10^{-31}$ kg.) [*W.*]

5. What do you understand by an electron?

Electrons in a certain cathode ray tube are accelerated through a potential difference of 2 kV between the cathode and the screen. Calculate the velocity with which they strike the screen. Assuming they lose all their energy on impact and given that 10^{12} electrons pass per second, calculate the power dissipation.
(Charge on the electron $= 1{\cdot}6 \times 10^{-19}$ C; mass of electron $= 9{\cdot}11 \times 10^{-31}$ kg.) [*O. and C. part qn.*]

6. Describe a method for measuring the ratio of the charge to mass (e/m) for an electron.

Given that e/m for an electron is $1{\cdot}76 \times 10^{11}$ C kg^{-1}, calculate (*a*) the speed acquired by an electron in undergoing a potential drop in an electrostatic field *in vacuo* of 1000 V, (*b*) the magnetic flux density which must be established perpendicular to the path of a beam of electrons of speed 5×10^7 m s^{-1} *in vacuo* to cause them to traverse a circular path of diameter 0·08 m. [*A.E.B.*]

7. Show that an electron projected at right angles to a uniform magnetic field describes a circular path. Derive an expression for the frequency of revolution.

An electron travelling at 10^7 m s^{-1} enters at right angles a uniform magnetic field of 5×10^{-4} T. Calculate the radius of the circular orbit it describes.
(e/m for electron = $1{\cdot}8 \times 10^{11}$ C kg^{-1}.)

8. A narrow horizontal beam of electrons passes symmetrically between two vertical metal plates mounted one on each side of the beam. The velocity of the electrons is $3{\cdot}00 \times 10^7$ m s^{-1}, the plates are 0·03 m long and 0·01 m apart. It is found that when a battery of 568 V is connected to the plates the electron beam just strikes the end of one of them. Calculate the value of e/m. [*J. part qn.*]

9. An electron emitted from a hot filament in an exhausted tube is accelerated by a potential difference of 4000 V and then enters at right angles a uniform magnetic field of flux density 1×10^{-3} T. Calculate the speed of the electron and determine its path in the magnetic field.

Calculate the intensity of the uniform electrostatic field which, when suitably applied, would compensate the effect of the magnetic field on the path of the electron and show in a diagram the relative directions of the electron and of the two fields.
(Assume that the ratio of the charge to the mass of an electron = $1{\cdot}76 \times 10^{11}$ C kg^{-1}.) [*J. part qn.*]

10. Describe a method for determining the ratio of the charge to mass of the electron, giving the theory on which the interpretation of the results rests.

An electron is injected with a velocity of $1{\cdot}5 \times 10^6$ m s^{-1} into a uniform magnetic field of flux density 0·10 T *in vacuo*. The angle between the field and the initial direction of the electron is 10°. By considering the components of the velocity of the electron parallel to and perpendicular to the field, calculate the axial distance between successive turns of the helical path which the electron will follow.
(e/m for electron = $1{\cdot}8 \times 10^{11}$ C kg^{-1}.) [*C. Schol.*]

3 Cathode ray oscilloscope

The cathode ray oscilloscope or oscillograph, usually called the C.R.O., is an instrument of wide application especially for examining waveforms. It consists essentially of a cathode ray tube, a device which has made television and radar possible and which comprises a highly evacuated glass envelope containing:

(*i*) *an electron gun*, i.e., an electrode assembly for producing a narrow beam of cathode rays,

(*ii*) *a deflecting system* to allow horizontal and vertical deflection of the beam and

(*iii*) *a fluorescent screen* on which the beam produces a spot of light.

Electron gun

A typical oscilloscope tube is shown in Fig. 3.1, connected to a potential divider R_1, R_2, R_3 which supplies appropriate voltages from an H.T. supply to the various electrodes of the electron gun.

The electron gun consists of a hot cathode C, directly or indirectly heated, a cylinder G known as the grid and two anodes A_1 and A_2. The grid is given a negative potential or *bias* with respect to the cathode and as well as concentrating the electrons along the axis of the tube by repulsion, it also controls the number leaving the neighbourhood of the cathode. If the bias is too negative no electrons pass through the hole in G and the spot on the screen S vanishes. Variable resistor R_1 determines the grid voltage and thus acts as a *brightness* control.

Anodes A_1 and A_2 are metal discs or cylinders with central apertures and both have positive potentials relative to the cathode. They accelerate the electrons to a high velocity, giving them sufficient energy to cause light emission where they hit the screen. In addition, the anodes provide further focusing of the beam to

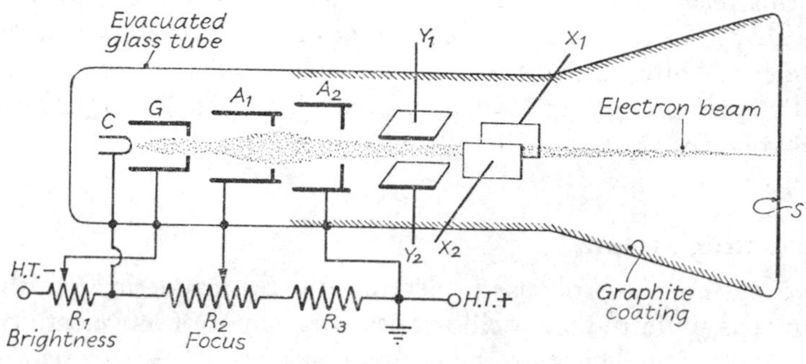

Fig. 3.1

offset the spreading which occurs due to mutual repulsion between the electrons after they leave G.

The focusing effect can be understood by considering a divergent beam of electrons entering the electric field created by A_1 and A_2. If the lines of force are as shown in Fig. 3.2, an electron

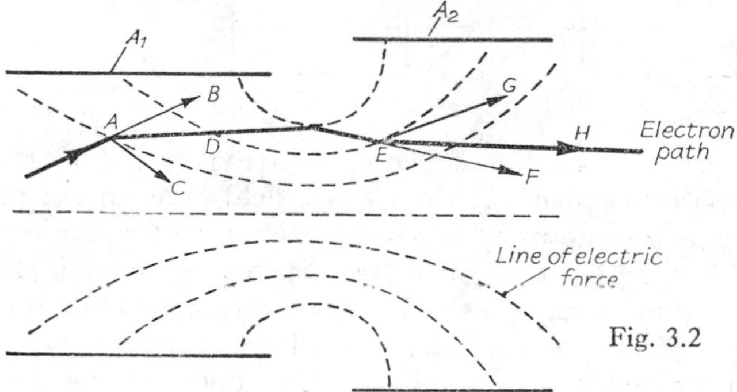

Fig. 3.2

at A, travelling in the direction AB, is accelerated by the field in the direction AC and follows an intermediate path AD. The electron suffers further bending and eventually the beam converges. At E the field intensity is decreasing and the electron is subject to a decelerating force in the direction EG so that instead of continuing along *EF*, it follows a path such as *EH*. A correctly designed field focuses the beam to a small spot on the screen; the shape of the field depends on the geometrical shape of the anodes and their potentials. A_2 has a higher potential than A_1 and adjustment of the potential of A_1 by variable resistor R_2, provides a *focus* control. The focusing effect of the electric field on the electron beam is analogous to that of a lens on light and the anodes are often called the 'electron lens' system.

Typical voltages for a small tube are 800 volts for A_2, 200 to 300 volts for A_1 and -50 volts to zero for *G*.

Deflecting system

Two systems can be used, electrostatic or magnetic, but the former is preferred for oscilloscopes on account of its versatility. In electrostatic deflection the beam passes first between a pair of horizontal metal plates, called the *Y* plates, and then between a

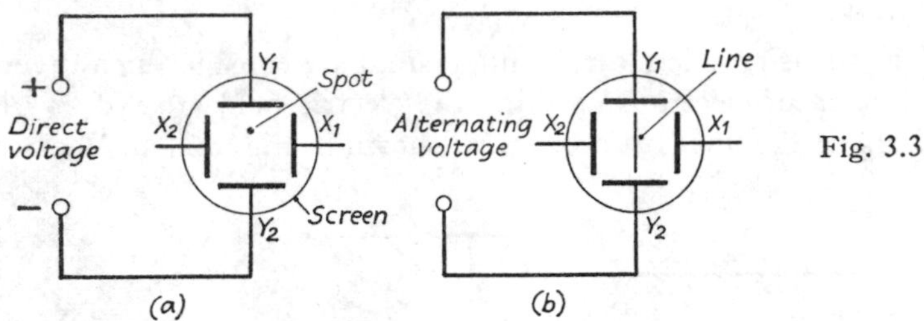

Fig. 3.3

similar vertical pair, the *X* plates, as in Fig. 3.1. If Y_1 is at a higher potential than Y_2, the electric field between the plates deflects the spot up from its central position on the screen, Fig. 3.3*a*. When Y_1 has a negative potential the deflection is down. An alternating voltage on the *Y* plates deflects the beam up and down and if the motion is fast enough (at mains frequency of 50 Hz for example) a vertical line appears due to the persistence of vision, Fig. 3.3*b*. A voltage applied to the *X* plates gives a horizontal deflection. In most C.R.O. applications, voltages are applied simultaneously to both pairs of plates and, when a waveform is to be displayed, the voltage on the *X* plates must vary linearly with time. More will be said later about this when the time-base circuit, which is responsible for producing this voltage, is considered.

If the deflecting plates are not at about the same potential as the final anode they have a defocusing effect on the electron beam. The simplest and safest way of preventing defocusing is to connect to earth one of each pair of deflecting plates, say X_2 and Y_2, and the final anode. H.T.+ is then at earth potential as shown in Fig. 3.1 and the other electrodes of the electron gun become negative with respect to A_2. So far as the acceleration of the beam is concerned the result is the same since there is still a high potential difference between the final anode and the cathode. In practice, X_2, Y_2 and the final anode are connected internally and brought out to a single terminal on the C.R.O. marked E (for earth). Deflecting voltages are then applied to Y_1 (usually marked Y or input) and E or to X_1 (marked X) and E.

Separate X and Y deflection amplifiers are often built into the C.R.O. to amplify alternating voltages too small to produce a measurable trace, before they are applied to the plates. X and Y shift controls are used to move the spot or trace 'manually' in the X and Y directions respectively. They apply a positive or negative voltage to one of the deflecting plates according to the shift required.

Fluorescent screen

Certain substances can absorb energy and emit light when they are struck by short-wavelength radiation (ultraviolet or X-rays) or by fast-moving particles such as electrons. They are called ***phosphors*** but this term is not strictly accurate since more than phosphorescence is involved. Two luminous effects occur. The first is the emission of light while the substance is actually being struck; this is called *fluorescence* and stops with the bombardment. The second effect, ***phosphorescence***, is the afterglow which may continue for many seconds after fluorescence has ceased.

Phosphors vary in the colour of the light they emit and in their persistence, i.e., the duration of the afterglow. Generally the basic phosphor material must be in an extremely pure state and requires a trace of a specific impurity, known as an 'activator'. A phosphor commonly used for the fluorescent screens of cathode ray tubes is zinc sulphide (with silver as activator) which gives a blue trace and no afterglow. When transients are to be observed, i.e., effects occurring briefly and not recurring, a phosphor such as calcium phosphate with a pronounced afterglow is necessary.

More advanced points

(*a*) *Internal graphite coating*

Electrons intercepted by the anodes in a cathode ray tube return to the H.T. supply in the normal way, but those forming the beam represent a small current of the order of microamperes and have no apparent return path since both the fluorescent screen and the glass envelope are insulators. It would appear that a negative charge must build up on the screen and repel later electrons. However, bombardment of the screen causes *secondary emission*, an effect occurring when high-speed particles strike a surface and eject electrons from it. These secondary electrons are collected by a coating of graphite on the inside of the tube, Fig. 3.1, which is connected to the final anode and provides a return path to H.T.+. The screen gains bombarding electrons but loses about the same number of secondary electrons, and thus has a potential roughly equal to that of the final anode. The electrons then travel with constant velocity between A_2 and the screen. In addition, the coating effectively shields the beam from the influence of external electric fields.

(*b*) *Deflection sensitivity*

This is defined as the deflection of the spot on the screen produced by a p.d. of 1 volt applied between the deflecting plates. It has been shown (p. 26) that the deflection D is given by

$$D = \frac{ElL}{2V}$$

where E is the intensity of the deflecting electric field, V the accelerating voltage, l the length of the plates and L the distance from the centre of the plates to the screen. Hence D is inversely proportional to V and therefore V should be small for large sensitivity. The electrons then pass the deflecting plates sufficiently slowly to suffer appreciable deflection. However, the production of a bright spot requires V to be large so that the electrons are fast-moving. The value chosen for V has to be a compromise to meet these conflicting demands. The sensitivity also increases with E which is itself increased for a given deflecting voltage by decreasing the plate separation. To prevent the beam then being intercepted by the edges of the plates, the latter are often splayed out towards the screen as shown in Fig. 3.4. A sensitivity of about 0·25 mm per volt is common for a small tube.

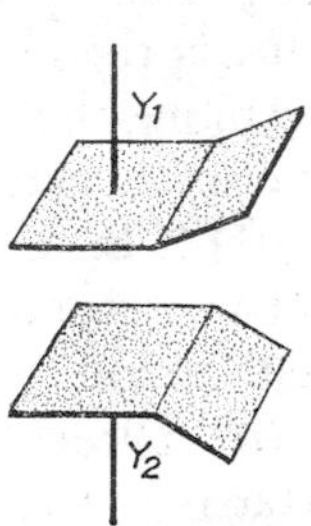

Fig. 3.4

C.R.O. as a voltmeter

Basically the C.R.O. is a voltmeter offering certain advantages, some of which are listed later, over other types of meter. Before using it for quantitative work it must be calibrated by applying various known d.c. voltages and measuring the corresponding deflections of the spot from its central or zero position. In the circuit of Fig. 3.5*a* the voltage is applied to the Y plates, the time

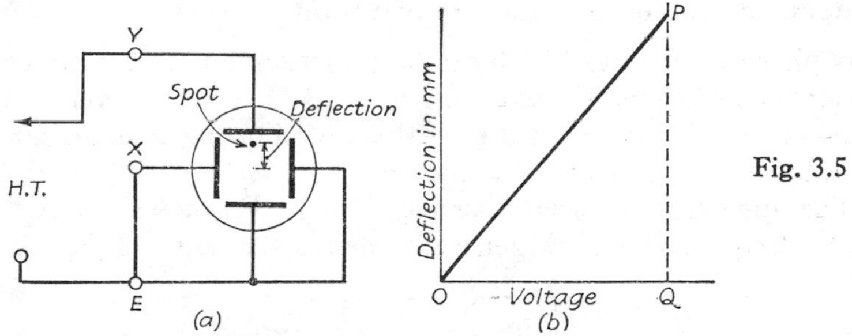

Fig. 3.5

base being switched off and the X plates connected together. The H.T. source can be either an ordinary H.T. dry battery with tappings which may be checked by a high-resistance voltmeter or a metered, variable H.T. power unit. A calibration graph is then drawn as in Fig. 3.5*b*; any unknown voltage is read off once the deflection it produces has been found. Since the graph is a straight line through the origin the deflections are proportional to the applied voltage and the slope PQ/OQ gives the deflection sensitivity of the tube in millimetres per volt. An alternating voltage produces a vertical line trace, the length of which gives the peak-to-peak value of the voltage, i.e., twice V_0. The r.m.s. value is then calculated from $V_{r.m.s.} = 0{\cdot}707 \times V_0$.

Among the advantages to be derived from using the C.R.O. as a voltmeter are:

(*i*) The electron beam behaves as a pointer of negligible inertia, responding instantaneously and having a perfect 'dead-beat' action.

(*ii*) Direct and alternating voltages can be measured and the latter may have frequencies of several million cycles per second.

(*iii*) It has an almost infinite resistance to direct current and a very large impedance to alternating current so that the circuit to which connection is made is little affected and a true reading is obtained.

It is also possible to measure other electrical quantities such as current, resistance, capacitance and inductance by arranging for a voltage representing the quantity, to be applied to the *Y* plates. In practice however more conventional methods using direct-reading meters are preferred.

Determination of the velocity of sound

Any physical property which can be translated into a voltage (or current) may be investigated using the C.R.O. Thus, the velocity of sound in air can be measured by investigating a stationary sound wave with the aid of a microphone.

The apparatus required is arranged as in Fig. 3.6. The A.F (audio-frequency) signal generator delivers a note of known

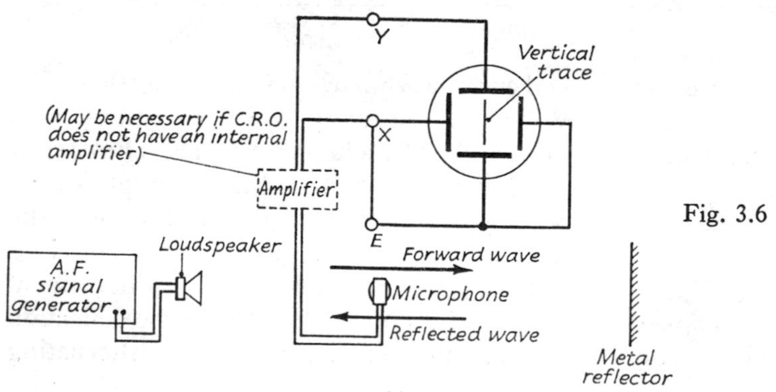

Fig. 3.6

frequency (2000 Hz is suitable) to a loudspeaker which is directed towards a reflecting metal sheet. Interference occurs between the forward and reflected sound waves and a stationary wave pattern with nodes and antinodes is established. If the reflector is slowly moved towards or away from the microphone the vertical trace on the C.R.O. varies from a maximum to a minimum and the distance moved by the reflector between two consecutive maxima or minima equals $\lambda/2$, where λ is the wavelength of the sound wave. By reading the frequency f of the note from the scale on the A.F. generator, the velocity of sound in air v is then given by $v = f\lambda$.

In engineering the C.R.O. can be used to study vibrations, pressure fluctuations, speed and other phenomena which can be converted into voltages or currents using appropriate conversion devices, i.e., transducers.

Measurement of phase relationship

When used in its simplest manner as a voltmeter only the Y plates of the C.R.O. are required. The more usual method of operation involves both pairs of deflecting plates and enables the relationship between two quantities to be studied in a way which is not possible with other instruments.

A typical measurement, often required in electronics, is the phase difference between two sinusoidal alternating voltages of the same frequency. The voltages V_x and V_y are applied as in Fig. 3.7. It is assumed that they are of equal amplitude and that each is positive when the beam is deflected, as shown by the arrows in the figure.

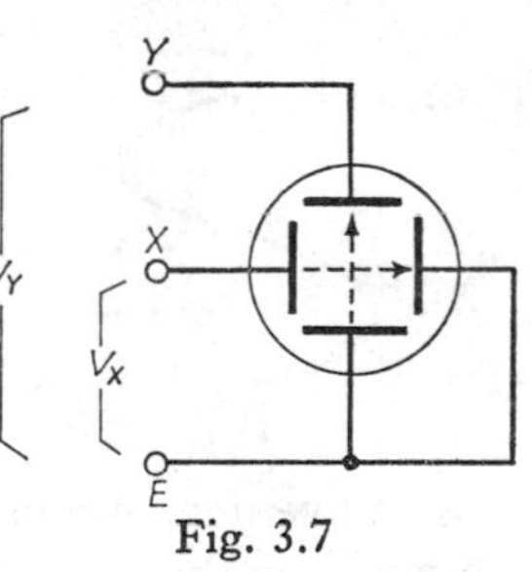

Fig. 3.7

If V_x and V_y are in phase (or antiphase) a straight line trace inclined at 45° to the axes is obtained. A phase difference of 90° gives a circle and intermediate values give an elliptical trace. These results are illustrated in Fig. 3.8 and in practice a transparent scale with similar markings may be used for finding the phase difference.

Graphical construction shows how the figures are formed. In

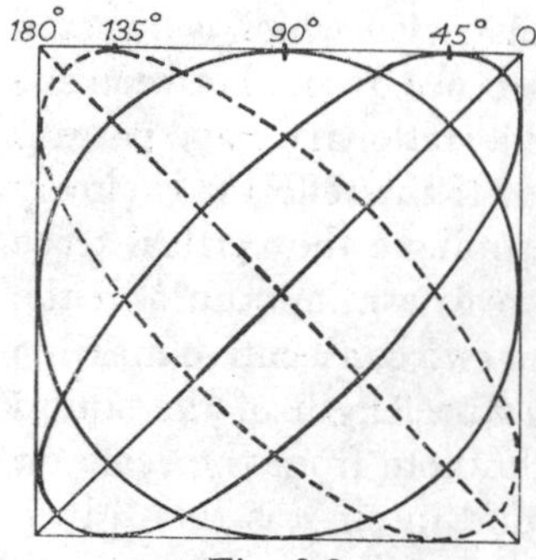

Fig. 3.8

Fig. 3.9, V_x and V_y are in phase, V_x alone would produce a horizontal trace and V_y a vertical trace. The resultant trace when they are applied simultaneously is obtained by projecting the corresponding points A, B, C on each waveform vertically and horizontally; the intersections *a*, *b*, *c* give the positions of the spot on the screen. The case in which the phase angle ϕ is 45° is represented by V'_x and V_y. The trace is then an ellipse.

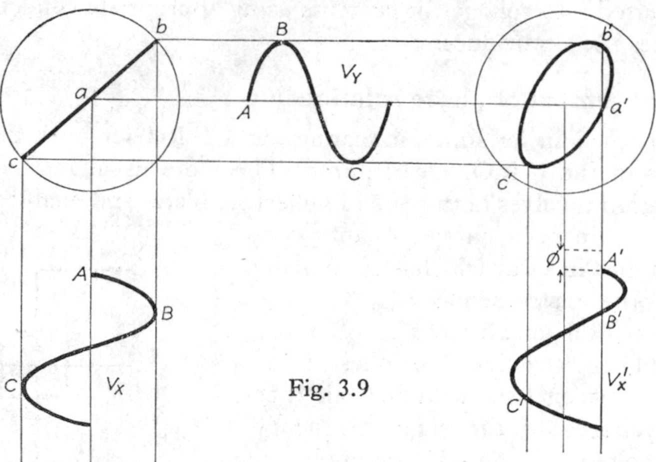

Fig. 3.9

A convenient circuit to investigate is shown in Fig. 3.10 in which V_y is the p.d. across the capacitor and variable resistor in series and V_x the p.d. across the fixed resistor. Since the current in a resistor is in phase with the voltage, V_x gives the current waveform in the resistor and therefore the current waveform in the capacitor, since the two are in series. The phase difference between V_x and V_y can be varied between 0° and 90° by adjusting the 1-MΩ resistor.

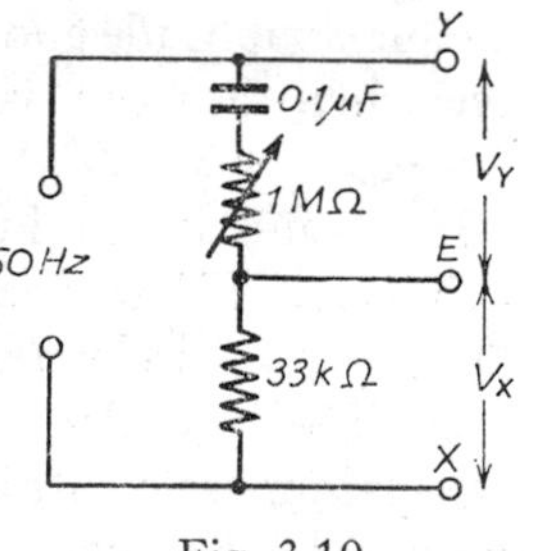

Fig. 3.10

Comparison of frequency

If two voltages having different frequencies f_x and f_y are applied to the X and Y plates of a C.R.O., as in Fig. 3.7, their frequencies may be compared or one calculated if the other is known. The case of $f_x = f_y$ was considered in the last section when it was seen that in general an elliptical trace is obtained depending on the phase difference. Other simple number frequency ratios give more complex figures, known as the *Lissajous figures*, some of which are shown in Fig. 3.11.

In any given case the frequency ratio can be found from inspection by imagining a horizontal and a vertical line to be

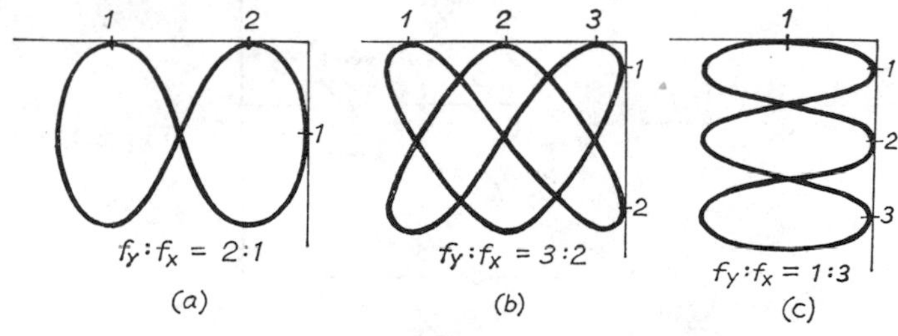

Fig. 3.11

drawn at the top and side of the trace. The number of loops touching each line is counted and the frequency ratio is given by

$$\frac{f_y}{f_x} = \frac{\text{number of loops touching horizontal line}}{\text{number of loops touching vertical line}}$$

Examples are given in Fig. 3.11.

The form of the figures changes if the phase difference or frequency ratio changes, but the pattern becomes stationary when $f_y:f_x$ is a ratio of whole numbers and the phase difference remains constant.

Many C.R.O.s provide a small 50 Hz calibrating voltage (available at a socket marked *cal*) and if this is applied to the X plates at the same time as a variable-frequency voltage from an A.F. signal generator is applied to the Y plates, the Lissajous figures are readily obtained.

Hysteresis loop display

A simple hysteresis loop display can be arranged with a C.R.O. to show the relationship between the magnetic induction of a ferromagnetic specimen and the magnetizing field.

The specimen is inserted in a magnetizing coil placed at right angles to the axis of the oscilloscope tube and close to the deflecting plates, Fig. 3.12. When current flows in the coil the specimen is magnetized and creates a magnetic field which deflects the electron beam along the *Y* axis (Fleming's left-hand

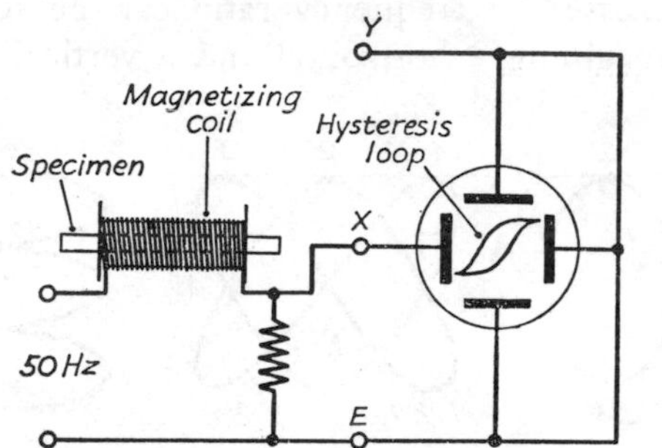

Fig. 3.12

rule). The *Y* deflection thus indicates the magnetic induction of the specimen. The p.d. across the resistor is applied to the *X* plates, the *X* deflection is then proportional to the magnetizing coil current and therefore to the magnetic field acting on the specimen. With an a.c. input the magnetizing current takes the specimen through complete magnetization cycles and the spot produces a hysteresis curve, provided the peak value of the current is sufficiently large to cause saturation, otherwise the trace is a distorted phase ellipse.

For this experiment the C.R.O. must have an easily accessible tube from which any mumetal screen (shielding the tube from magnetic fields) can be removed.

Time base of the C.R.O.

When it is desired to study the variation of a quantity with time, an alternating voltage representing the quantity is applied to the *Y* plates and a sawtooth voltage from the time-base circuit is applied to the X plates. The sawtooth voltage must be of the form shown in Fig. 3.13 and has to satisfy three conditions. First, it should start at a maximum negative value, thus attracting the spot to the extreme left of the screen, and then rise linearly through zero to a maximum positive value which sweeps the spot to the

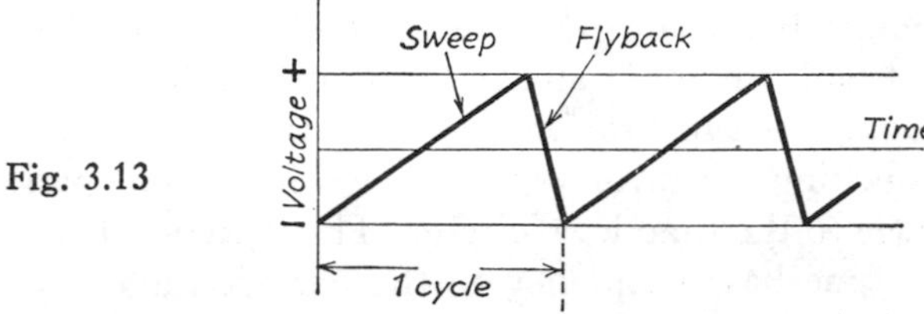

Fig. 3.13

far right of the screen. The sweep must be linear so that the deflection of the spot is proportional to time, the X-axis then represents time. Second, the time taken to return the spot to the left before it starts the next sweep, i.e. the flyback time, should be negligible; and third, the frequency must be variable.

As the spot is drawn horizontally across the screen by the time base, it is also deflected vertically by the alternating voltage under study which is therefore 'spread out' on a time axis and its waveform displayed. The waveform will be a faithful representation,

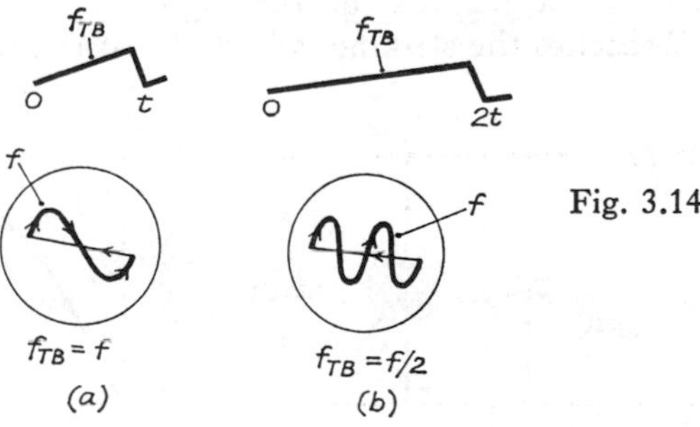

Fig. 3.14

free from distortion, only if the time base has a linear sweep. When the time-base voltage has the same frequency as the input voltage, one complete wave is formed on the screen, Fig. 3.14*a*; if the time-base frequency is half that of the input voltage two waves are exhibited, Fig. 3.14*b*. The time-base frequency must either equal or be a sub-multiple of the frequency of the voltage being analysed. Otherwise the trace from each sweep will not be superimposed on earlier traces and the picture will not be still.

An approximately correct adjustment of the time-base frequency can be achieved by setting the coarse and fine time-base controls to give as steady a trace as possible. This, however, is generally not enough because of the difficulty of ensuring that the frequencies of both the input and the time-base voltages remain constant. Complete synchronization of the two frequencies is obtained by adjusting a control marked *sync* which feeds part of the input voltage to the time-base circuit. This synchronizing voltage pulls the time-base frequency to the correct value and 'locks' the picture. In some C.R.O.s the time base is triggered by the input and does not start by itself, thus giving a steady trace automatically.

The spot is usually suppressed during flyback so that the return trace is not visible. This is done by applying a large voltage, negative relative to the cathode, to the grid of the tube during the flyback period, thereby cutting off the electron beam.

Simple time-base circuits

The simplest time-base circuit is shown in Fig. 3.15*a*. The capacitor C charges through the high resistor R until the p.d. across C reaches the striking voltage V_s of the neon lamp (about

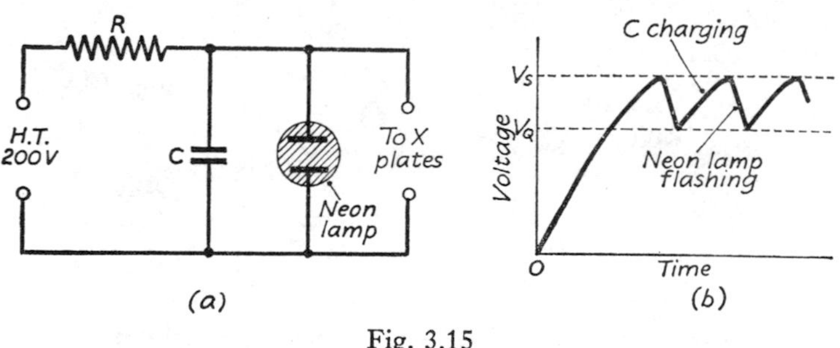

Fig. 3.15

170 volts depending on the lamp). The lamp conducts, glows and C rapidly discharges through it. When the p.d. across C falls to the quenching voltage V_Q of the lamp (about 140 volts), it is no

longer able to maintain the discharge through the neon, the glow disappears and the p.d. starts to rise again as C recharges. The cycle of operations is then repeated.

The voltage across C has a sawtooth form, Fig. 3.15*b*, and its frequency can be altered by varying C and R. Small values of C and R cause a rapid sweep. The two main objections to this circuit are the non-linearity of the sweep (C charges exponentially) and the limited amplitude of the voltage applied to the X plates (due to the small difference between V_s and V_Q).

A more linear time base is given by the arrangement of Fig. 3.16. The resistor R is replaced by a diode valve with the H.T. supply such that the diode is always in the saturated condition. The diode current, which charges C, is constant and so the p.d. across C rises uniformly. This circuit has been used but better methods are now available giving large-amplitude, linear sweeps. In one time base the saturated diode is replaced by a pentode valve and the neon lamp by a thyratron valve. The latter is a gas-filled device (a 'soft' valve) with an action similar to the neon lamp so far as the sawtooth voltage is concerned. For further details of this and other time-base circuits reference should be made to more advanced textbooks on electronics.

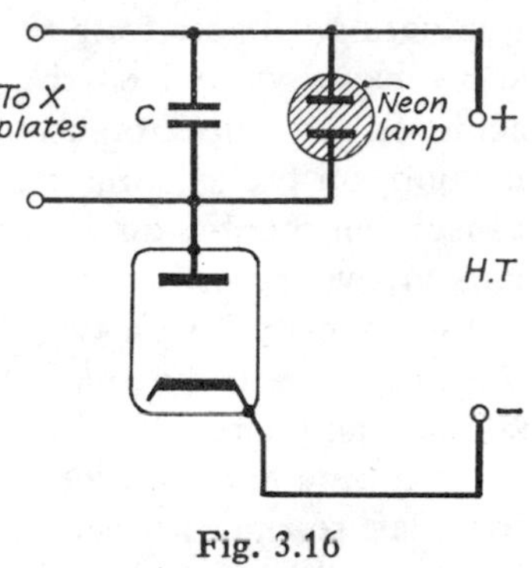

Fig. 3.16

Double beam C.R.O.

The double beam C.R.O. uses a cathode ray tube in which the electron beam emerging from the final anode is split into two parts by an earthed metal plate S placed between the Y plates as

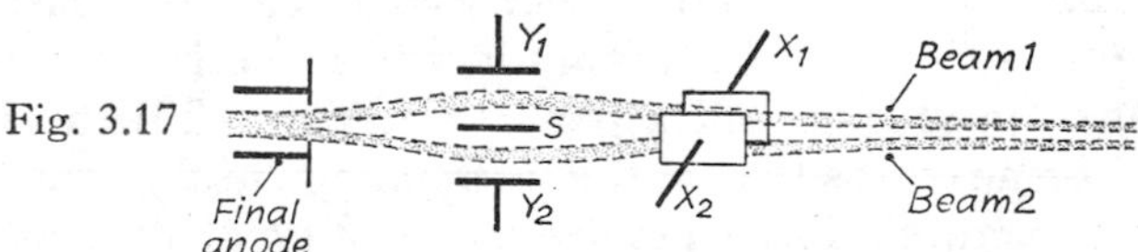

Fig. 3.17

in Fig. 3.17. Besides splitting the beam S acts as a common deflecting plate to both beams. A voltage applied between Y_1 and S deflects the first beam, while one applied between Y_2 and S gives independent deflection of the second beam. Both beams pass between normal X plates and are deflected by any voltage on the X plates. Two traces can thus be studied simultaneously.

It is also possible to make a single beam tube simulate a double beam tube by employing an electronic switching device.

Television receiver

(*a*) BLACK AND WHITE. A television receiver converts small fluctuating voltages from the receiving aerial into a picture of the scene being viewed by the television camera. The operation is achieved by superimposing the signal voltage, after amplification, on the existing steady bias of a cathode ray tube. This causes the number of electrons in the beam from the electron gun to vary according to the signal. To spread the variation of beam intensity into a two-dimensional black and white picture the beam has to be made to scan the fluorescent screen horizontally and vertically.

Two time bases are necessary, the one which moves the spot from left to right across the screen and returns it quickly ready for the next line is called the *line* time base. The other, called the *frame* time base, operates simultaneously and draws the spot at a much slower rate down to the bottom of the screen and then rapidly restores it to the top. The spot thus covers the screen by tracing a series of parallel lines, the process being similar to that when reading a page of print. Both time bases use magnetic deflection; special circuits generate sawtooth currents, at the line and frame frequencies, which are passed through two pairs of coils VV and HH arranged round the neck of the tube as in Fig. 3.18.

In Britain the screen is scanned in 405 lines or in the latest receivers in 625 lines (to conform to general practice in Europe), the process being repeated 25 times per second. Picture flicker is reduced by using interlaced scanning in which the beam scans alternate lines, producing half a picture every one-fiftieth of a second, and then returns to scan the intervening lines, Fig. 3.19. The complete picture is formed in one-twenty-fifth of a second, a time well within the one-tenth of a second allowed by the persistence of vision to give the impression of continuity. The line and frame time bases have the same frequencies as their counterparts in the camera (p. 122) and to ensure that the scanning of a line or a frame starts at the same time as in the camera, synchronizing pulses are transmitted with the signal to trigger the

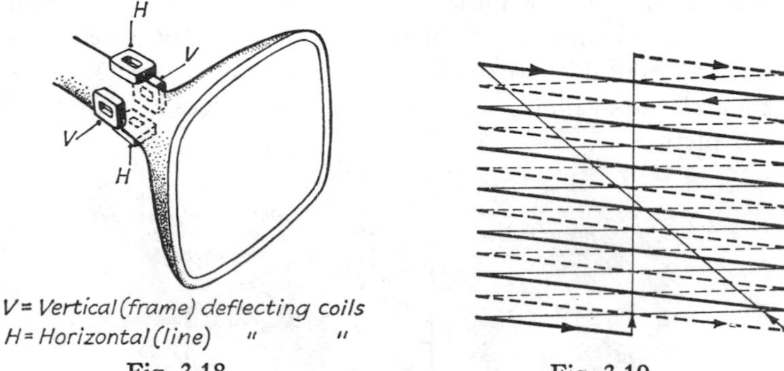

Fig. 3.18

Fig. 3.19

receiver time bases. The signal also carries a 'blanking' pulse to suppress the spot during flyback.

The screen of a television tube contains a mixture of two or more phosphors each contributing colours from different parts of the spectrum to give a white trace. On the inner side of the screen there is a film of aluminium, thin enough to allow the electron beam to pass, which acts as a mirror and reflects out to the viewer light emitted by the phosphor that would otherwise pass into the tube. This, together with the very high final anode voltage (about 16 kV), ensures a bright picture under most conditions.

(*b*) COLOUR. A colour TV tube has three electron guns all similar to the single gun in a black and white tube. The fact is used that any colour of light can be produced by mixing in the right proportions the three primary colours (in light but not for paints) red, green and blue.

The screen is coated with about a million tiny light-emitting 'dots' arranged in triangles. Three different phosphors are used for the 'dots', one which emits red light when struck by electrons, another which emits green light and the third emits blue light. Each dot contains only one phosphor and so emits light of one colour only.

As the three electron beams scan the screen, an accurately placed 'shadow mask' consisting of a perforated metal plate with about one third of a million holes ensures that each beam strikes only dots of one phosphor, e.g. electrons from the 'red gun' strike only 'red dots', Fig. 3.20. Therefore when a particular triangle of dots is struck it may be that the red and green electron beams are intense but not so the blue. In this case the triangle would emit red and green light strongly and so appear yellowish. The triangles of dots are excited in turn and since the dots are so small and the scanning so fast, the viewer sees a continuous colour picture.

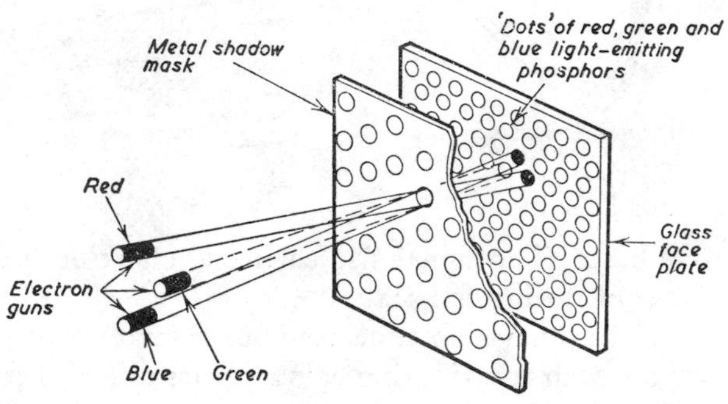

Fig. 3.20

QUESTIONS

1. Draw a sketch to show the essential parts of a cathode ray oscillograph having electrostatic deflection.

With the help of your sketch explain how in a cathode ray oscillograph:

(*a*) The electrons are produced.
(*b*) The electrons are focused.
(*c*) The spot is made visible.
(*d*) The brightness of the spot is controlled.

What is meant by stating that a cathode ray oscillograph is fitted with a linear time base of variable frequency? [*J*.]

2. A diode valve and a resistance are connected in series with a supply of alternating current as shown in Fig. 3.21. Draw diagrams showing the appearance of the trace on the screen when the *Y* plates of a cathode ray oscilloscope are connected (*a*) to *A* and *C*, (*b*) to *B* and *C*. You may assume that during each sweep the spot moves uniformly with time in the *X* direction.

How would the trace be modified in (*b*) if the voltage of the supply were increased so that the diode valve became saturated during part of each cycle? [*C. part qn.*]

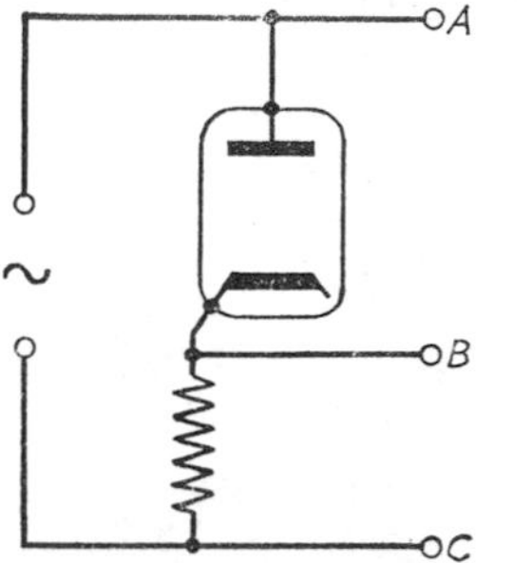

Fig. 3.21

3. A voltage alternating at 50 Hz is connected across the Y plates of a cathode ray oscillograph. Sketch and explain the forms of the traces on the oscillograph screen when a linear time-base of frequency (*i*) 10 Hz, (*ii*) 100 Hz is connected across the X plates. What would be the effect of disconnecting the time base and connecting the X and Y plates in parallel? [*J. part qn.*]

4. Potential differences of 10, 30 and 50 V from a battery are connected in turn between the Y plates of a cathode ray oscillograph causing the horizontal time-base trace to be deflected vertically upwards by amounts 1, 3 and 5 cm respectively. The battery is replaced by an alternating voltage of 20 V, as measured by a moving iron voltmeter. Draw the curve seen on the oscillograph marking the observed vertical deflections at appropriate points on the curve. [*J. part qn.*]

5. Electrons in a cathode ray tube are accelerated through a potential difference of 300 V and the axis of the tube is placed at right angles to the magnetic meridian.

Find how the earth's magnetic field will affect the position of the spot on the screen, if the axial distance from anode to screen is 0·20 m and the flux density of the earth's magnetic field is $6{\cdot}5 \times 10^{-5}$ T. (e/m for an electron $= 1{\cdot}76 \times 10^{11}$ C kg^{-1}.) [*L. Schol. part qn.*]

6. Describe the cathode ray oscilloscope. Draw a circuit diagram showing how the various voltages are applied to the electrodes in the beam system, and how the time-base and signal voltages are applied to the deflector plates.

How would you obtain a circular trace on the screen?

Why is the cathode ray tube preferable to a mechanical form of oscilloscope for showing rapidly changing effects? [*O. Special*]

4 Rectification

Rectification is the process which results in direct current being obtained from alternating current by means of a device called a rectifier. It is one of the three basic operations in electronics, the other two being amplification and oscillation.

The chief source of electrical power is the mains supply in the form of alternating current. However, electrical circuits using valves, transistors, cathode ray tubes, X-ray and Geiger–Müller tubes require direct current. While small amounts of d.c. power can be obtained from batteries a power unit operated from the a.c. mains is usually necessary. In such cases some means of rectification must be incorporated.

Rectifiers

Rectifiers have a low resistance for current flow in one direction, known as the forward direction, and a high resistance in the opposite or reverse direction. They are conductors which are largely unidirectional. When connection is made to a supply so that a rectifier conducts, it is said to be forward biased; in the non-conducting state it is reverse biased. The standard symbols for any rectifier are shown in Fig. 4.1 together with the forward and reverse bias connections. The arrowheads on the symbols indicate the forward direction of conventional current flow; electron flow is in the opposite direction. Three types of rectifier will be considered:

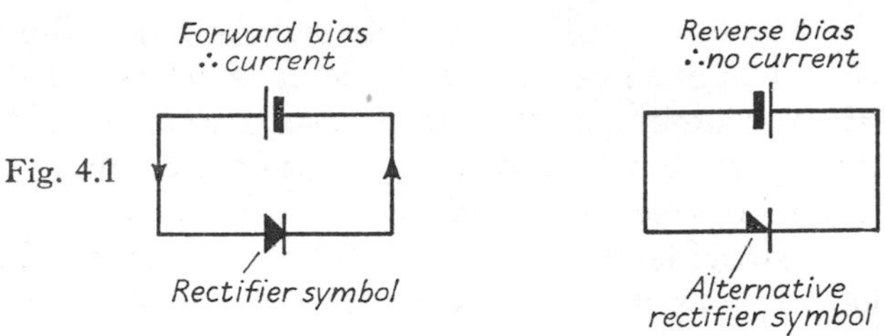

Fig. 4.1

(*i*) RECTIFIER VALVE. The thermionic vacuum diode was described in Chapter 2 and is suitable as a rectifier. It is forward biased when the anode is at a positive potential with respect to the cathode, Fig. 4.2. Any diode rectifies but some are specially designed for the purpose and are called rectifier valves. The double

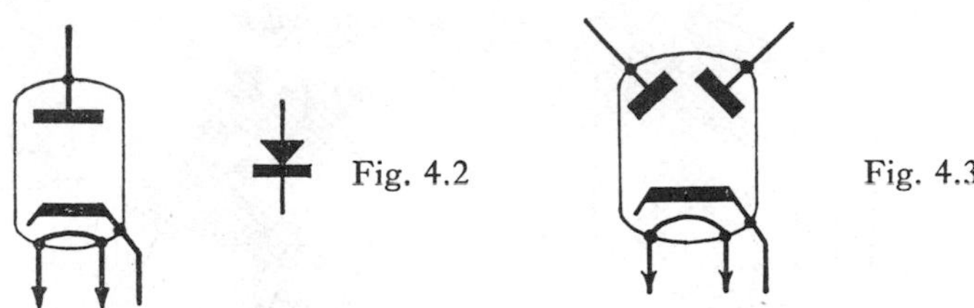
Fig. 4.2

Fig. 4.3

diode is used in certain rectifying circuits and has two diodes in the same glass bulb, each anode having a cathode inside it. The cathodes are often connected in series internally; Fig. 4.3 shows the double-diode symbol.

(*ii*) METAL RECTIFIERS. These consist of a conductor in contact with a semiconducting layer of either cuprous oxide or selenium.

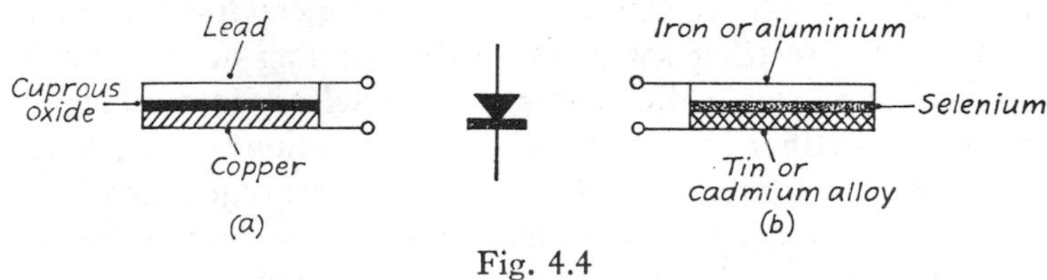

Fig. 4.4

In the copper-oxide rectifier, Fig. 4.4*a*, one face of a copper disc has a thin layer of cuprous oxide formed on it and a lead disc is pressed against the oxide to provide good electrical contact. The forward direction for conventional current flow is from oxide to copper. The selenium rectifier, Fig. 4.4*b*, has an iron or aluminium disc coated on one side with selenium on which is deposited a layer of tin or cadmium alloy to act as a surface electrode. The low-resistance direction is from selenium to tin or alloy. The action of a metal rectifier is not fully understood but it is thought to be due to a barrier layer, a few millionths of a centimetre thick, which is known to exist between conductor and semiconductor. This allows the movement of electrons from the conductor where electrons are plentiful, to the semiconductor where they are scarce.

Single metal rectifier elements can only withstand small reverse voltages, about 10 volts for copper-oxide and 25 volts for selenium, before breakdown occurs; for use on higher voltages

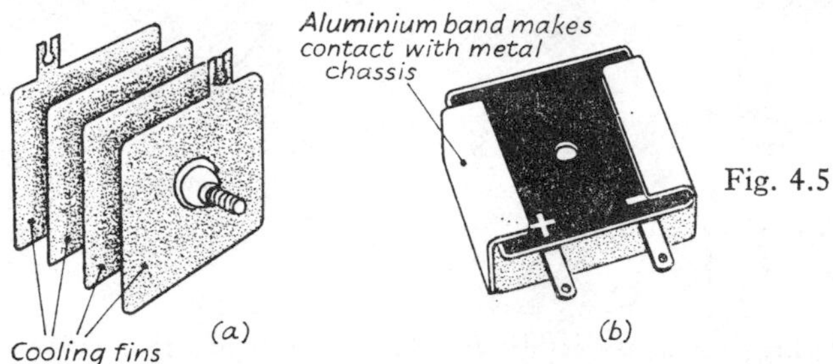

Fig. 4.5

several elements are joined in series. If the temperature of the rectifier increases, the difference between the resistances in the forward and reverse directions decreases and the device becomes less efficient. It is therefore important to ensure that the rectifier current does not create more heat than the rectifier can dissipate. Heat dispersal is achieved either by inserting metal fins at regular intervals in the rectifier assembly so that cooling occurs chiefly by convection or, as in the contact-cooled selenium rectifier, by securing the rectifier so that it cools by conduction to the chassis on which it is mounted. Fig. 4.5 shows both arrangements.

(*iii*) SEMICONDUCTOR DIODE RECTIFIERS. The limitations of metal rectifiers stimulated research into new types of rectifiers which could supply larger currents, withstand higher voltages, be made smaller and yet be reliable and robust. This work led to the introduction in the early 1950's of the germanium diode rectifier and shortly afterwards of the silicon rectifier which has now superseded germanium for power rectification. Silicon rectifiers can operate at a current density of 100 A cm^{-2} of rectifier surface (compared with 100 mA cm^{-2} for metal rectifiers); they can withstand reverse voltages of several hundred

Fig. 4.6

volts and have a maximum working temperature of about 150°C. Fig. 4.6 is a full-size illustration of a typical silicon diode rectifier. The construction and rectifying action of semiconductor diodes will be explained in Chapter 14.

Half-wave rectification

The rectifying circuit of Fig. 4.7 consists of a rectifier in series with the a.c. input to be rectified and the 'load' requiring the d.c.

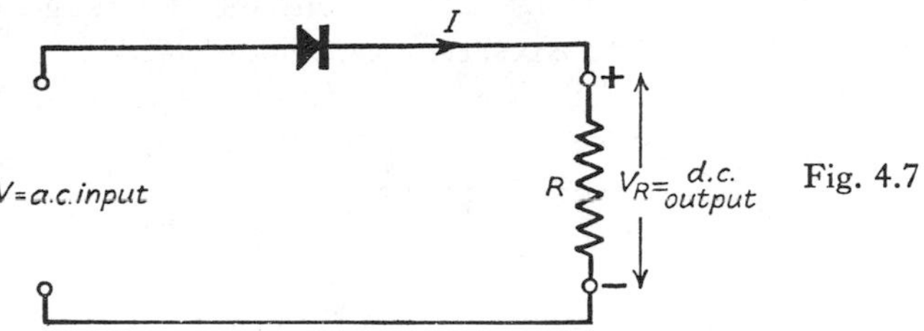

Fig. 4.7

output. For simplicity the 'load' is represented by a resistor *R* but might actually be a radio receiver or some piece of electronic equipment.

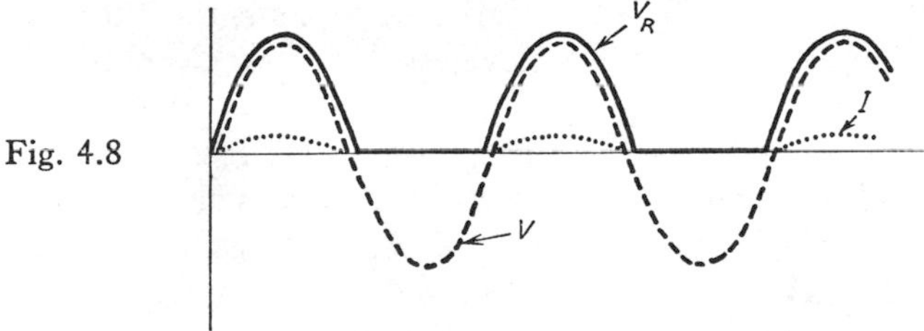

Fig. 4.8

In Fig. 4.8, *V* represents the alternating input voltage applied to the rectifier and load. If the first half-cycle acts in the forward direction of the rectifier a pulse of current I flows round the circuit, creating a p.d. across R where $V_R = IR$. If the forward resistance of the rectifier is small compared with R then V_R will be almost equal to V during this half-cycle. The second half-cycle will reverse bias the rectifier, little or no current flows and V_R is zero. This is repeated for each cycle of a.c. input. The current pulses are unidirectional and so V_R is direct, for although it fluctuates it never changes direction. The top of R in the diagram is always positive. This process is called half-wave rectification since I only flows during positive half-cycles of the input voltage.

If the fluctuating, unsmoothed d.c. output from a half-wave circuit was used to operate a radio receiver it would cause unbearable mains hum in the loudspeaker. To produce steady d.c. some form of smoothing is necessary.

Reservoir capacitor

The simplest smoothing circuit consists of a large capacitor, 16 μF or more, called a reservoir capacitor, placed in parallel with the load R. In Fig. 4.9, C_1 is the reservoir capacitor and its action

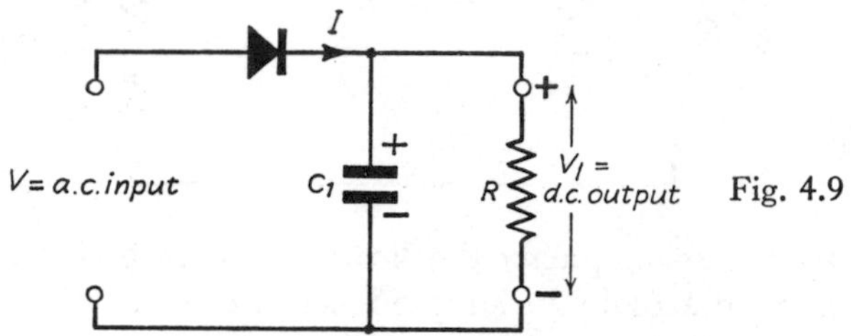

Fig. 4.9

can be followed from Fig.4.10 where V represents the alternating input voltage, V_1 the voltage developed across C_1 and I the rectifier current.

When V acts in the forward direction of the rectifier, current flows through R and at the same time C_1 becomes charged almost to the peak value of V as shown by OA. At A, V becomes less than V_1 and C_1 starts to discharge. It cannot do so through the rectifier since the polarity is wrong, but it does through the load and thus maintains current flow by its charge storing or reservoir action. Along AB, V_1 thus falls. At B, when the applied voltage V equals

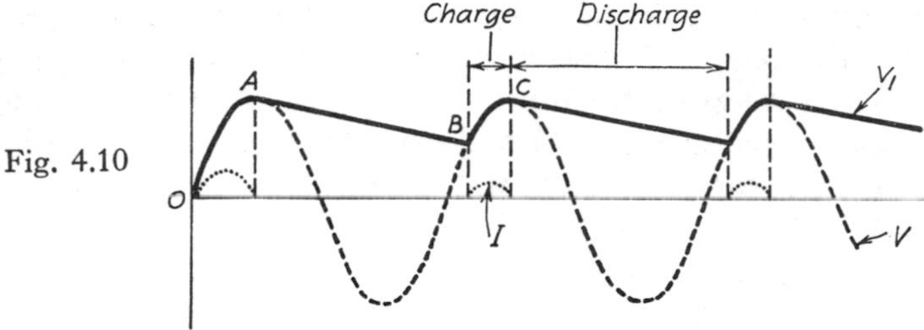

Fig. 4.10

the value to which V_1 has fallen, rectifier current I again flows to recharge the reservoir capacitor to the peak voltage, as shown by BC. The cycle of operations is then repeated. The d.c. output developed across the load is V_1 and although it fluctuates at the frequency of the supply (50 Hz for mains input), the amplitude of the fluctuations is much less than when C_1 is not used.

The following points should be noted:

(*a*) The smoothing action of C_1 is brought about because its large capacitance makes the time constant C_1R very long and so C_1 is unable to follow the variations of V.

(*b*) A large value of C_1 would give better smoothing but initially the uncharged reservoir capacitor would act almost as a short circuit and the resulting surge of current might damage the rectifier.

This type of circuit, employing a valve rectifier, is used to provide E.H.T. of about 16 kV for the final anode of the cathode ray tube in a television receiver. The smoothing of such a high

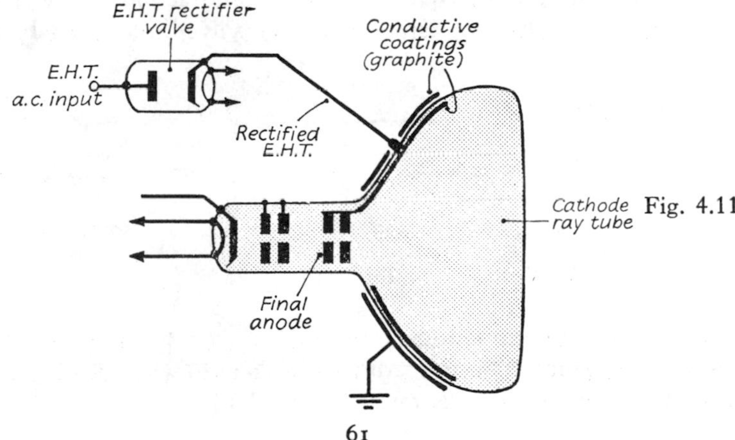

Fig. 4.11

voltage makes severe demands on the insulation of any capacitor used for the purpose. The difficulty is overcome by having conductive coatings on the inner and outer walls of the cathode ray tube as shown in Fig. 4.11 and using them as the plates of a reservoir capacitor. The glass wall of the tube acts as the dielectric.

Capacitor-input filter

A reservoir capacitor has a useful smoothing effect but it is usually supplemented by a filter circuit consisting of a choke L having

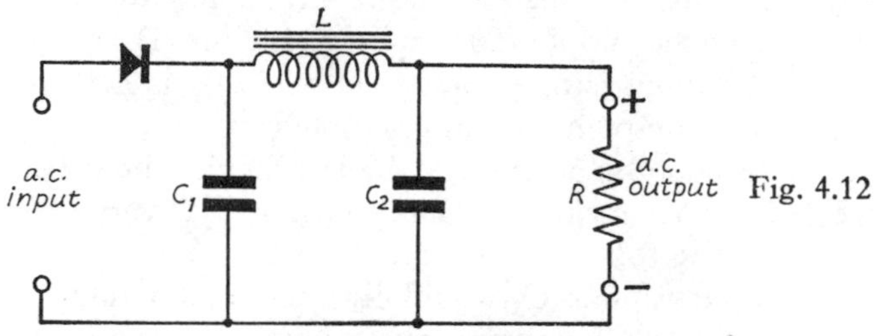

Fig. 4.12

an inductance of about 15 henries and a large capacitor C_2 arranged as in Fig. 4.12. The reservoir capacitor C_1 and the filter capacitor C_2 may be electrolytics enclosed in the same can.

C_1 behaves as explained in the last section and the voltage across it is similar to V_1 in Fig. 4.10. The action of the filter circuit L–C_2 can be understood if V_1 is resolved into a steady d.c.

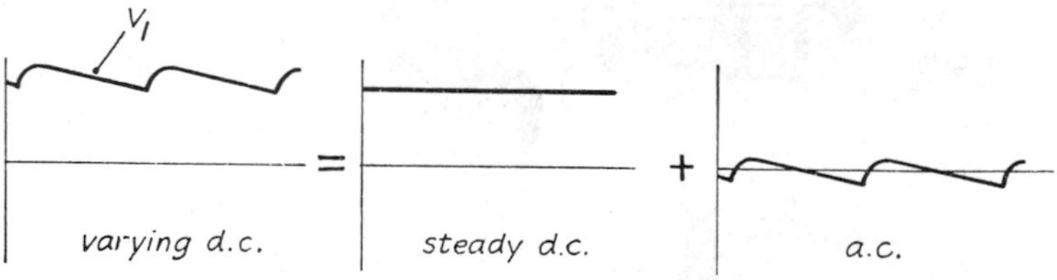

V_1

varying d.c. = steady d.c. + a.c.

Fig. 4.13

voltage (the d.c. component) and an a.c. voltage (the a.c. component or ripple). This procedure is often used when dealing with a varying d.c. and is illustrated in Fig. 4.13.

By redrawing the smoothing circuit as in Fig. 4.14 we see that V_1 is applied across L and C_2 in series. L offers a much greater impedance to the a.c. component than C_2 and most of the unwanted ripple voltage appears across L. For the d.c. component, C_2 has infinite resistance and the whole of this component is developed across C_2 except for the small drop due to the resistance of the choke. The filter thus acts as a potential divider, separating d.c. from a.c. A steady d.c. output is available across

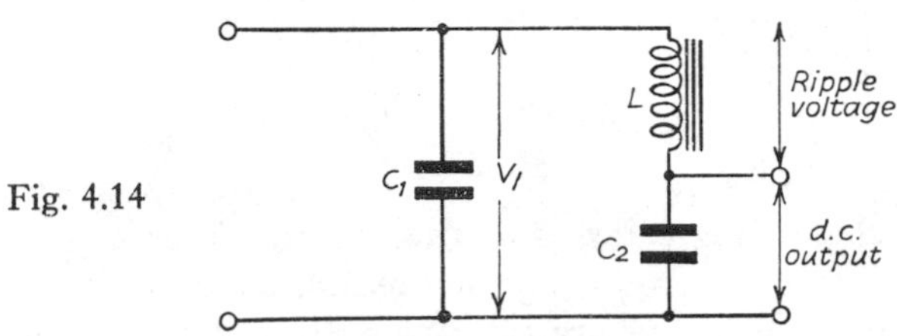

Fig. 4.14

C_2 and can be used, for example, as the H.T. supply to the valves of the circuit forming the load.

When the load current required is small, the choke is often replaced by a resistor to reduce weight and cost but this may result in more of the d.c. component being lost.

The H.T. supply for the valves in the latest television receivers is obtained from a silicon diode half-wave rectifier connected directly to the a.c. mains. A capacitor-input filter provides smoothing, C_1 and C_2 having values between 100 μF and 300 μF.

Full-wave rectification

Half-wave rectification, if followed by adequate smoothing, is quite satisfactory for many purposes but where a very steady ripple-free voltage is required, as in a good quality amplifier, full-wave rectification is necessary.

In this process both halves of every cycle of input voltage v produce current pulses which, if applied directly to the load without smoothing, would develop a fluctuating d.c. output voltage as shown by V_R in Fig. 4.15. The output can be smoothed by a capacitor-input filter, as explained for half-wave rectification, but since the ripple frequency in this case is twice the input frequency (100 Hz for a.c. mains input) the smoothing circuit is more effective. This is so for two reasons. First, the reservoir capacitor has a shorter time to discharge because the pulses of rectified current charging it follow one another twice as fast as in half-wave rectification; the voltage across the reservoir capacitor therefore falls by a smaller amount between pulses. Second, the impedance

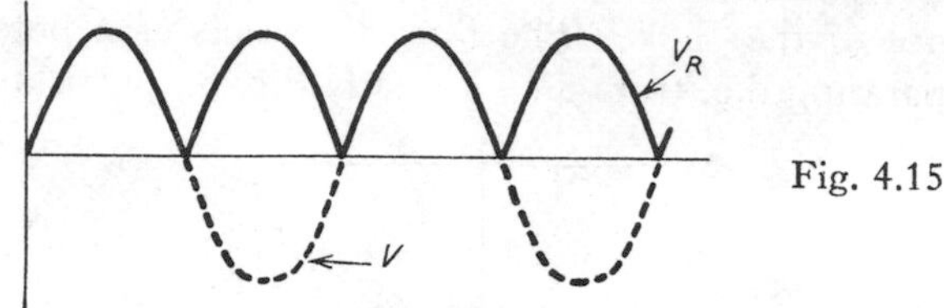

Fig. 4.15

of the filter choke is greater, and that of the filter capacitor smaller, the higher the frequency of the a.c. component. This results in more complete separation of a.c. from d.c. and a very smooth output.

There are two types of full-wave rectification circuit.

Centre-tap full-wave rectifier

This circuit uses two rectifiers and a transformer with a centre-tapped secondary. A common arrangement is shown in Fig. 4.16 where a double-diode valve provides both rectifiers.

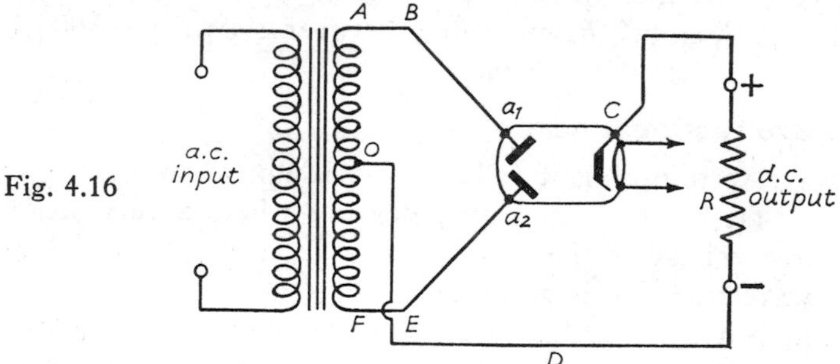

Fig. 4.16

The centre tap O of the secondary winding has a potential half-way between that of A and F and it is convenient to take O as a reference point having zero potential. If the first half-cycle of input makes A positive, anode a_1 is positive with respect to the cathode C and diode a_1–C conducts, giving a current pulse in the circuit ABa_1C, R, DO. During this half-cycle the other diode a_2–C is non-conducting since the voltage across FO makes anode a_2 negative with respect to C. On the other half of the same cycle F becomes positive with respect to O, and A negative. Diode a_2–C conducts to give current in the circuit FEa_2C, R, DO; diode a_1–C is now reverse biased.

In effect the circuit consists of two half-wave rectifiers working into the same load on alternate half-cycles of applied voltage. The important point is that the current through R is in the same direction during both half-cycles and creates a fluctuating d.c. voltage across R like that shown for V_R in Fig. 4.15.

A disadvantage of the centre-tap circuit arises from the fact that the transformer really consists of two secondaries in series (AO and OF). The total secondary voltage is thus twice that required by one diode, for example a 300–0–300 volt transformer develops an r.m.s. voltage of 600 volts (about 800 volts peak) across the whole secondary but only 300 volts is effective during each half-cycle.

Bridge full-wave rectifier

Four rectifiers are arranged in a bridge network as in Fig. 4.17. If A is positive during the first half-cycle, rectifiers 1 and 2 conduct and current takes the path ABC, through R, DEF. On the next half-cycle when F is positive, rectifiers 3 and 4 are forward

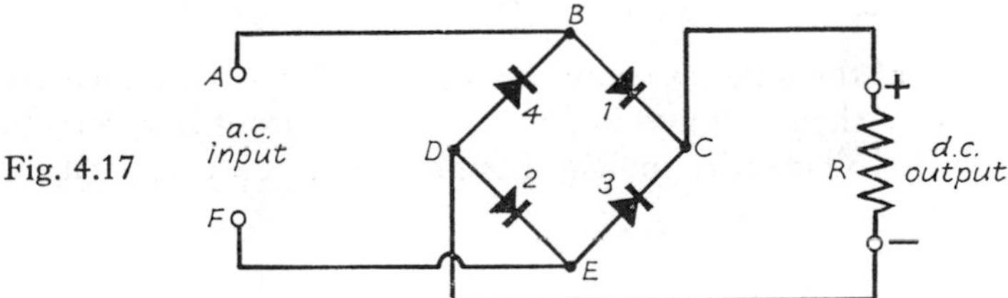

Fig. 4.17

biased and current follows the path FEC, through R, DBA. Once again current flow through R is unidirectional during both half-cycles of input voltage and a d.c. output is obtained.

The bridge rectifier circuit is frequently employed with metal rectifiers, all four rectifiers being mounted on the same spindle and forming one physical unit. The arrangement is adopted in the copper-oxide instrument rectifier which converts d.c. meters to a.c. working. One is shown in Fig. 4.18, the four connections being taken from points corresponding to *B*, *E*, *C* and *D* in Fig. 4.17. Copper-oxide rectifiers are now only used as instrument rectifiers and in certain telephone circuits.

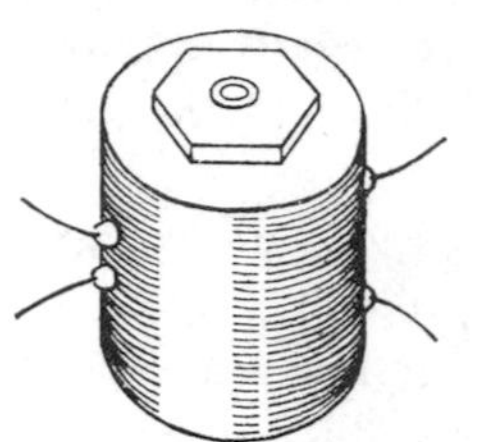

Fig. 4.18

Voltage doubling

In the rectifying circuits considered so far the output voltage never exceeds the peak input voltage. Certain high-voltage devices such as cathode ray oscilloscopes, require only a small current and in such cases a voltage doubling circuit is suitable using two rectifiers and two capacitors connected as in Fig. 4.19.

Each capacitor charges to the peak voltage during alternate

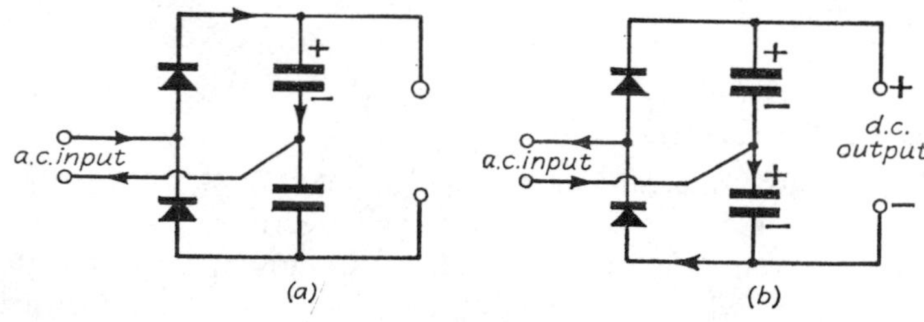

Fig. 4.19

half-cycles of the input as shown by *a* and *b*. Since the capacitors are in series, their voltages add and the d.c. output is twice the peak supply voltage without a load but less when current is taken.

Laboratory H.T. power pack

A typical laboratory power pack for experimental work is shown in Fig. 4.20; it employs a selenium bridge rectifier fed by a step-up mains transformer and provides a smooth d.c. supply of 0–400 volts at 100 mA, as well as 6·3 volts a.c. The 25-kΩ variable resistor acts as a potential divider giving a continuously variable output and also allowing the capacitors to discharge when the pack is switched off—this eliminates any risk of shock should the output terminals be touched subsequently.

The use of a transformer in a power pack offers certain advantages:

(*a*) If the input is taken directly from the 240-volt a.c. mains, the value of the output is determined by the mains voltage and may not be suitable for the load. The transformer allows the

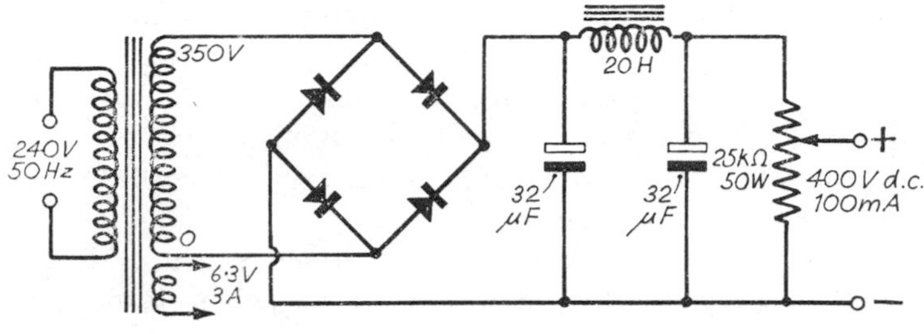

Fig. 4.20

input to be increased or decreased depending on its turn-ratio with a corresponding rise or fall of the direct voltage output.

(*b*) A low-voltage supply for valve heater currents can be obtained from a step-down secondary winding on the transformer.

It should be noted that r.m.s. voltages are usually quoted for the secondary of a transformer but, depending on the current taken by the load, rectification and smoothing can result in a d.c. output which approaches the peak value, i.e., 1·4 times the r.m.s. value. Thus in the circuit shown the nominal 350-volt secondary gives a d.c. output of about 500 volts at no load current and 400 volts when 100 mA is supplied.

Diode valve voltmeter

A valve voltmeter has a very high impedance and does not appreciably disturb the circuit to which it is connected. It can also measure alternating p.d.s of low and high frequency and thus has advantages over moving coil and moving iron instruments.

A simple valve voltmeter employing the rectifying action of a diode valve is shown in Fig. 4.21. The diode conducts during positive half-cycles of input voltage and the moving coil milliammeter records the mean value of rectified anode current. A calibration curve is obtained by applying alternating voltages of known r.m.s. values (usually at 50 Hz) and noting the corresponding anode currents. Unknown voltages may then be found and may be of other frequencies. *R* is a resistance of several hundred kilohms whose exact value depends on the diode and the sensitivity of the milliammeter. It is included to increase the resistance of the voltmeter.

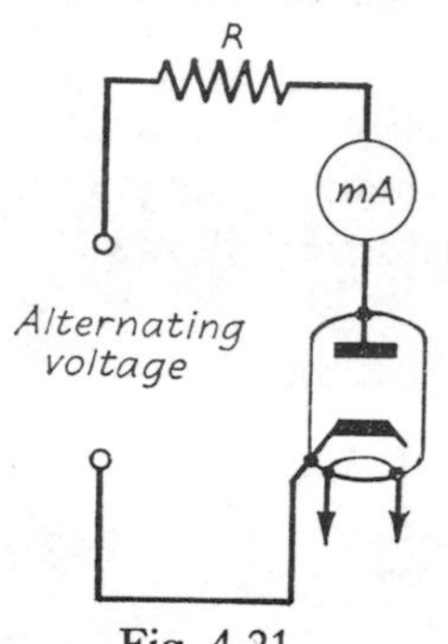

Fig. 4.21

Triode valve voltmeters are preferable in practice because they have higher impedances and also amplify.

QUESTIONS

1. (*a*) What is meant by rectification?
   (*b*) What properties should a rectifier possess?
   (*c*) Explain briefly the terms half-wave and full-wave rectification.

2. In each case name one type of rectifier which is suitable for supplying
   (*a*) E.H.T. (16 kV, 120 μA) to the cathode ray tube in a television receiver.
   (*b*) L.T. (12 V, 5 A) for battery charging.
   (*c*) H.T. (220 V, 300 mA) for the valves in a television receiver.
   (*d*) d.c. to a 1 mA moving coil meter which is to be used in an a.c. circuit.

3. Draw a circuit diagram of one type of rectifier–smoother circuit which will give a well-smoothed, direct voltage from the a.c. mains. Explain the function of each component.

4. Give a labelled circuit diagram of a half-wave diode rectifier to provide a smoothed but very small current at about 680 volts. Assume that the circuit is to be supplied from 240-volt a.c. mains through a transformer and deduce the appropriate turns ratio for the anode voltage. [*W. part qn.*]

5. Explain the meaning of *rectification* of an alternating current. Describe the use of (*a*) a metal rectifier, (*b*) a diode valve, as a rectifier of alternating current. [*A.E.B.*]

6. Describe in detail the construction and action of a thermionic diode. How would you produce (*a*) half-wave, (*b*) full-wave, rectification of alternating current using diode valves? [*S.*]

7. Give a circuit diagram for a low-voltage unit operating from the a.c mains which will supply a fairly smooth d.c. supply of 20 V at 6 A maximum.

5 Amplification

Amplification is the changing of a small alternating voltage into a large alternating voltage and the device performing the operation is called an amplifier. The process is necessary in many types of electronic equipment; thus in a radio set a signal of a few millionths of a volt from the aerial has to be amplified to drive a loudspeaker, and the same is true of the small output from the pick-up in a record player or the microphone in a public address system.

Amplification can be brought about by a triode valve.

Triode valve

The triode has three electrodes. The anode and cathode are as in the diode valve but the third electrode, called the *grid*, is a thin wire wound in a spiral close to but not touching the cathode so that electrons can pass through the spaces between its windings, Fig. 5.1.

In the diode, the anode current can be changed by changing the anode voltage; in the triode, alteration of the voltage of the grid with respect to the cathode provides an additional and more effective way of controlling the anode current. Thus, the more negative the voltage or *bias* of the grid the fewer the number of electrons reaching the anode from the space charge near the cathode. When the grid is sufficiently negative to just reduce the anode current to zero, the triode is said to be biased to 'cut-off'. A positive grid bias increases the anode current but also attracts some electrons to the grid, causing a flow of grid current which, we shall see later, is undesirable. Care is therefore generally taken to ensure that the bias on the grid is always negative.

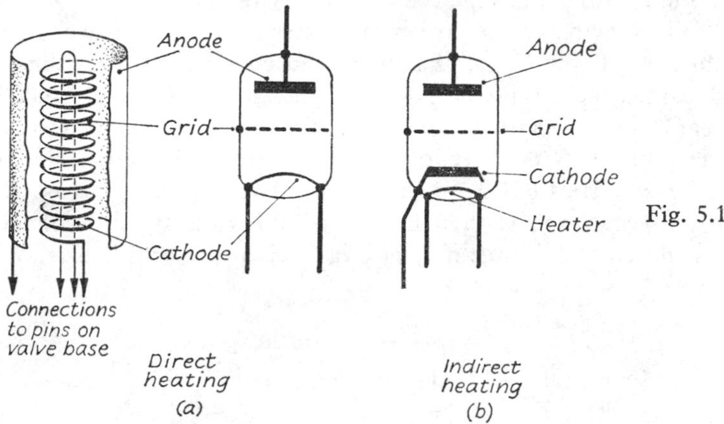

Fig. 5.1

These effects may be studied using the circuit of Fig. 5.2, various negative voltages being applied to the grid from the grid bias supply *G.B.* When *X* is connected to *Y* the grid potential

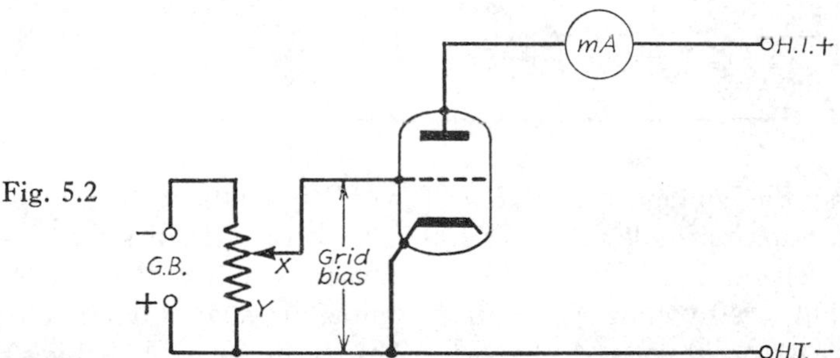

Fig. 5.2

is zero, i.e., the same as the cathode potential. Positive bias is provided by reversing the connections to *G.B.* A negative bias of a few volts cuts off the valve even when the anode voltage is 100 volts or more.

Triode as a voltage amplifier

The proximity of the grid to the cathode results in a small change of grid voltage causing an appreciable change in anode current and it is this, in effect, which enables a triode to amplify. The anode current change is usually converted into a voltage change by connecting a *load*, such as a resistor, between the anode and H.T. The anode current change then produces a voltage change across the load which may be many times greater than the voltage change on the grid. The valve and load *together* act as a voltage amplifier.

Consider the circuit of Fig. 5.3 with a resistor R of 10,000 ohms (10 kΩ) as the load and an H.T. supply of 120 volts. The anode current I_a flows (conventionally) from H.T.+, through R and the valve to H.T.− and causes a voltage drop across R. The anode voltage is then less than 120 volts by the voltage dropped across R. Thus if I_a is 2 mA when the grid bias is −3

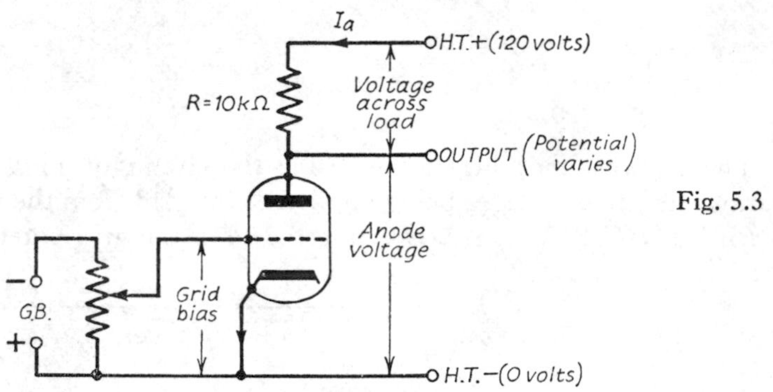

Fig. 5.3

volts, the voltage across $R = I_a \times R = 0{\cdot}002 \times 10{,}000 = 20$ volts and the anode voltage is 100 volts. If the grid bias changes to −1 volts and I_a becomes 4 mA the voltage across $R = 0{\cdot}004 \times 10{,}000 = 40$ volts and the anode voltage is now only 80 volts, a decrease of 20 volts. A change of 2 volts on the grid changes the anode voltage by 20 volts. The ***voltage amplification*** or ***gain*** A is defined as

$$\frac{\text{change in anode voltage}}{\text{change in grid voltage}}$$

and in this case is $20/2 = 10$.

In practice the grid voltage is changed by applying the small alternating voltage to be amplified, i.e., the input, between grid and cathode, and to ensure that it never drives the grid positive, a

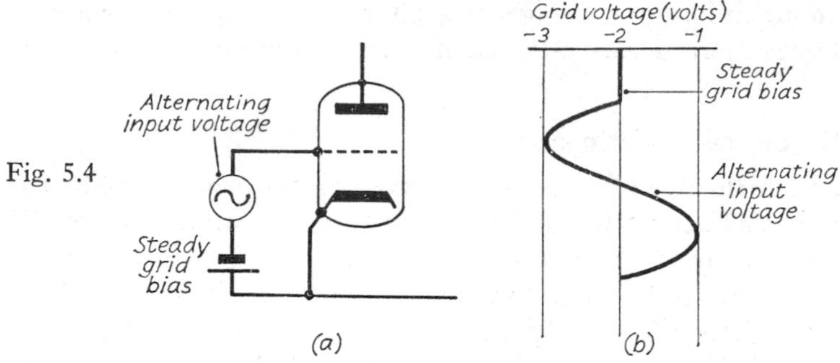

Fig. 5.4 (a) (b)

steady negative bias, represented by a battery in Fig. 5.4*a*, is applied in series with the input. If the input has a peak value of 1 volt and the steady bias is −2 volts, the grid voltage varies from −3 to −1 volts, Fig. 5.4*b*. For the triode under consideration the anode voltage will then fluctuate between 100 and 80 volts.

The anode voltage variations which form the output may be tapped off by connecting across the valve, i.e., between the output and H.T.− terminals as in Fig. 5.3. Similar variations occur across the load and although the output could be obtained by connecting across the output and H.T.+ terminals, this is not usual. The output is a varying direct voltage which can be considered to consist of a steady direct voltage with an alternating voltage superimposed upon it. Here the steady component has a value of 90 volts and the alternating component has peak value of 10 volts, Fig. 5.5. Only the alternating voltage is required and it may be separated from the direct component by inserting a capacitor, to block the direct component, in the output connection from the anode. It can be seen from Figs. 5.4*b* and 5.5 that

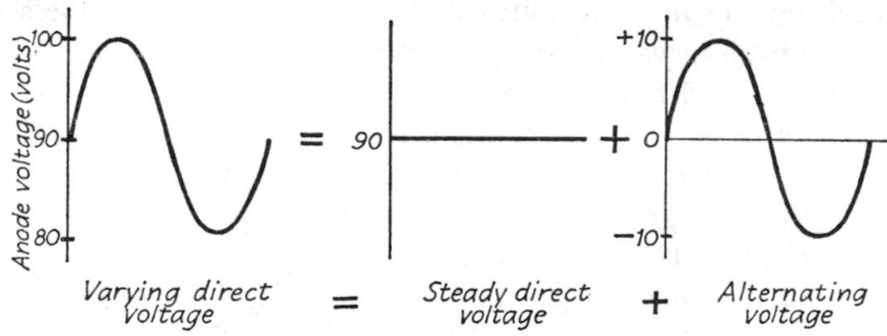

Fig. 5.5

the input and output voltages are 180° out of phase, i.e., when the grid goes more negative the anode becomes more positive.

Static characteristic curves

The performance of a triode in a given circuit can be predicted when its characteristics are known. The anode current I_a depends on both the anode voltage V_a and the grid voltage V_g and either V_a or V_g must be kept fixed while the other is varied when studying their effect on I_a. The circuit of Fig. 5.6 is suitable for investigating the relationships using a directly heated valve. Two sets of curves, called *static characteristics*, can be obtained.

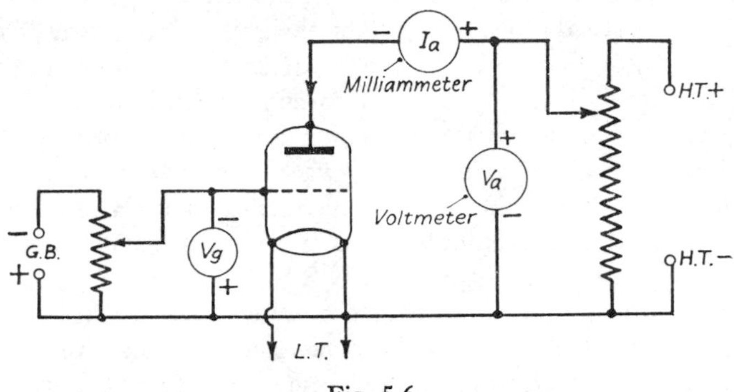

Fig. 5.6

The *anode characteristic* curves show how I_a varies with V_a when V_g is constant. Curves relating to the triode considered in the last section are shown in Fig. 5.7 for four different grid voltages. Each one is found by keeping V_g fixed while V_a is increased up to the maximum value permitted for the valve and the corresponding values of I_a measured.

It will be noted that (*i*) the curves are approximately straight and parallel over a good part of their length and (*ii*) a greater anode voltage is required to obtain a given anode current the more negative the grid, e.g., for $I_a = 4$ mA, $V_a = 60$ volts when $V_g = 0$ volt, but $V_a = 100$ volts when $V_g = -2$ volts.

The *mutual characteristic* curves relate I_a and V_g when V_a is constant and are derived using the same circuit. Four curves, also for the previous triode, are shown in Fig. 5.8; their general form

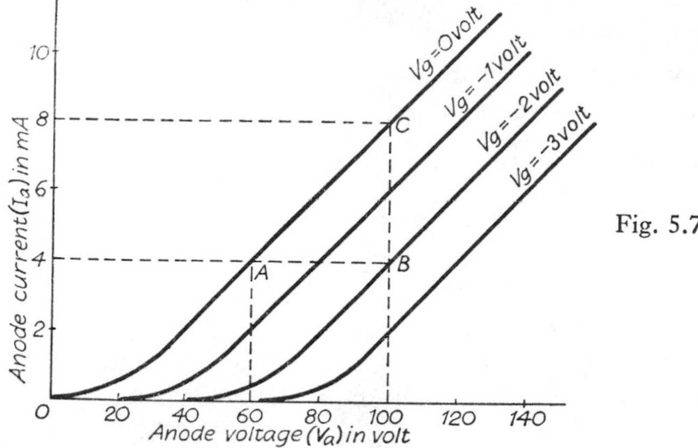

Fig. 5.7

is similar to that of the $I_a - V_a$ characteristics. Note that at higher anode voltages a more negative grid cut-off voltage is required.

The anode characteristics and the mutual characteristics are two different ways of giving exactly the same information about a valve.

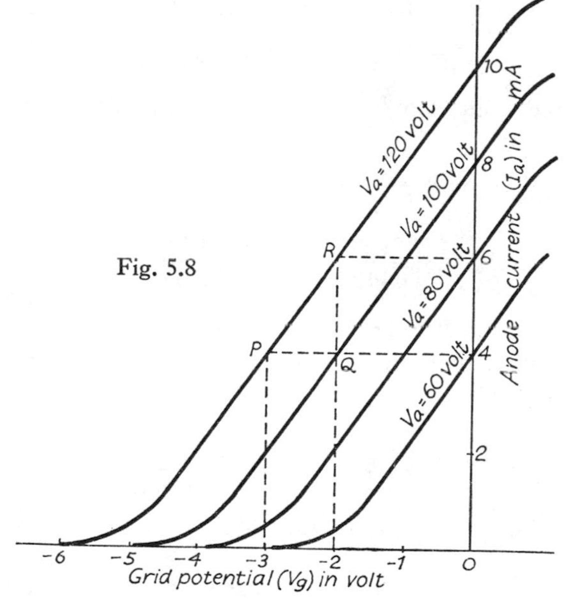

Fig. 5.8

Valve constants

Much of the information contained in the static characteristic curves can be summarized by three valve constants or parameters.

1. A.C. OR ANODE RESISTANCE. The d.c. resistance of a triode equals the ratio V_a/I_a for corresponding values but this quantity is of little importance since in amplification we are usually concerned with a.c. and so it is the internal opposition of the valve to *changes* in voltage and current which matters. The a.c. or anode resistance denoted by R_a is defined thus:

$$R_a = \frac{\text{change in anode voltage } (\delta V_a)}{\text{change in anode current } (\delta I_a)}$$

when the grid voltage V_g is constant and the straight part of the characteristic is used. Referring to points A, B and C on the anode characteristic curves, Fig. 5.7, we have

$$R_a = \frac{\delta V_a}{\delta I_a} = \frac{\text{AB}}{\text{BC}} = \frac{(100 - 60)\text{ volts}}{(8 - 4)\text{ mA}} = \frac{40\text{ volts}}{4\text{ mA}}$$

$$= 10{,}000\text{ ohms} = 10\text{ k}\Omega$$

The same value is obtained from the mutual characteristics.

2. MUTUAL CONDUCTANCE. This has the symbol g_m and is given by

$$g_m = \frac{\text{change in anode current } (\delta I_a)}{\text{change in grid voltage } (\delta V_g)}$$

when V_a is constant and the changes are measured on the straight part of the characteristic. It is readily obtained from the mutual characteristic and in Fig. 5.8

$$g_m = \frac{\delta I_a}{\delta V_g} = \frac{\text{QR}}{\text{PQ}} = \frac{(6 - 4)\text{ mA}}{1\text{ volt}}$$

$$= 2\text{ mA per volt.}$$

g_m indicates the control the grid exerts on the anode current.

3. AMPLIFICATION FACTOR. A small change of grid voltage can cause the same change in anode current as a large change of anode voltage. The amplification factor μ of a valve is defined by

$$\mu = \frac{\text{change in anode voltage } (\delta V_a)}{\text{change in grid voltage } (\delta V_g)}$$

to give the same change of anode current. In Fig. 5.8 an increase of I_a from 4 mA to 6 mA can be achieved by either (*i*) increasing V_a from 100 volts to 120 volts, keeping $V_g = -2$ volts (points Q and R), or (*ii*) changing V_g from -3 volts to -2 volts, keeping $V_a = 120$ volts (points P and R). Therefore

$$\mu = \frac{\delta V_a}{\delta V_g} = \frac{20}{1} = 20$$

From the definitions of μ, g_m and R_a it follows that

$$\mu = \frac{\delta V_a}{\delta V_g} = \frac{\delta V_a}{\delta I_a} \times \frac{\delta I_a}{\delta V_g} = R_a \times g_m$$

For the triode considered $R_a = 10\ \text{k}\Omega$, $g_m = 2$ mA per volt, hence $\mu = R_a \times g_m = 10{,}000 \times 2/1000 = 20$, which agrees with the value found from the static characteristics.

The values of the three parameters are determined by the geometry of the electrodes; valves intended for different purposes have different parameters.

The amplification factor μ is not to be confused with the voltage amplification or gain A. μ is a constant of the valve alone and measures the amplification of which it is capable. By contrast A is a constant of the whole circuit including the load and indicates the amplification actually attained. For the triode discussed previously $\mu = 20$ but when used as an amplifier in the circuit of Fig. 5.3 the gain A is only 10.

This discrepancy between the theoretical capability of the valve and its performance in practice is due to the fact that under working conditions the anode voltage does not remain constant. If the valve has a load in its anode circuit, an increase of anode current (caused by the grid voltage becoming less negative) results in an increased voltage *drop* across the load and so a decrease of anode voltage, as was explained earlier. The increase of anode current is therefore not as great as it would have been if the anode voltage had remained constant. Hence A is always less than μ.

Gain formula for an amplifier

It follows from the definition of g_m that a change of δV_g in the grid voltage of a valve produces an anode current change of $g_m . \delta V_g$, provided the anode voltage remains constant. Similarly from the definition of R_a, a change of δV_a in the anode voltage causes an anode current change of $\delta V_a / R_a$ if the grid voltage remains constant. In a triode amplifier having an anode load R, the grid and anode voltages change simultaneously and are such that the anode voltage change reduces the variation of anode current produced by the variation of grid voltage. The resultant anode current change δI_a is then given by

$$\delta I_a = g_m . \delta V_g - \frac{\delta V_a}{R_a} \tag{1}$$

Also, since the anode voltage change created by the anode current change δI_a equals the change of voltage across R,

$$\delta V_a = R . \delta I_a \tag{2}$$

Eliminating δI_a from (1) and (2)

$$\frac{\delta V_a}{R} = g_m . \delta V_g - \frac{\delta V_a}{R_a}$$

$$\therefore \quad \delta V_a \left(\frac{1}{R} + \frac{1}{R_a} \right) = g_m . \delta V_g$$

$$\therefore \quad \frac{\delta V_a}{\delta V_g} = \frac{g_m . R_a . R}{R_a + R} = \frac{\mu R}{R_a + R}$$

But the gain $A = \delta V_a / \delta V_g$ under working conditions

$$\therefore \quad A = \frac{\mu R}{R_a + R} \tag{3}$$

This expression enables the gain of an amplifier to be calculated if the valve parameters R_a and μ and also the anode load R, are known. When $\mu = 20$, $R_a = 10 \text{ k}\Omega$ and $R = 10 \text{ k}\Omega$ then

$$A = \frac{20 \times 10}{(10 + 10)} = 10$$

From (3), we see that when R is large compared with R_a, $A \simeq \mu$. However this would require the H.T. supply to be inconveniently high for the valve to operate satisfactorily. A common compromise is to make $R \simeq 2R_a$ then $A \simeq 2\mu/3$.

Dynamic characteristic

A graph showing the variation of anode current I_a with grid voltage V_g under certain working conditions, i.e., for a given load and H.T. voltage, is called a *dynamic characteristic*. It can be

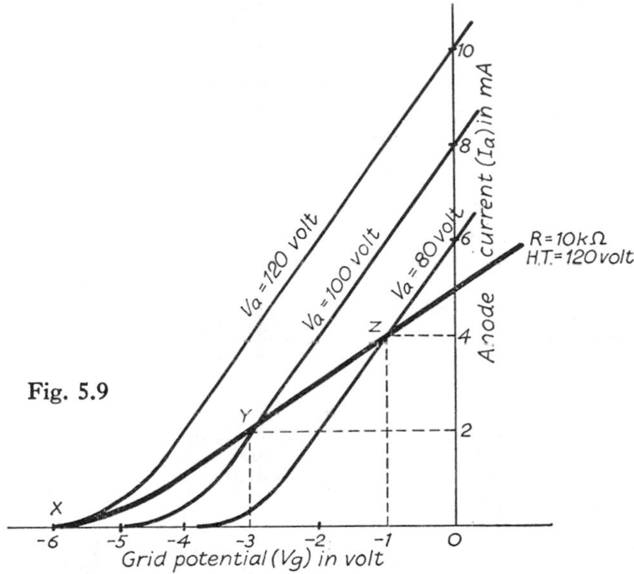

Fig. 5.9

found experimentally in the same way as the static characteristics (but with the load in the anode circuit), or it may be derived from the mutual characteristics. Thus the dynamic characteristic for an anode load of 10 kΩ and an H.T. voltage of 120 volts can be deduced for the triode whose mutual characteristics were shown in Fig. 5.8 and are repeated in Fig. 5.9.

When $I_a = 0$, there is no voltage drop across R and the anode voltage V_a equals the H.T. voltage of 120 volts. Point X therefore lies on the dynamic characteristic. If $I_a = 2$ mA, the voltage across R is 20 volts and V_a equals 100 volts; this gives point Y on the dynamic characteristic. Similarly Z, corresponding to $I_a = 4$ mA and $V_a = 80$ volts, is a third point and XYZ is the required curve. It is characteristic not of the valve itself but of the valve when connected to an anode load of 10 kΩ.

The dynamic characteristic provides another method of determining the gain of an amplifier. The curve shown in Fig. 5.10 is

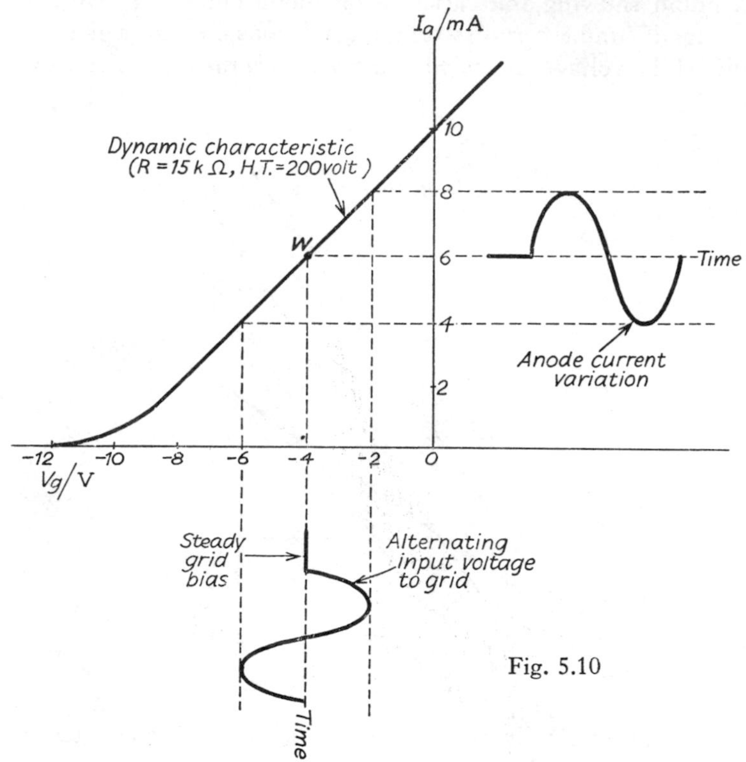

Fig. 5.10

for a triode having an anode load of 15 kΩ and an H.T. supply of 200 volts. If a steady bias of −4 volts is applied to the grid, the anode current remains constant at 6 mA in the absence of a signal. The point W on the dynamic characteristic is called the *working point*. Application of an alternating input of ±2 volts causes the grid voltage to vary between −2 and −6 volts and the anode current between 8 and 4 mA. The anode current may be treated as a steady direct current of 6 mA plus an alternating current of peak value ± 2 mA and it is the latter which develops the amplified output voltage across the load. Here the output voltage has a peak value which equals the anode load × peak value of the alternating component of anode current, i.e., 15 kΩ × 2 mA = 30 volts. The gain A is 30/2, i.e., 15.

If the output voltage waveform is to be a true, but amplified, copy of the input voltage waveform the working point must be on the straight part of the dynamic characteristic. This is achieved by correct selection of the steady negative grid bias value. If the

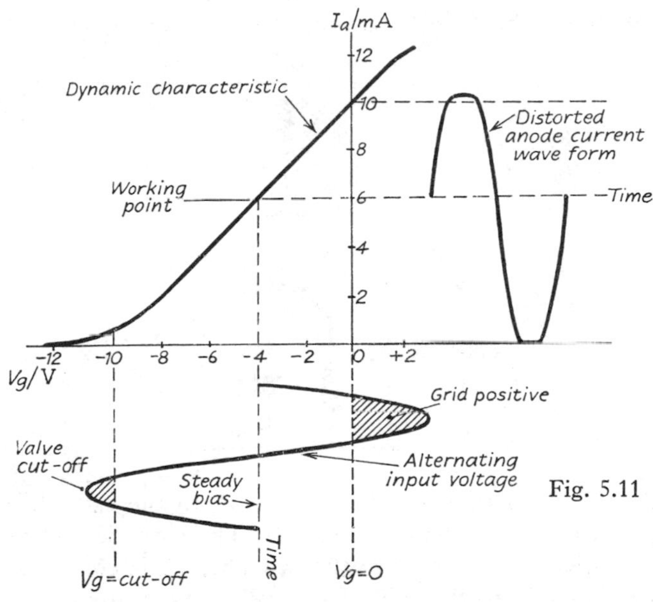

Fig. 5.11

bias is too negative the alternating input voltage may drive the valve beyond cut-off during the negative half-cycles. On the other hand, too small a negative bias may cause the input to drive the grid positive during positive half-cycles and the grid then attracts some electrons which normally would go to the anode. In both cases the result is a distorted anode current waveform. Even with the correct grid bias, distortion occurs if the input voltage swings are excessive, as shown in Fig. 5.11.

In practice the steady bias is often chosen so that it has a value mid-way between $V_g = 0$ and $V_g =$ cut-off. This is called *mid-point biasing* and the amplifier is said to be operating under *Class A* conditions.

Grid bias

Grid bias may be applied from a battery and although simple, it is generally only employed in the laboratory for experimental work. Bias batteries are made up from several (often six) 1·5-volt cells in series and are tapped for intermediate voltages.

A method known as *cathode bias* is commonly used and is shown in Fig. 5.12. With no input signal the anode current is

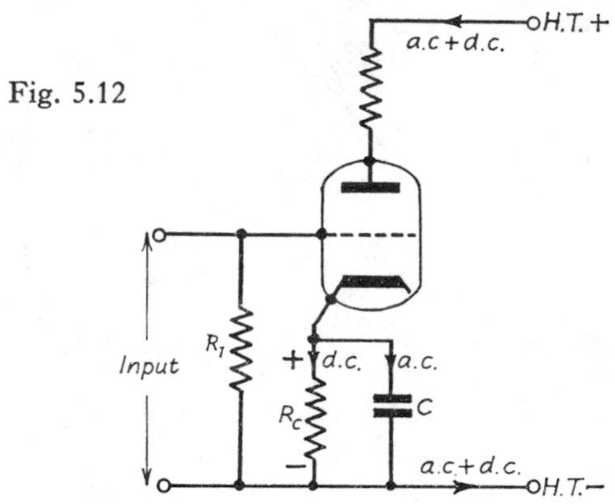

Fig. 5.12

steady and flows through the resistor R_c in the cathode circuit causing a drop in potential across it. The cathode end of R_c is thus positive with respect to the other which is connected by a high resistor R_1 to the grid. R_1 is called the *grid resistor* and it ensures that the grid is at the same potential as the lower end of R_c. This is so because there is no grid current flowing through R_1 to create a p.d. between its ends. Both ends are at the same potential, i.e., the potential of the lower end of R_c. (It will be understood shortly, when the coupling of amplifier stages is considered, why R_1 must have a large value.) The cathode is therefore at a higher potential than the grid, i.e., the grid is negative with respect to the cathode. For example, if the valve requires a steady bias of -3 volts to operate properly and the anode current is 6 mA with this bias, then by Ohm's law $R_c = 3/0{\cdot}006 = 500$ ohms.

When a signal is applied to the grid the anode current has an a.c. component which will vary the bias if it passes through R_c. To eliminate this a by-pass or *decoupling* capacitor C is connected across R_c and provides a low-capacitive reactance to the lowest frequency to be amplified. The value of C is such that the combined impedance of R_c and C in parallel is negligible to the a.c. component, and therefore the a.c. voltage developed across them is also negligible. Typical values of C for a low-frequency amplifier are 50 μF and for a high-frequency amplifier 0·1 μF.

Types of amplifier

The basic principles of amplification are the same for all frequencies but it is usual to classify amplifiers according to whether they handle low or high frequencies.

(*a*) An *audio frequency* (A.F.) amplifier amplifies frequencies from about 15 Hz to 15,000 Hz (15 kHz), i.e., those resulting from speech or music. It is required to give uniform amplification of all frequencies in this range.

(*b*) A *radio frequency* (R.F.) amplifier is designed to amplify one frequency (more exactly a narrow band) exceeding 30 kHz such as is produced in the aerial of a radio set by the signal from a broadcasting station. A typical radio frequency is one million hertz, usually called one megahertz and written 1 MHz.

We shall see shortly that, depending on the type of amplifier, the anode load is not always a resistor. Furthermore, most amplifiers require more amplification than that obtained with one valve and several 'stages' are employed in which the output of one stage is applied to the input circuit of the next. This coupling of stages can be done in various ways.

Resistance-capacitance coupling

A two-stage resistance-capacitance coupled amplifier is shown in Fig. 5.13, the coupling taking its name from the resistive load R and the coupling capacitor C.

The alternating component of anode voltage from the first valve V_1 has to be applied to the grid of the second valve V_2. Direct connection cannot be made because this would also couple the steady component and subject the grid of V_2 to a high positive potential. If a capacitor C is interposed, the direct voltage is blocked but the alternating component successively charges and discharges C, causing an alternating current to flow in the grid resistor R_1. The voltage developed across R_1 is therefore alternating and acts as the input to the next stage. The presence of grid resistor R_1 is essential to make the cathode bias circuit of valve V_2 effective.

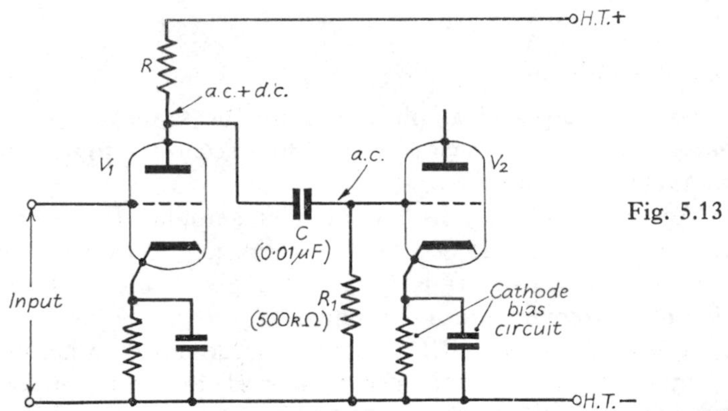

Fig. 5.13

To prevent loss of amplification in the coupling both C and R_1 should be large. This follows since these two components form a potential divider to the alternating output from V_1, and the greater the value of R_1 compared with the reactance of C, i.e., $1/2\pi fC$, the larger is the fraction of the output applied to V_2.

Resistance-capacitance coupling is used in A.F. amplifiers, a typical value for C being 0·01 μF and for R_1 about 500 kΩ. The frequency response is uniform on account of the resistive load R being independent of frequency. A disadvantage arises from the drop of H.T. volts occurring across R.

Transformer coupling

In the transformer coupled A.F. amplifier of Fig. 5.14 the anode circuit of valve V_1 contains the primary of an iron-cored transformer whose secondary is connected to the grid-cathode circuit of valve V_2. The inductive reactance of the primary acts as the load across which the a.c. component of anode current develops an amplified alternating voltage. This induces the output voltage of the stage in the secondary.

One advantage of this method is that by using a transformer

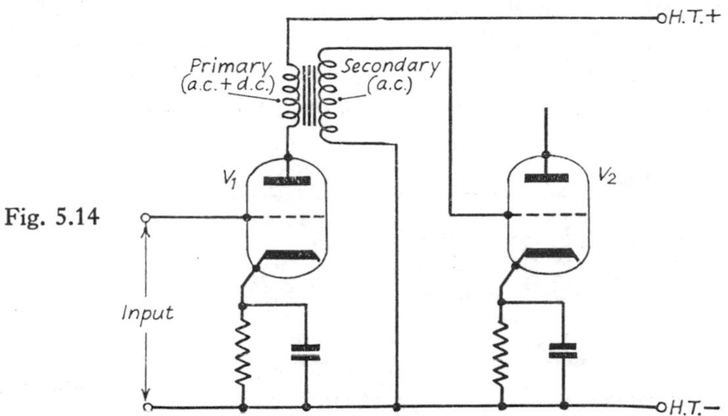

Fig. 5.14

with more turns on the secondary than the primary, a voltage step-up results from the coupling, 1 to 3 being usual. Another advantage is that the d.c. resistance of the primary is small and so there is no appreciable drop of H.T. volts in the load. Furthermore, since the secondary connects the grid to the cathode bias resistor, no grid resistor is required.

Despite these advantages transformers are not much used for interstage coupling of A.F. amplifiers on account of the unequal amplification produced by the variation of the reactance of the primary with frequency. In addition they are bulky and expensive components.

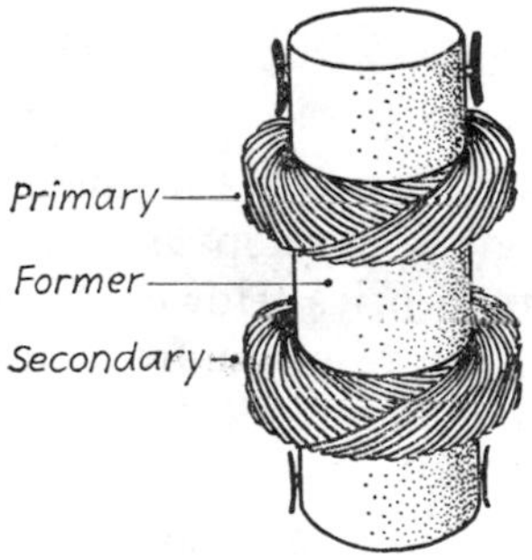

Fig. 5.15

Tuned transformer coupling

Transformer coupling is used to connect an R.F. amplifier to the next stage in a radio receiver. An R.F. transformer is shown in Fig. 5.15 having a primary and a secondary coil wound on a tube, called the 'former', made of cardboard, bakelite or other insulating material. The former frequently has a dust-iron or ferrite core, these being materials with a high magnetic permeability and low eddy current loss. A metal can is often used to screen the coils from stray electric fields.

The action of an R.F. transformer is essentially the same as that of an A.F. transformer in a transformer-coupled audio amplifier but the secondary is generally tuned by a variable capacitor, since an R.F. amplifier is required to select as well as

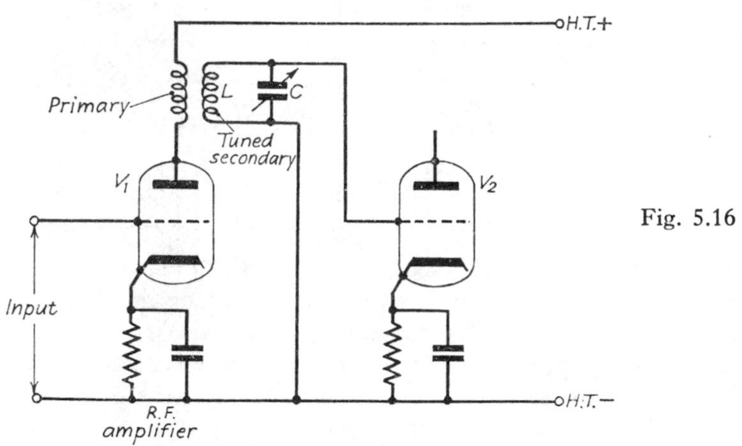

Fig. 5.16

amplify. The primary, which has a high impedance at radio frequencies, is the anode load for V_1, Fig. 5.16, and all input signals develop an amplified voltage across it whatever their frequencies. However, only the signal having a frequency equal to the resonant frequency of the tuned secondary builds up a large induced voltage across L–C. Induced voltages due to other frequencies are very much smaller and are in effect rejected. Usually the input (grid-cathode) circuit of an R.F. amplifier is also tuned to give increased selectivity, the two tuning capacitors being 'ganged', i.e., the movable plates are mounted on the same spindle, so that both circuits can be tuned by one control.

Tetrode valve

In a triode each pair of electrodes behaves as if it were a very small capacitor, and at radio frequencies the reactance of the grid to anode capacitance becomes sufficiently small for energy to be fed back from the anode circuit to the grid circuit. This causes unwanted oscillations which prevent the triode from amplifying properly. In the tetrode the anode to grid capacitance is found to be reduced by having a second grid between the first grid and the anode. The first grid is called the *control grid* and is constructed and acts in the same way as the grid in a triode. The second grid, known as the *screen grid*, is kept at a steady positive potential approaching that of the anode.

The passage of electrons from the cathode to the anode is little

Fig. 5.17

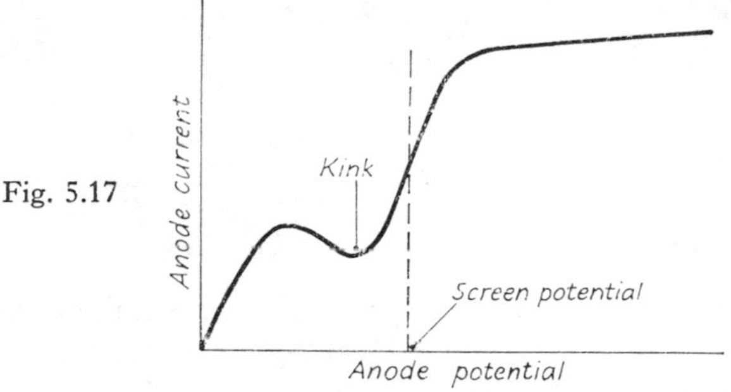

affected by the screen since it is an open spiral of thin wire at a positive potential and the electrons have enough energy to pass through. However, as in all valves, secondary emission occurs at the anode due to its bombardment by the high-speed electrons from the cathode, each primary electron ejecting several secondary electrons. In the triode this is not important because the secondary electrons are attracted back to the anode, but in the tetrode, whenever the anode voltage is less than the screen voltage, some secondary electrons go to the screen, and produce a reduction of anode current and a kink in the anode characteristic, Fig. 5.17. When the tetrode is giving high amplification the anode voltage varies considerably and if it falls below the screen voltage the output is distorted. One remedy would be to have a very high H.T. voltage but the problem has been overcome in the pentode and the tetrode is seldom used today.

Pentode valve

The pentode eliminates the flow of secondary electrons from anode to screen by including a third grid, called the *suppressor grid*, between the anode and screen. The suppressor is connected internally or externally to the cathode and is thus very negative with respect to the anode, Fig. 5.18. Any secondary electrons

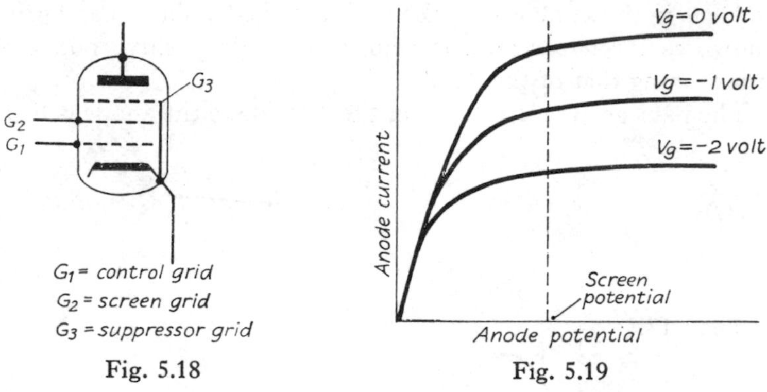

Fig. 5.18

Fig. 5.19

between the anode and suppressor are unable to reach the screen. Primary electrons from the cathode have sufficient energy to pass through the suppressor grid to the anode.

Anode characteristic curves for a pentode are shown in Fig. 5.19. Beyond a quite small anode potential the anode current changes very little with anode potential, consequently the a.c. resistance R_a of a pentode is extremely high, being of the order of 1 MΩ. The expression $\mu = g_m \times R_a$ also applies to a pentode, and since g_m is about the same as for a triode, it follows that μ is very much greater for a pentode than a triode. Greater voltage amplification as well as R.F. operation are therefore possible with pentodes.

Power amplifiers

The amplifiers considered so far have been voltage amplifiers designed to develop a large output voltage for application to the next stage. However, if the output has to operate a device such as a loudspeaker, mechanical power is required to produce sound waves from the vibration of a coil attached to the speaker diaphragm. The valve and its associated circuit is then called a *power amplifier*.

The volume of sound from a loudspeaker depends on the alternating *current* supplied to it and therefore only the a.c. component of anode current is important. It can be shown that a generator delivers maximum power to an external load when the

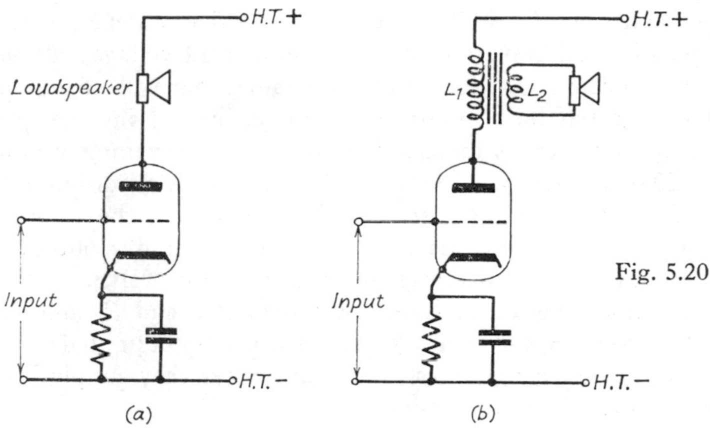

Fig. 5.20

internal impedance of the generator equals the external impedance. Considering the generation of the a.c. component of anode current by a valve, the maximum power will be delivered when the impedance of the anode load equals the a.c. resistance of the valve. Thus if a triode power amplifier of $R_a = 10{,}000$ ohms has to operate a moving-coil loudspeaker with a speech coil of impedance 4 ohms, direct connection of the speaker as the anode load, Fig. 5.20*a*, would give very poor results.

The difficulty is resolved by using a *matching transformer* in the anode of the power amplifier, Fig. 5.20*b*. If the primary L_1 of the transformer has impedance 10,000 ohms, the valve will deliver maximum power to L_1 and if the secondary L_2 has impedance 4 ohms, L_2 delivers maximum power to the speaker.

From the theory of the transformer $n_p/n_s = V_p/V_s = I_s/I_p$, where n_p and n_s are the numbers of turns on the primary and secondary respectively, V_p and V_s are the primary and secondary voltages and I_p and I_s the corresponding currents. It follows that

$$\left(\frac{n_p}{n_s}\right)^2 = \frac{V_p}{I_p} \times \frac{I_s}{V_s} = \frac{Z_p}{Z_s}$$

where Z_p and Z_s are the primary and secondary impedances. Therefore, when $Z_p = 10{,}000$ ohms and $Z_s = 4$ ohms, $n_p/n_s = \sqrt{10{,}000/4} = 50/1$. A 50 to 1 *step-down* matching transformer is necessary.

While a 1-volt change of grid voltage produces most power in the load when $Z_p = R_a$, it can be shown that when $Z_p = 2R_a$ it is possible to have a *greater variation* of grid voltage without distortion occurring. Less power is obtained per volt change of grid voltage but more input volts can be applied and the *total* power output thereby increased. If in the above example we put $Z_p = 20{,}000$ ohms, $n_p/n_s = 50\sqrt{2}/1$. The above condition, i.e., $Z_p = 2R_a$, holds only for triodes. With pentodes the value of the anode load giving maximum undistorted power output is supplied by the manufacturer for each particular valve.

Power amplifier valves have low values of μ and R_a and can handle large swings of grid voltage. Their use is not limited to the audio-frequency range; in a radio transmitter they supply R.F. power to the transmitting aerial.

QUESTIONS

1. Describe the construction of a triode valve and briefly indicate its properties.

Sketch a typical curve relating the anode current with grid-to-cathode voltage for a fixed value of anode-to-cathode voltage, discuss the main features of this curve, and show how a triode may be employed as a voltage amplifier.

Give a circuit diagram of a single-stage triode amplifier showing clearly where the input voltage is applied and whence the amplified output voltage is obtained. [*O. and C.*]

2. For a triode sketch curves to show (*a*) the form of the anode current/grid voltage static characteristics, (*b*) the form of the anode current/anode

voltage static characteristics. How may the amplification factor of the valve be deduced from these curves?

Explain, with the aid of a circuit diagram and with reference to the static characteristics, how the triode may be used to amplify a small alternating voltage. [*J.*]

3. Distinguish between *voltage amplification* or *gain* and *amplification factor*.

(*a*) A triode has an amplification factor of 40 and a mutual conductance of 2·0 mA per volt. Calculate the gain for an anode load of 30,000 ohms.

(*b*) The gain of a triode amplifier is 20 with an anode load of 30 kΩ and 25 with a load of 50 kΩ. Determine the valve constants.

4. Draw the circuit diagram of a simple class A amplifier which employs a triode valve. Explain carefully, with the aid of a suitable chart, how this amplifier can produce an output alternating voltage of waveform which is a magnified replica of the input signal to the grid.

A triode valve of anode slope resistance 20 kΩ is used with an anode load resistance of 50 kΩ. If an alternating signal is applied to the grid of 0·5 volt r.m.s., find the output voltage if the amplification factor of the valve is 15. Deduce from first principles the gain formula you use. [*A.E.B.*]

5. Define and explain what is meant by the impedance and amplification factor of a triode valve. Give a circuit diagram to show how an a.c. voltage applied in the grid circuit of a triode can be amplified and applied to the grid circuit of a second triode by means of a resistance-capacitance coupling. Discuss the conditions to be satisfied if the variations of voltage are to be faithfully reproduced after this amplification. [*W. Special*]

6. Discuss the factors affecting the choice of the steady bias applied to the grid of a valve. Explain how cathode bias works.

A triode requires a steady negative bias of 3 volts; calculate the value of the cathode resistor when the d.c. component of anode current is 6 mA. If a 50 μF decoupling capacitor is placed in parallel with this cathode resistor what is its capacitive reactance at 1 kHz? Comment on your answers.

7. Draw a circuit diagram for a three-stage audio-frequency amplifier in which the first stage is resistance-capacitance coupled, the second transformer coupled and the third is a power amplifier.

If the first stage gives a gain of 15 and the second 20, what is the overall voltage amplification due to these two stages?

6 Radio : oscillation : detection

In this chapter the principles involved in the transmission, generation and reception of radio signals will be considered.

Electromagnetic radiation

The idea that fields of force exist in the space surrounding electric charges, conductors and magnets is useful when 'explaining' electrical and magnetic effects. The flow of current in a conductor may also be considered to be due to the existence of an electric field in the conductor and since current can be induced by a changing magnetic field it follows that *a changing (or moving) magnetic field creates an electric field* in the medium where the change occurs (whether it be free space or a material medium). This effect, known as electromagnetic induction, was discovered by Faraday in 1831.

The converse effect, i.e., *a changing (or moving) electric field sets up a magnetic field*, was proposed by Clerk Maxwell in 1864 on the grounds that if this assumption is made, the mathematical equations expressing the laws of electricity and magnetism (in terms of Faraday's ideas of fields of force) become both simple and symmetrical. There is no easy way of demonstrating Maxwell's assumption directly on account of the difficulty of detecting a weak magnetic field, but one consequence is that any electric field produced by a changing magnetic field must inevitably create a magnetic field and vice versa, i.e., one effect is coupled with the other. On this basis Maxwell predicted that when a moving electric charge is oscillating it should radiate an *electromagnetic wave* consisting of a fluctuating electric field accompanied by a fluctuating magnetic field of the same frequency and phase. The intensity of each field varies periodically like the amplitude of a wave motion, and since the directions of the fields are perpendicular to one another and to the direction of travel of the wave, the latter resembles a transverse wave. Fig. 6.1 is an attempt to represent an electromagnetic wave diagrammatically.

Maxwell also showed that the velocity of all electromagnetic waves, no matter what their wavelength or origin, should be the same as the velocity of light and inferred that light itself is electromagnetic in nature. A full treatment of the production and

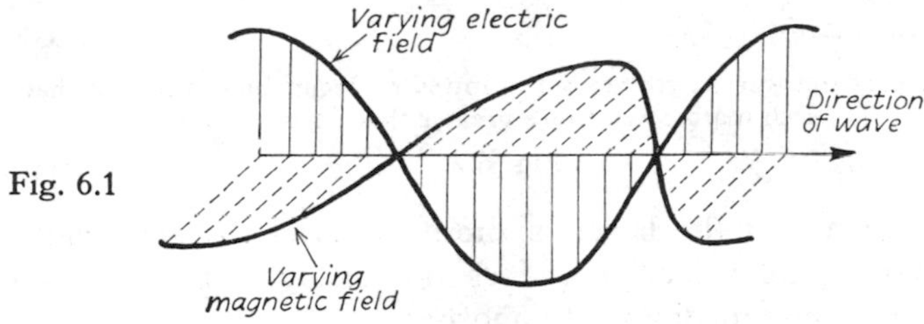

Fig. 6.1

transmission of electromagnetic waves requires considerable mathematics.

The search for other forms of electromagnetic radiation resulted in the discovery by H. Hertz in 1887 of waves having the same velocity as light but with wavelengths of several metres compared with a very small fraction of a millimetre for light. These waves, now called ***radio waves***, were generated by Hertz by means of an oscillatory electrical discharge.

A whole family of electromagnetic radiations is now known extending from gamma rays of very short wavelength to very long radio waves. Fig. 6.2 shows the wavelength and frequency ranges occupied by the various members of the electromagnetic spectrum. Although methods of production and detection differ from member to member all exhibit interference, diffraction and polarization, properties considered to be typical of transverse waves.

For any wave motion the product of the frequency f and the wavelength λ equals the velocity. With electromagnetic waves the velocity c is that of light, i.e., 3×10^8 m s^{-1}, and hence, if the frequency or the wavelength of a particular type of radiation is given, the other can be calculated. Thus for violet light of wavelength 0·4 μm $= 4 \times 10^{-7}$ m we have $c = f\lambda$; therefore $f = c/\lambda = 3 \times 10^8/(4 \times 10^{-7}) = 7{\cdot}5 \times 10^{14}$ hertz. By contrast, a 1 MHz radio signal has a wavelength of 300 metres. Electromagnetic waves may be distinguished either by their wavelength

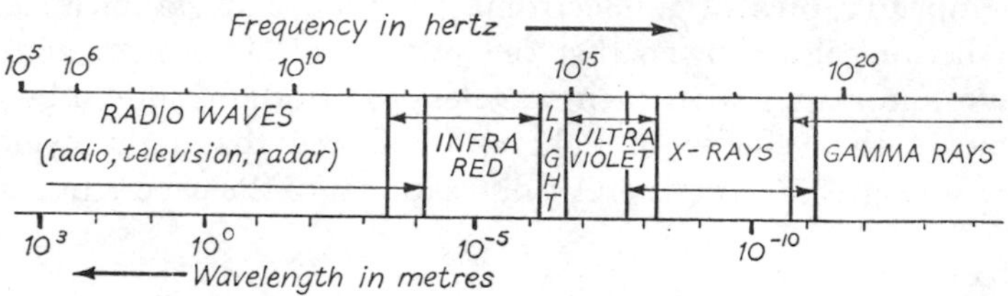

Frequency and wavelength are both plotted on logarithmic scales so that each mark is ten times greater than its predecessor.

Fig. 6.2

or frequency but the latter is more fundamental since unlike wavelength (and velocity) it does not change when the wave travels from one medium into another.

In general, electromagnetic waves are generated when electrons suffer an energy change. In Chapter 12 we shall consider how changes within an atom produce certain types of radiation. For the present it suffices to say that radio waves are emitted when free electrons in a conductor undergo changes of kinetic energy as a result of being accelerated or decelerated in a transmitting aerial.

Radio waves and aerials

Consideration of the way in which a transmitting aerial produces radio waves shows that the electric field comes off parallel to the aerial and the magnetic field at right angles to it. If the transmitting aerial is vertical, both fields will have their maximum inducing effect if the receiving aerial is also vertical. In this case the radio waves are said to be vertically polarized, the direction of polarization being given by the direction of the electric field. This follows the practice adopted with light waves where experiments show that it is the electric field which is responsible for most of the common optical effects caused by the interaction of light with matter.

The radiation from a transmitting aerial is divided into three parts, Fig. 6.3.

(*i*) The *ground wave* travels along the ground following the curvature of the earth.

(*ii*) The *sky wave* leaves the aerial at an angle exceeding that between the aerial and the horizon and travels skywards.

(*iii*) The *space wave* takes a straight line path and strikes the ground between the aerial and the horizon.

Which one of the three is most effective in reaching a particular location depends on the frequency of the radiated signal as well as on the power of the transmitter. A common classification of frequencies is given in Table 6.1, page 96.

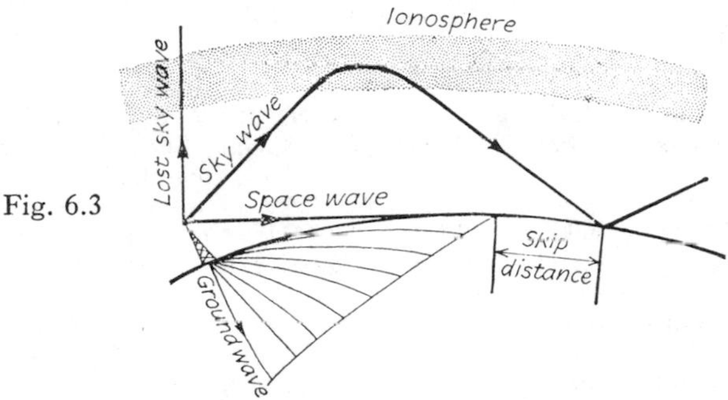

Fig. 6.3

The range of the ground wave is limited mainly by the extent to which energy is absorbed from it by the ground; thus poor conductors such as sand absorb more strongly than water. This absorption attenuates the wave and the higher the frequency the greater the attenuation. The range may be about 1500 km at low frequencies (long waves) but only a few kilometres for V.H.F. waves.

The sky wave, so long as it is below a certain *critical frequency*, is returned to earth by layers of ionized gas, collectively called the *ionosphere*. This extends from a height of about 80 km above the earth to 500 km and it changes the direction of travel of the sky wave by gradual refraction. On striking the earth the sky wave bounces back to the ionosphere where it is once again directed to earth, and the process continues until the wave is completely attenuated. Since sky waves leave a transmitting aerial at many angles, the waves returning from the ionosphere cover quite large areas of the earth's surface. Those radiated at too steep an angle pass into space due to the refraction being insufficient to direct the wave earthwards. As a result no sky waves reach the area around the aerial and the distance between the limit of the ground wave and the point where the first sky wave returns to earth is called the 'skip distance' and receives no signals. The critical frequency (i.e., the frequency above which no sky wave, whatever its angle of radiation, will return to earth) varies with the time of day, the seasons and the eleven-year sun-spot cycle. Whereas in the long and medium wavebands the sky wave can be used for long-distance communications over several thousand

TABLE 6.1

	Long Waves 30 kHz–300 kHz	*Medium Waves* 300 kHz–3 MHz	*Short Waves* 3 MHz–30 MHz	*V.H.F.* (very high frequency) 30 MHz–300 MHz	*U.H.F.* (ultra high frequency) 300 MHz–3000 MHz	*Micro-waves* Above 3000 MHz
Ground wave	Medium-range communication	Local sound broadcasts				
Sky wave	Long-range communication	Distant sound broadcasts	Distant sound broadcasts and communication			
Space wave				F.M. sound broadcasts T.V. (B.B.C. 1 and I.T.A. 1)	T.V. (B.B.C. 2	Radar. Radio-astronomy. Satellite communication

kilometres, in the short waveband it is erratic and unreliable. If both the ground wave and sky wave from a particular transmitter are received at the same place interference can occur if the two waves are out of phase. When the phase difference varies the signal 'fades'.

Above the critical frequency the ground wave is rapidly attenuated and the sky wave passes through the ionosphere. Therefore for V.H.F., U.H.F. and microwave transmissions only the space wave, travelling in a direct line from transmitter to receiver, is effective. When the transmitting aerial is at the top of a tall mast standing on high ground a range of up to 150 km or so is possible. Microwave frequencies approach those of light waves and in radar and radioastronomy where microwaves are used, the aerial is often in the form of a huge curved metal bowl which collects and reflects the incoming signal to a focus just as an optical aerial, i.e., a telescope objective, focuses light.

A recent development in world-wide communications is the use of artificial satellites. These are not only more dependable than the ionosphere but they contain amplifiers to boost the microwave signals used.

Table 6.1 shows some applications of the various frequency bands.

Outline of radio

The radiation from an aerial is appreciable only when the length of the aerial is comparable with the wavelength of the electromagnetic wave produced by the a.c. flowing in it. A 50 Hz alternating current corresponds to a wavelength of 6×10^6 metres and so in practice R.F. currents must be supplied. However, since speech and music generate A.F. currents some means of combining the two is necessary if intelligence is to be conveyed over a distance. In a transmitter, an *oscillator*, consisting of a valve and an associated circuit, generates a radio-frequency alternating current which if applied directly to the aerial would produce an electromagnetic wave, called the *carrier wave*, of constant amplitude and having the same frequency as the R.F. current. If a normal receiver picked up such a signal nothing would be heard. The R.F. signal can be modified or *modulated* in various ways so that it carries the A.F. intelligence.

In *amplitude modulation* (A.M.) the amplitude of the R.F. is varied so that it depends on the A.F. current from the microphone. The process occurs in a valve circuit known as the modulator, Fig. 6.4*a*. This type of transmission is used for medium- and long-wave broadcasting in Great Britain. V.H.F.

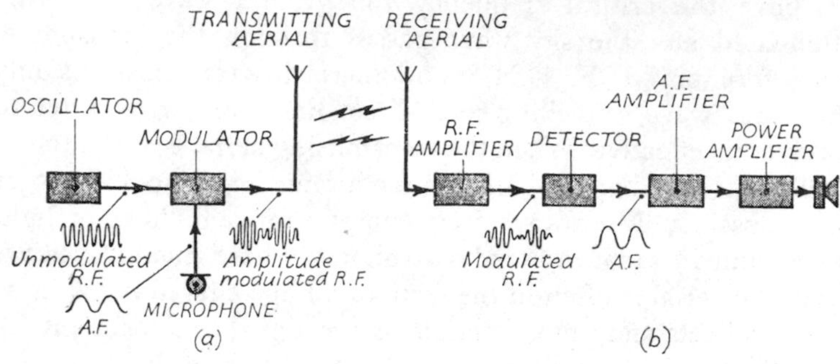

Fig. 6.4

broadcasts use *frequency modulation* (F.M.) in which the frequency of the carrier is altered at a rate equal to the frequency of the A.F. signal but the amplitude remains constant, Fig. 6.5. F.M. signals are relatively free from various kinds of electrical interference.

A block schematic diagram of a simple receiver for A.M.

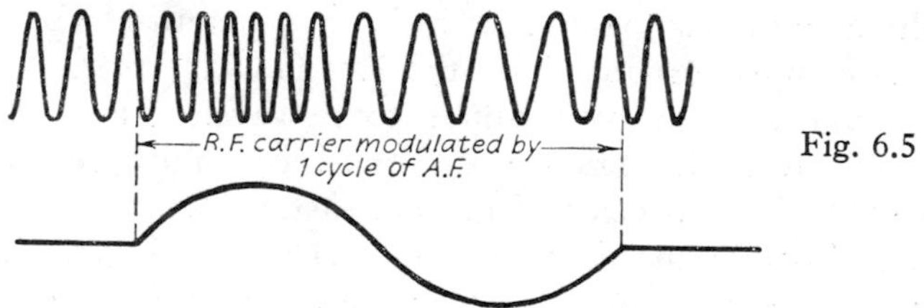

Fig. 6.5

signals is shown in Fig. 6.4*b*. A weak current, a replica of that in the transmitting aerial, is induced in the receiving aerial and then boosted by an R.F. voltage amplifier. The *detector* or *demodulator* separates the A.F. intelligence from the R.F. carrier and after A.F. amplification, an A.F. power amplifier supplies the power necessary to drive a loudspeaker.

Oscillatory circuit

The production of a radio-frequency alternating current is impossible with a mechanical generator but is readily achieved electrically with the aid of a capacitor and coil.

In Fig. 6.6*a* a capacitor *C*, charged previously by a battery, is

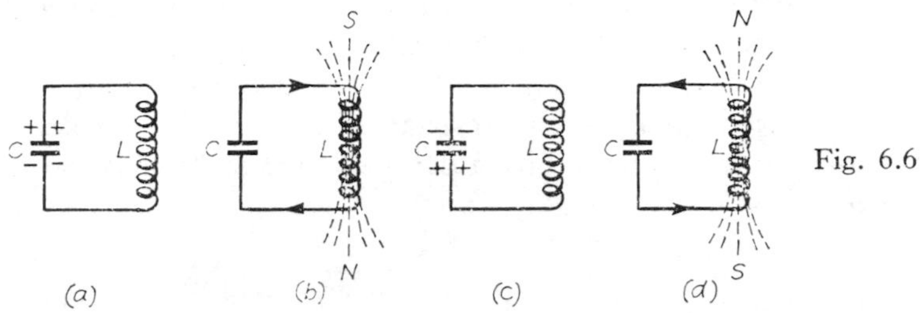

Fig. 6.6

shown connected across a coil *L*. *C* immediately starts to discharge, current flows and a magnetic field builds up which induces an e.m.f. in the coil. This e.m.f. opposes the current. *C* cannot discharge instantaneously and the greater the inductance of *L* the longer does the discharge take. When *C* is completely discharged the electrical energy originally stored in it has been transferred to the magnetic field around *L*, Fig. 6.6*b*.

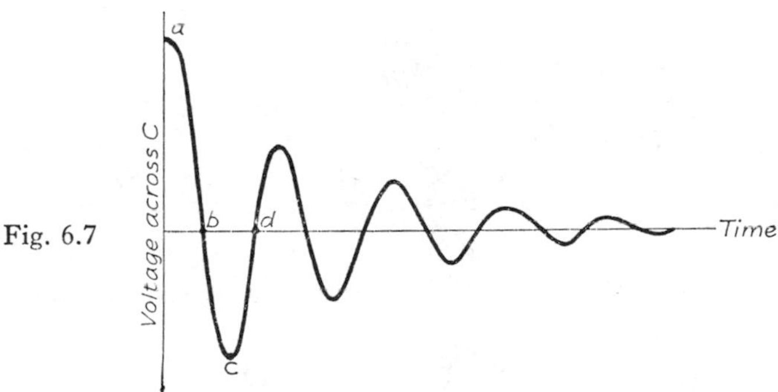

Fig. 6.7

At this point the magnetic field begins to collapse and a voltage is induced in *L* which tries to maintain the field. Current therefore flows in the same direction as before and charges *C* so that the lower plate is positive. By the time the field has collapsed completely the energy of the magnetic field is stored as electrical energy in C, Fig. 6.6*c*. Once more C starts to discharge but current now flows in the opposite direction creating a magnetic field of opposite polarity, Fig. 6.6*d*. When this field has decayed, C is again charged with its upper plate positive and conditions are the same as at the start.

In the absence of resistance in any part of the circuit this cycle would repeat itself over and over again and a C.R.O. connected across C would show the rise and fall of voltage as a sine wave. Resistance cannot be eliminated in practice and energy is gradually dissipated by the resistance as heat. The voltage decreases in each cycle to give a damped electrical oscillation as shown in Fig. 6.7.

Frequency of the oscillations

The circuit of Fig. 6.8 contains capacitance C, inductance L and resistance R. Suppose C is charged and then left to discharge. At time t later let C have charge Q and a voltage V across it. If the instantaneous current is I, then the back e.m.f. due to L is $L.dI/dt$ and the voltage drop across R is IR, hence

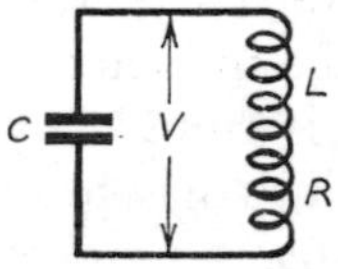

Fig. 6.8

$$V = L \cdot \frac{dI}{dt} + IR \qquad (1)$$

If R is very small

$$V = L \cdot \frac{dI}{dt}$$

But $V = Q/C$ and $I = -dQ/dt$ (the negative sign shows Q decays with t)

$$\therefore \quad \frac{Q}{C} = -L \cdot \frac{d^2Q}{dt^2}$$

$$\therefore \quad \frac{d^2Q}{dt^2} = \frac{-Q}{LC}$$

This represents a simple harmonic motion of period T given by

$T = 2\pi\sqrt{LC}$. If f is the natural frequency of the oscillations, $f = 1/T$ and

$$\therefore f = \frac{1}{2\pi\sqrt{LC}} \tag{2}$$

If L is in henries and C in farads, f is in hertz.

The following points should be noted:

(*i*) To generate R.F. oscillations L and C must be small.

(*ii*) From equation (2) we see that the natural frequency of oscillation of a circuit equals its resonant frequency provided the circuit has negligible resistance.

(*iii*) The full solution of equation (1) gives

$$f = \frac{1}{2\pi}\sqrt{\frac{1}{LC} - \frac{R^2}{4L^2}}$$

which reduces to (2) if R is small.

As R increases the amplitude of the oscillations decays more rapidly and when R is too large the capacitor discharge is unidirectional and no oscillations occur.

Triode as an oscillator

The oscillations set up by the discharge of a capacitor through an inductor can be maintained indefinitely by using a triode to feed

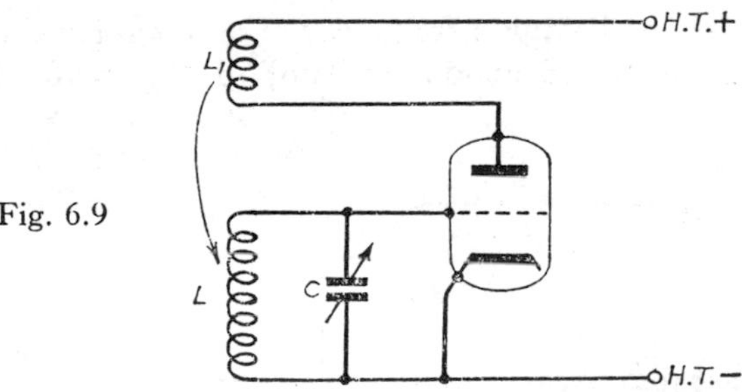

Fig. 6.9

back energy into the oscillatory circuit. The energy is provided by the H.T. supply to the valve; it compensates for that dissipated as heat in the resistance of the inductor.

A tuned grid oscillator is shown in Fig. 6.9 with the oscillatory circuit L–C connected between grid and cathode of the triode. The anode circuit contains a coil L_1, the feedback coil, arranged close to L so that it is inductively coupled to it. When the H.T. supply is switched on, the anode current rises from zero to its steady value and a magnetic field builds up around L_1, inducing a voltage in L which charges C. Once the anode current has reached its steady value no further induction occurs and C discharges by oscillation. Left to itself the oscillation would decay, but the alternating voltage across C, being connected between grid and cathode, acts as an input to the triode and produces an a.c. component of anode current at the same frequency. If the coils are connected so that the current induced in L is in the same direction as the oscillatory current, positive feedback occurs and undamped oscillations are obtained.

The circuit acts as an amplifier supplying its own input. The triode itself is not primarily responsible for the oscillations; the L–C circuit is, but by using the valve feedback is possible.

Many valve oscillator circuits have been developed. Some are used in A.F. signal generators to supply an alternating voltage at any frequency up to about 15 kHz for testing audio equipment. Others working in the radio-frequency range are employed in transmitters, in the superheterodyne type of radio receiver and for fault finding.

Low-frequency demonstration oscillator

Very slow oscillations having a frequency of about 2 Hz can be produced using the tuned anode oscillator of Fig. 6.10. Two

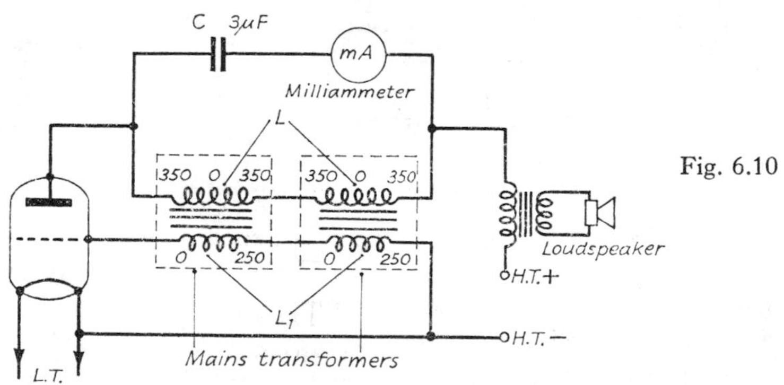

Fig. 6.10

350–0–350 volt mains transformers with their secondaries in series act as a large inductor L for the oscillatory circuit and the primary windings are used as the feedback coil L_1 in the grid circuit. The oscillations can be 'seen' from the movement of the pointer on a centre-zero milliammeter and 'heard' on a loudspeaker. The H.T. and L.T. supplies are chosen to suit the valve.

Points which may be demonstrated include:

(*i*) The frequency of the oscillations increases if C is decreased to 2 μF.

(*ii*) When L is reduced by using only one or one and a half secondary windings the frequency also increases.

(*iii*) If the number of turns on L_1 is decreased, feedback becomes smaller and oscillations of smaller amplitude result. This is shown by using the 0–200 volt tapping on the primaries instead of the whole winding.

(*iv*) Reversing the connections on the primary windings gives negative feedback and oscillation stops.

Detection by a diode

In *detection* or *demodulation* the A.F. modulation is derived from the R.F. carrier on which it was impressed at the transmitter. The process involves rectification and the reservoir action of a capacitor.

Let the amplitude modulated R.F. signal V, represented in Fig. 6.11*a*, be applied to the detecting circuit of Fig. 6.12 comprising a diode, a capacitor C and a receiving earphone. The rectifying action of the diode creates unidirectional pulses of R.F. current as in Fig. 6.11*b*. These charge up C whenever V exceeds the voltage across C, i.e., during part of each positive half-cycle. During the rest of the cycle when the diode is non-conducting, C partially discharges through the phones. The action of the circuit is very similar to that discussed under rectification (p. 60). The process of partial and intermittent discharge causes the voltage across C to vary as shown by V_c in Fig. 6.11*c*. V_c may be regarded as having

(*i*) a steady direct component
(*ii*) an A.F. component at the modulating frequency
(*iii*) a small R.F. ripple at the frequency of the carrier.

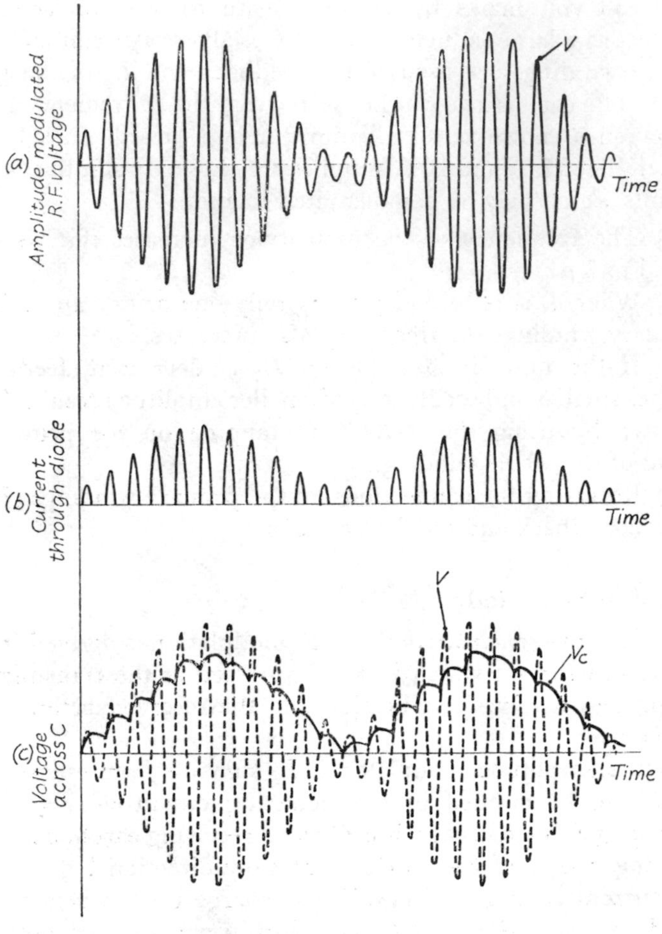

Fig. 6.11

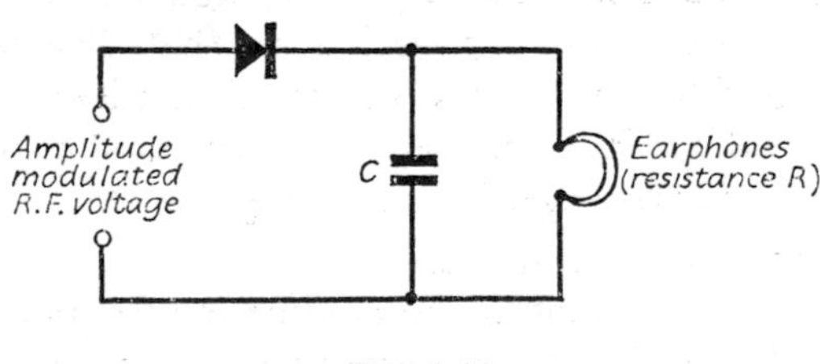

Fig. 6.12

All three are applied to the earphone but the A.F. component alone is reproduced as sound.

For V_c to vary in the way indicated, the value of C and the resistance R of the earphone must be correctly chosen. The important factor is the time constant CR; if it is too large, C charges and discharges too slowly and V_c does not respond to the A.F. modulation; on the other hand too small a time constant allows C to discharge so rapidly that V_c follows the R.F. variations. The product CR should have a value between the time for one cycle of R.F. and one cycle of A.F. (mean).

When it is desired to operate a loudspeaker the detector is followed by one or more stages of A.F. amplification. A suitable resistor (500 kΩ) then replaces the earphone as the load for the detector; C is usually 0·0001 μF (100 pF).

Nowadays a germanium diode is generally used as the rectifying device in detection circuits. It requires no power supply, it has a very long life and will work with a small input voltage. By contrast the diode valve is insensitive to weak signals but it can handle larger inputs than the germanium diode.

Triode as a detector

A diode detector does not amplify and is generally used in a receiver having several stages of amplification. When the number of valves has to be restricted a more sensitive detector can be obtained by using a triode valve to detect and amplify simultaneously. Fig. 6.13 shows a triode *leaky grid detector* having a

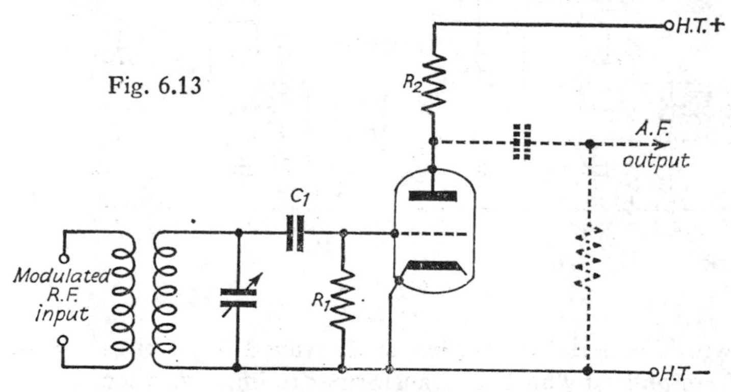

Fig. 6.13

tuned input circuit to which a modulated R.F. signal is applied from an R.F. transformer. The primary of the latter may be connected either to an R.F. amplifier or, in a very simple receiver, to an aerial.

The grid-cathode circuit can be treated as a diode detector with C_1 and R_1 acting as the reservoir capacitor and detector load respectively. Since no steady bias is applied to the grid it is driven positive during positive half-cycles of the input voltage. The grid then collects some electrons from the cathode giving rise to grid current which charges C_1. During negative half-cycles C_1 partially discharges through R_1, the grid leak resistor. If the time constant C_1R_1 has a suitable value, the voltage across R_1 contains A.F. and R.F. components, and since R_1 is in the input circuit of the triode, A.F. and R.F. amplified voltages appear across the anode load R_2. The A.F. component produces sound when R_2 is a receiving earphone; otherwise it is coupled to the next stage for further amplification. The grid leak R_1 can also be connected across C_1.

A straight receiver

In Fig. 6.14 a simplified circuit is given for a 'straight' or 'tuned radio frequency' (T.R.F.) radio receiver. It has four stages as

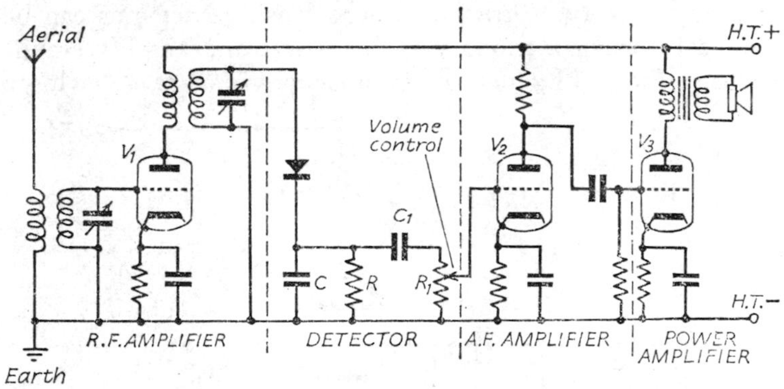

Fig. 6.14

shown. The aerial is coupled to the tuned input circuit of the R.F. amplifier by an R.F. transformer to improve selectivity. In the detector, resistor R acts as the load across which the detector output is developed, C being the reservoir capacitor. C_1 blocks the d.c. component and the A.F. component appears across the variable resistor R_1 which has a higher impedance to A.F. than C_1. R_1 acts as a volume control by altering the input to the A.F. amplifier. Sometimes a filter circuit is included to bypass the R.F. ripple and prevent it reaching the audio stages where it can cause certain undesirable effects.

In practice the triodes V_1 and V_3 would be replaced by tetrodes and pentodes and additional 'decoupling' capacitors and resistors would be necessary to eliminate unwanted coupling between the various stages. This last point is explained in more advanced textbooks.

Nowadays most receivers are 'superhets'. These give greater sensitivity and selectivity but are more complex.

QUESTIONS

1. Explain as fully as possible what is meant by the term electromagnetic wave.

In what respects are the various types of electromagnetic radiation (*a*) similar, (*b*) different?

2. Describe the methods by which radio waves are propagated.

Explain why distant European medium-wave broadcasting stations are received more strongly in Great Britain after sunset when the layers of the ionosphere are at a greater height.

3. Why is *modulation* necessary in a radio transmitter? Explain with the help of diagrams (*a*) *amplitude modulation*, (*b*) *frequency modulation.*

4. (*a*) What conditions are necessary for the discharge of a capacitor to be oscillatory? Discuss the energy changes occurring when the discharge is oscillatory.

(*b*) Explain how a triode valve can be used as an oscillator for a radio transmitter. Give a circuit diagram.

(*c*) Calculate the maximum and minimum frequencies of the oscillations which could be generated by a variable capacitor of maximum capacitance 0·0005 μF and minimum capacitance one-tenth of this value connected to a coil having inductance 100 μH.

5. What is meant by detection in a radio receiver? Draw a diode detector circuit, explain its action pointing out the function of each component.

6. Draw the circuit of a three-valve receiver consisting of an R.F. amplifier, a leaky grid detector and a power amplifier.

7. What are the essential processes involved in the communication of speech (or music) by radio?

Explain in detail any arrangement used in either the generation or the reception of radio signals. [*J. Schol.*]

7 Photoelectric emission

By the end of the nineteenth century Maxwell's electromagnetic wave theory of radiation had established itself as one of the great intellectual pillars of physics, a unifying principle linking electricity, magnetism and light. It appeared that the physicist had almost completed his work and only a few minor 'mopping-up' operations remained. This complacency was, within a few years, rudely shattered and the wave theory suffered an unexpected blow from which it has never quite recovered.

The present century has seen two major revolutions in scientific thinking, each resulting in a break with the fundamental ideas of classical physics as developed by Newton, Maxwell and others. One is the theory of relativity and the other the quantum theory; only the latter will be considered here. Two phenomena, both concerned with electromagnetic radiation, were responsible for the rise of the quantum theory.

Photoelectric effect

In photoelectric emission electrons are ejected from metal surfaces when X-rays, ultraviolet, light or infrared fall on them. Thus zinc emits electrons when exposed to X-rays or ultraviolet. Sodium gives emission with X-rays, ultraviolet and all colours of light except orange and red, while caesium responds to infrared as well as to higher frequency radiation. The effect may be shown by allowing ultraviolet from a mercury vapour lamp to fall on a small sheet of zinc, freshly cleaned with emery cloth and connected to an electroscope as in Fig. 7.1. If the electroscope is given a positive charge the pointer is unaffected by the ultraviolet radiation and scarcely falls. When negatively charged, however, the electroscope discharges quite rapidly when the zinc is illuminated with ultraviolet. A sheet of glass between the lamp and the zinc plate halts the discharge.

The photoelectric effect was discovered by H. Hertz in 1887 and, although the above experiment was first performed by Hallwachs in 1888, it was not until after the identification of the electron by

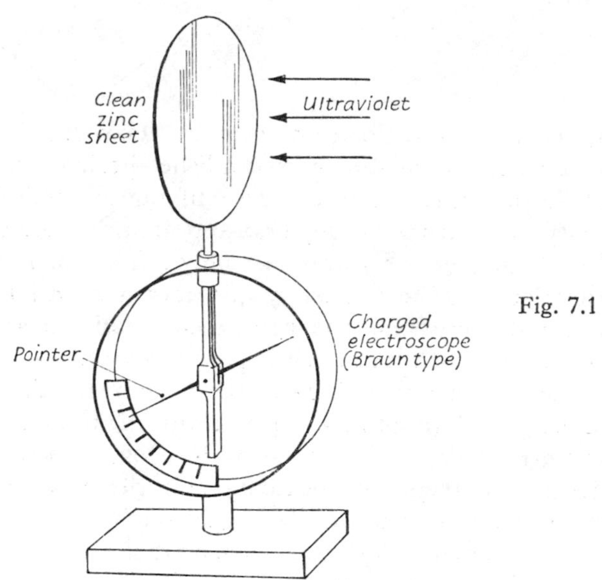

Fig. 7.1

J. J. Thomson that the true explanation emerged. When the zinc plate is positively charged the electrons ejected from it by the ultraviolet fail to escape, being attracted back to the plate. A negative charge on the zinc repels the emitted electrons and both the zinc and the electroscope lose negative charge. The insertion of the sheet of glass cuts off the ultraviolet but allows the passage of violet light, also emitted by the lamp, and shows that violet light does not produce the effect with zinc.

Subsequently Lenard deflected the photoelectric 'emission' by a magnetic field and obtained a value for the charge to mass ratio agreeing with the value for e/m of electrons. Electrons obtained in this way are often called 'photoelectrons' but they are exactly the same as electrons produced by other means.

Laws of photoelectric emission

An experimental study of the photoelectric effect reveals some surprising results which may be summarized as follows.

Law I—the *number* of photoelectrons emitted per second is proportional to the *intensity* of the incident radiation.

Law II—the photoelectrons are emitted with a range of velocities from zero up to a *maximum velocity* which increases as the *frequency* of the radiation increases and is independent of the intensity of the radiation.

Thus a faint blue light produces electrons with a greater maximum velocity than those produced by a bright red light, but the latter releases a greater number.

Law III—for a given metal there is a certain minimum frequency of radiation, called the *threshold frequency*, below which no emission occurs irrespective of the intensity of the radiation. For zinc, the threshold frequency is in the ultraviolet.

Can the wave theory explain these facts? *Law I* is readily vindicated since if the radiation has greater intensity, more energy is absorbed by the metal and it is possible for more electrons to escape. It is also reasonable to suppose that the range of emission velocities from zero to a maximum is caused by electrons having a range of possible kinetic energies inside the material. The electrons with the highest kinetic energy are emitted with the maximum velocity. However we would expect a certain number of photoelectrons to be ejected with greater velocities when the radiation intensity increases; this is not so according to *Law II*. The increase of maximum velocity with frequency and the existence of the threshold frequency are even more enigmatic. Furthermore, according to the wave theory, radiation energy is spread over the wave front and since the amount incident on any one electron would be extremely small, some time would elapse before an electron gathered enough energy to escape. No such time lag between the start of radiation and the start of emission is observed, even when the radiation is very weak. Most of the facts of photoelectric emission appear to be inexplicable on the wave theory.

Black body radiation

The second aspect of the behaviour of electromagnetic radiation to defy explanation by classical physics was *black body radiation.* A black surface is a better absorber and so also a better emitter of radiation than any other colour. The theoretical concept of a perfect black body (cf., a perfect gas) was introduced to represent an ideal absorber and emitter of radiation and although the perfect black body cannot be made in practice, a close approximation for experimental work is a sphere with dull black interior walls and a very tiny hole, Fig. 7.2. Radiation entering from outside is reflected internally and eventually absorbed by the walls

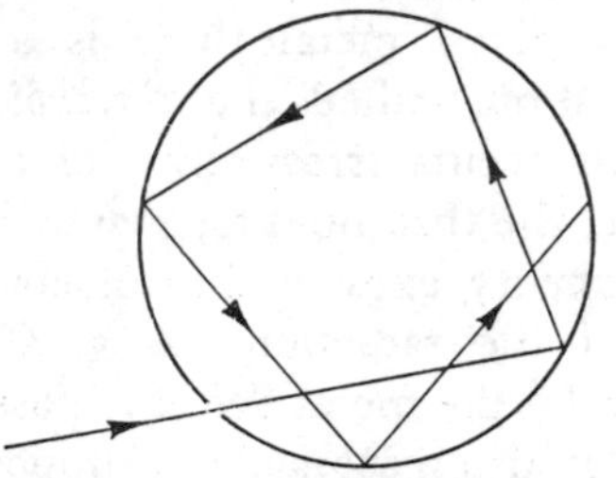

Fig. 7.2

so that none escapes. The *hole* in the sphere thus acts as a perfect black body since it absorbs all the radiation falling on it.

If the sphere is heated to a definite temperature, a spectrum of the radiation emitted can be formed by viewing the *hole* with a prism or grating spectrometer. Measurement of the intensity E_λ of a small band of wavelengths in different parts of the spectrum enables a graph of E_λ against the wavelength λ to be drawn for various temperatures, Fig. 7.3. The following points emerge:

(*i*) Only a very small proportion of the energy is carried by very long and very short wavelengths.

(*ii*) There is a certain wavelength λ_{max} for which E_λ is a maximum.

(*iii*) As the temperature of the black body increases λ_{max} decreases. This agrees with the observation that a body becomes red-hot before reaching white heat.

The wave theory is quite unable to account even for the presence of a maximum in the E_λ–λ curves, far less for their shape.

Fig. 7.3

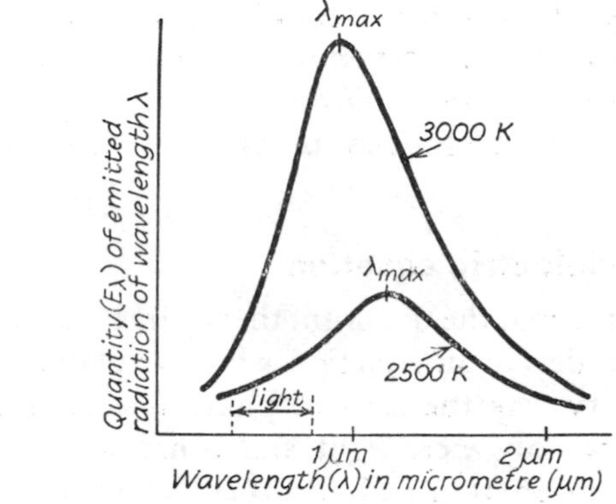

Planck's quantum theory

In 1900 Max Planck tackled the problem of finding a theoı which would fit the facts of black body radiation. Whereas others had considered the radiation to be emitted or absorbed continuously, Planck supposed it to be emitted or absorbed intermittently in integral multiples of an 'atom' or *quantum* of energy, the size of which depends on the frequency of the oscillator. A body would thus emit or absorb one, two, three, etc., quanta of energy but no fractional amounts. For the success of his theory it was unnecessary for Planck to make any assumptions about the method of travel of the radiation and so he held to the conventional view that it travels as a wave motion.

According to Planck the quantum E of energy for radiation of frequency f is given by the expression

$$E = hf \qquad (1)$$

where h is a constant, now called Planck's constant. For electromagnetic radiation of wavelength λ, $c = f\lambda$, where c is the velocity of light and it follows that

$$E = \frac{hc}{\lambda}$$

The energy of a quantum is thus inversely proportional to the wavelength of the radiation. It is convenient to express many quantum energies in electron-volts; the energy of a quantum of red light is about 2 eV and of blue light about 4 eV.

Using equation (1) Planck derived an expression for the variation of E_λ with λ for a black body which agreed with the experimental curves at all wavelengths and temperatures. At the time the quantum theory was too revolutionary for most scientists and little attention was paid to it. Nevertheless the interpretation of black body radiation was the first of its many successes.

Einstein's photoelectric equation

Albert Einstein revived the quantum theory in 1905 by extending Planck's ideas to derive an equation which explained in a completely satisfactory way the laws of photoelectric emission. He assumed that not only were light and other forms of electromagnetic radiation emitted and absorbed in whole numbers of energy quanta but that they also travelled through space with the speed of light as streams of quanta, sometimes called *photons*, the number of photons increasing with the intensity of the radiation. This idea apparently rejected the wave theory in favour of a moving-particle theory not unlike Newton's corpuscular theory.

When dealing with thermionic emission it was explained that to liberate an electron from the surface of a metal a quantity of energy, called the *work function*, Φ, which is characteristic of the metal, has to be supplied. In photoelectric emission, Einstein proposed that a photon of energy hf causes an electron to be emitted if $hf > \Phi$. The excess energy $(hf - \Phi)$ appears as kinetic energy of the emitted electron which escapes with a velocity having any value up to a maximum v_{max}. The actual value depends on how much energy the electron has inside the metal. Hence

$$hf - \Phi = \tfrac{1}{2}mv_{max}^2 \qquad (2)$$

This is Einstein's photoelectric equation.

If the photon has only just enough energy to liberate an electron, the electron gains no more kinetic energy. From (2) it follows that since Φ is constant for a given metal, there is a minimum frequency, the *threshold frequency* f_0 given by $hf_0 = \Phi$, below which no photoelectric emission is possible. Alternatively, for every metal there is a maximum wavelength, the *threshold wavelength* λ_0 above which electrons are not released.

We may also write equation (2)

$$h(f - f_0) = \tfrac{1}{2}mv^2_{max}$$

The increase of maximum emission velocity with higher frequency radiation can now be seen to be due to the greater photon energy of such radiation. It should also be noted that the photon imparts all its energy to one electron and then no longer exists.

Millikan's experiment on photoelectric emission

In 1916 Millikan verified Einstein's photoelectric equation experimentally and provided irrefutable evidence for the existence of photons. He also obtained an accurate value for Planck's constant h. His apparatus is shown in simplified form in Fig. 7.4.

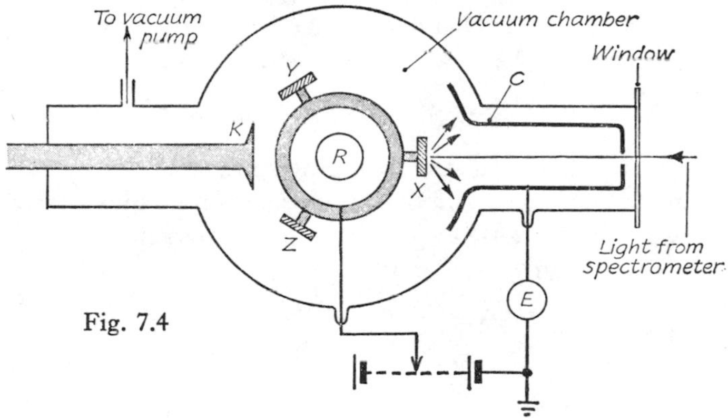

Fig. 7.4

Monochromatic light from a spectrometer entered the window of the vacuum chamber and fell on a metal X mounted on a turntable R controlled by an electromagnet outside the chamber. The photoelectrons emitted were collected by an electrode C and detected by a sensitive current measuring device E. The minimum positive potential, called the *stopping potential*, which had to be applied to X to prevent the most energetic photoelectrons reaching C and causing current flow, was found for different frequencies of the incident radiation. The procedure was repeated with Y and then Z opposite C. X, Y and Z were made from the alkali metals lithium, sodium and potassium, since these metals emit photoelectrons with light and each one can therefore be studied over a wide range of frequencies. Immediately before taking a set of readings R was rotated and the knife K adjusted so that a fresh surface was cut on the appropriate metal, thus eliminating the effects of surface oxidation.

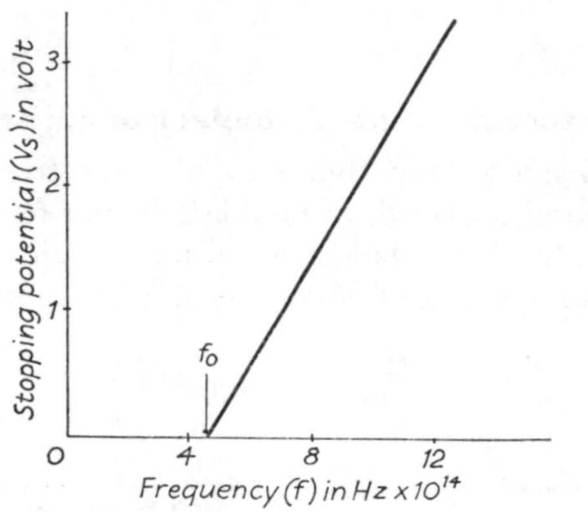

Fig. 7.5

The relation between the stopping potential V_s and the maximum kinetic energy of the photoelectrons is given by the energy equation (p. 24), $eV_s = \frac{1}{2}mv^2_{max}$. Einstein's equation may then be written

$$\tfrac{1}{2}mv^2_{max} = eV_s = hf - \Phi$$

$$\therefore\ V_s = \frac{h}{e}\cdot f - \frac{\Phi}{e} \qquad (3)$$

The graph of V_s against f should be a straight line, a fact which Millikan's results confirmed. Einstein's relation was thus verified. Furthermore the stopping potential for a given frequency of light was independent of the intensity of the light. One of Millikan's graphs is shown in Fig. 7.5. He found that whatever the metal all graphs had the same slope and from equation (3) this is seen to be h/e. Knowing e, h can be calculated and the value obtained agrees with that found from black body radiation experiments. The threshold frequency f_0 and the work function Φ are characteristic for each metal and may also be deduced from the graph. The values of Φ are in good agreement with those determined from thermionic emission.

Planck's constant h is one of the fundamental physical constants and, like the velocity of light, occurs in a wide variety of atomic physics formulae. The accepted value of Planck's constant is, to three figures,

$$h = 6{\cdot}63 \times 10^{-34} \text{ joule second}$$

It is because of its smallness that quantum effects are not normally apparent.

Worked example

If a photoemissive surface has a threshold wavelength of 0·65 μm *calculate (a) its threshold frequency, (b) its work function and (c) the maximum velocity of the electrons emitted under the action of violet light of wavelength* 0·40 μm.

Velocity of light = $3{\cdot}0 \times 10^8$ m s^{-1};
Planck's constant = $6{\cdot}6 \times 10^{-34}$ J s;
1 eV = $1{\cdot}6 \times 10^{-19}$ J; mass of electron = $9{\cdot}1 \times 10^{-31}$ kg.

$$\begin{aligned}
(a)\ \lambda_0 &= 0{\cdot}65\ \mu\text{m} = 6{\cdot}5 \times 10^{-7}\ \text{m} \\
c &= 3 \times 10^8\ \text{m s}^{-1} \\
f_0 &= c/\lambda_0 \\
&= \frac{3 \times 10^8}{6500 \times 10^{-10}} \\
&= 4{\cdot}6 \times 10^{14}\ \text{Hz}
\end{aligned}$$

$$\begin{aligned}
(b)\ h &= 6{\cdot}6 \times 10^{-34}\ \text{J s} \\
\Phi &= hf_0 \\
&= 6{\cdot}6 \times 10^{-34} \times 4{\cdot}6 \times 10^{14}\ \text{J} \\
&= \frac{6{\cdot}6 \times 4{\cdot}6 \times 10^{-20}}{1{\cdot}6 \times 10^{-19}}\ eV \\
&= 1{\cdot}9\ eV
\end{aligned}$$

(*c*) *For violet light*

$$f = c/\lambda$$
$$= \frac{3 \times 10^8}{4 \times 10^{-7}} \text{ Hz}$$
$$= 7{\cdot}5 \times 10^{14} \text{ Hz}$$

Using the photoelectric equation $\frac{1}{2}mv_{max}^2 = hf - \Phi$

$$\tfrac{1}{2}mv_{max}^2 = (6{\cdot}6 \times 10^{-34} \times 7{\cdot}5 \times 10^{14} - 1{\cdot}9 \times 1{\cdot}6 \times 10^{-19}) \text{ J}$$
$$= 1{\cdot}91 \times 10^{-19} \text{ J}$$
$$\therefore v_{max} = \sqrt{\frac{2 \times 1{\cdot}91 \times 10^{-19}}{9{\cdot}1 \times 10^{-31}}} \text{ m s}^{-1}$$
$$= 6{\cdot}5 \times 10^5 \text{ m s}^{-1}$$

Wave-particle duality of radiation

Is electromagnetic radiation to be thought of as a wave motion or as a stream of particle-like packets of energy? The wave theory provides a completely satisfactory explanation of interference, diffraction and polarization while the quantum theory accounts for the photoelectric effect and black body radiation. Two such apparently contradictory interpretations of the nature of radiation posed an embarrassing problem to physicists in the early decades of this century. Are both theories correct, wrong or incomplete?

We shall return to this question later (Chapter 12) since it is of fundamental importance in modern physics. For the present we shall accept the duality of radiation and treat it accordingly when one aspect is more in evidence than the other. In this connection it is worth noting that with the long wavelengths and small frequencies of radio and infrared radiation, photon energies are small and particle effects difficult to observe. Large numbers of photons are required for detection and large numbers tend to obscure the graininess of radiation. In this case the wave-like nature predominates and interference, diffraction and polarization are readily obtained.

At the other extreme where wavelengths are short and frequencies high, single X- and gamma-ray photons may have energies of several million electron-volts and even one photon can be observed. The particle aspect is then most apparent and interference, etc., more difficult to show.

The intermediate wavelength and frequency values of light are such that both wave and particle behaviour is evident. In interference, diffraction and polarization many photons are involved and the wave model gives a satisfactory picture. But when we consider the intimate interaction between light and matter involving single photons and electrons, as in the photoelectric effect, the particle nature is dominant.

The equation $E = hf$ does in fact imply that radiation has a dual nature, since E is the energy of the photon of radiation considered as a particle and f the frequency of the radiation considered as a wave.

Photocells

The photoelectric cell or photocell changes radiation into an electric current. There are three main types.

1. PHOTOEMISSIVE CELL. A typical cell and its symbol are shown in Fig. 7.6. Two electrodes are enclosed in a glass bulb

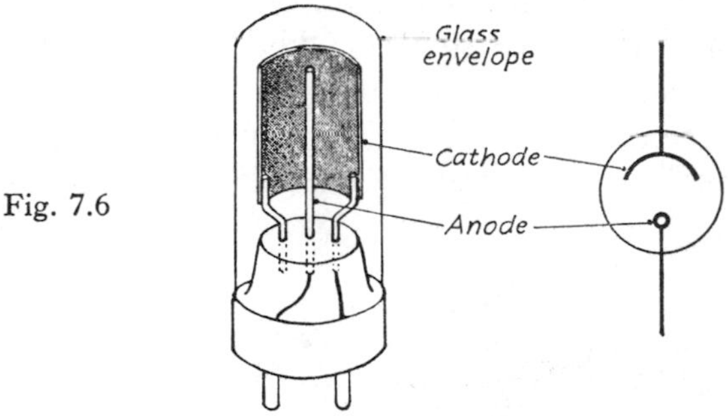

Fig. 7.6

which may be evacuated or contain an inert gas at low pressure. The cathode, often called the photocathode, is a curved metal plate having an emissive surface facing the anode, here shown as a single metal rod. When radiation falls on the cathode, photoelectrons are emitted and are attracted to the anode if it is at a suitable positive potential. A current of a few microamperes flows and increases with the intensity of the incident radiation. An inert gas in the cell gives greater current but causes a time lag in the response of the cell to very rapid changes of radiation. This may make it unsuitable for some purposes.

The choice of material for the cathode surface depends on the frequency range over which the cell is to operate and should be such that a good proportion of the incident photons yield photoelectrons. Ideally every photon should release one electron but in practice the yield is much lower. Pure metals are rarely used because of their high reflecting power; most photocathode surfaces are composite. Caesium on oxidized silver has a peak response near the red end of the spectrum and a threshold wavelength of 12 μm which makes it suitable for use with infrared.

2. PHOTOCONDUCTIVE CELL. This type of cell has been developed considerably in recent years. It consists of a plate of a material called a photoconductor, whose resistance decreases when it is illuminated by light or infrared, mounted in an evacuated glass bulb. An applied voltage causes current flow which increases with the intensity of radiation due to the release of more electrons in the photoconductor. The sensitivity of the cell is such that infrared sources can be detected at a distance of many miles. At present cadmium sulphide, with a peak response to red light, is most commonly used in light-controlled cells. The resistance of such a cell in the dark may be 10 MΩ and in daylight less than 1 kΩ.

3. PHOTOVOLTAIC CELL. If a very thin layer of cuprous oxide is formed on a copper disc and a translucent metal film deposited

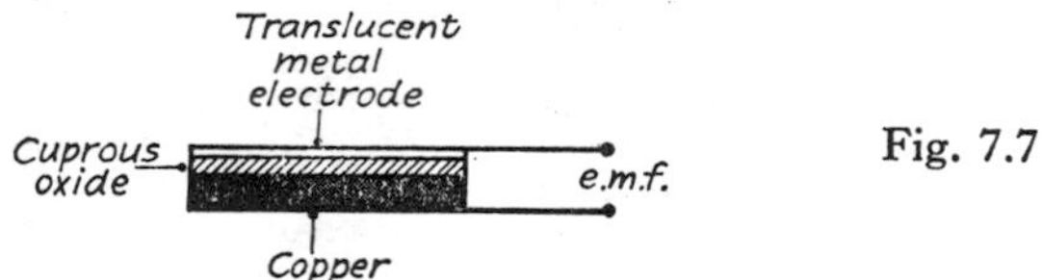

Fig. 7.7

on the oxide to provide electrical contact, an e.m.f. is generated between oxide and copper when the oxide is illuminated, Fig. 7.7. A thin layer of selenium on iron behaves similarly. Currents of about 1 mA are obtained and the current follows variations in the intensity of illumination so long as these are not rapid. The photovoltaic cell is a true cell since no external battery is required.

Some uses of photocells

1. COUNTING SYSTEMS. The photoemissive cell helps to count objects on a conveyor belt in a factory. When the beam of light or other radiation falling on the cell is cut off by the passing object the photocell operates the counting mechanism.

2. INTRUDER ALARMS. Something in the wrong place, e.g., a safe-breaker in a bank vault or the hand of a worker too close to a piece of machinery, can be detected if it interrupts a beam, often infrared, falling on a photocell connected to an alarm.

3. SOUND REPRODUCTION FROM FILM. Light from an exciter lamp, Fig. 7.8*a*, is focused on the 'sound track' at the side of the moving film and then falls on a photocell. The sound track varies

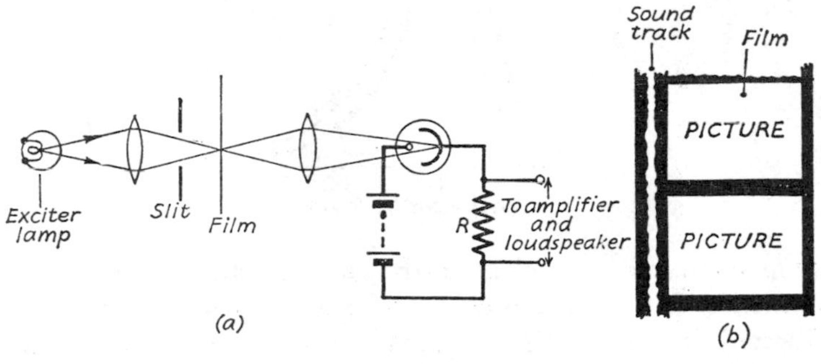

Fig. 7.8

the intensity of the light passing through it so that the photocell creates a varying current which is a replica of that obtained in the recording microphone when the film was made. The fluctuating voltage developed across the load R is amplified and the output converted to sound by a loudspeaker.

In the *variable area* sound track the width of the 'white' part, Fig. 7.8*b*, varies in the same way as the original sound wave. The track is produced by allowing the electrical variations from the recording microphone to control the width of a narrow slit through which light passes on its way to the side of the moving film. The finished track is obtained by developing the film.

4. ARTIFICIAL LIGHTING. This is often controlled automatically in factories, streets, etc., by a clock mechanism which turns on

the lights at a prearranged time. A controlling device employing a photoconductive cadmium sulphide cell has a switching action related to the prevailing light conditions rather than to time, and can cater for abnormal dark periods at dusk, dawn and during the day.

5. LIGHT-METER. The copper-oxide photocell is very suitable as a portable light-meter for measuring illumination since its

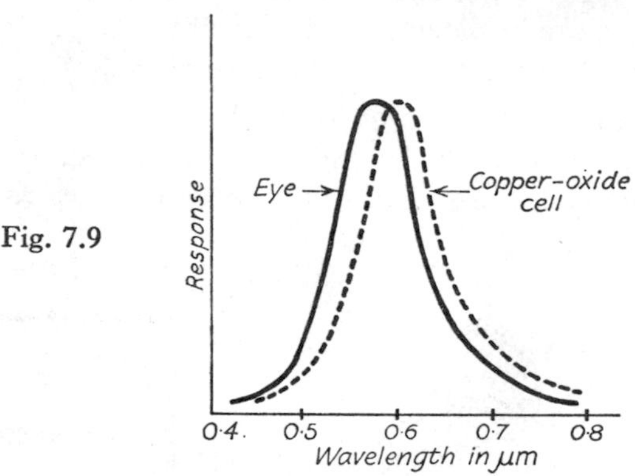

Fig. 7.9

response curve is very close to that of the human eye, Fig. 7.9. In practice the cell is connected to a galvanometer having a scale calibrated in lux; it is frequently used as a photographer's exposure meter.

Television camera

The television camera changes the optical image of a scene into an electrical signal. The principle of the *image orthicon*, a type of camera tube in common use, is illustrated in Fig. 7.10.

Light falling on the semi-transparent photocathode causes the emission of photoelectrons which are accelerated towards the target. The electrons are emitted at right angles to the cathode and so maintain the pattern of the optical image. At the target every incident electron ejects several other electrons by secondary emission and points on the target are thus left with positive charges. The target is a very thin glass plate (about 2 μm thick), electrical conduction can occur *through* it and a positive electrical image thus appears on its back surface. The image on the target is preserved because the glass is a good insulator *across* its surface. Having achieved their purpose of creating positive charges on the target, the secondary electrons are attracted by a fine wire mesh, on the cathode side of the target (not shown), which is a few volts positive with respect to the target.

A beam of electrons from the electron gun at the other end of the tube scans the back of the target point by point. Those points having a large positive charge, corresponding to bright parts of the optical image, remove more electrons from the scanning beam

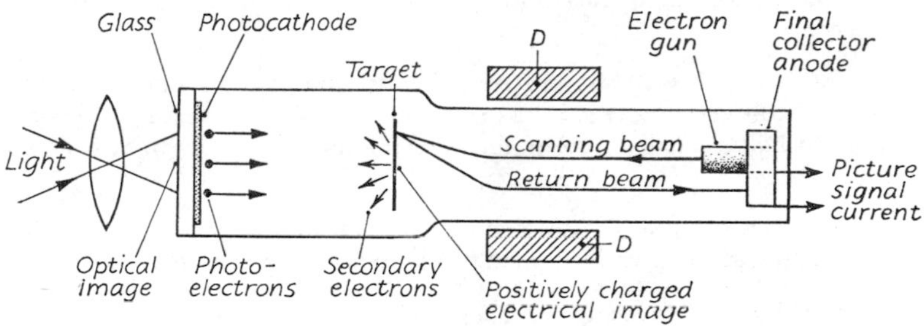

Fig. 7.10

than do 'dark' parts of the image which have little positive charge. The intensity of the return electron beam is therefore changing continuously, i.e., is modulated, according to the optical image. The varying current intercepted by the final collector anode provides the picture signal current for subsequent transmission. Two pairs of coils *DD* provide magnetic deflection (as in the receiver) of the scanning and return beams so that the whole target is covered. When the target has been scanned and its positive charge neutralized, it is ready to receive a new electrical image.

A recent type of camera tube is the '*Plumbicon*' tube which has features that make it attractive for colour television. Whereas the optical image in the *image orthicon* is converted into a pattern of electrostatic charges by means of photoemission and secondary emission, in the '*Plumbicon*', the charge pattern is produced by photoconduction using a layer of lead monoxide.

QUESTIONS

[Velocity of light = 3×10^8 m s^{-1}; Planck's constant = $6{\cdot}6 \times 10^{-34}$ J s; mass of electron = $9{\cdot}1 \times 10^{-31}$ kg; 1 eV = $1{\cdot}6 \times 10^{-19}$ J.]

1. (*a*) What is meant by photoelectric emission?
(*b*) State the main experimental facts relating to this effect.
(*c*) What does it contribute towards an understanding of the nature of light?

2. The B.B.C. Radio 2 transmitter at Droitwich operates on a wavelength of 1500 metres and at a power of 400 kilowatts. Calculate (*a*) the frequency corresponding to this wavelength, (*b*) the energy of a Radio 2 photon in joules and (*c*) the number of photons emitted per second.

3. A modern 200-watt sodium street lamp emits yellow light of wavelength 0·6 μm. Assuming it is 25 per cent efficient in converting electrical energy to light, calculate the number of photons of yellow light it emits per second.

4. If a surface has a work function of 3·0 eV, find the longest wavelength light which will cause the emission of photoelectrons from it.

5. When light of wavelength 0·5 μm falls on a surface it ejects photoelectrons with a maximum velocity of 6×10^5 m s^{-1}. Calculate (*a*) the work function in electron-volts, and (*b*) the threshold frequency for the surface.

6. What is the maximum velocity of the photoelectrons liberated from a surface having a work function of 4·0 eV by ultraviolet radiation of wavelength 0·2 μm?

7. When light is incident in a metal plate electrons are emitted only when the frequency of the light exceeds a certain value. How has this been explained?

The maximum kinetic energy of the electrons emitted from a metallic surface is $1{\cdot}6 \times 10^{-19}$ joule when the frequency of the incident radiation is $7{\cdot}5 \times 10^{14}$ Hz. Calculate the minimum frequency of radiation for which electrons will be emitted. Assume that Planck's constant = $6{\cdot}6 \times 10^{-34}$ J s. [*J.*]

8. Give an account of the photoelectric effect, and describe one practical application of it. State the factors that determine (*a*) the number of electrons emitted from unit area of the irradiated surface, and (*b*) the energy with which these electrons leave the surface. Discuss these results briefly in terms of the quantum theory of radiation.

Taking the work function for caesium to be 1·9 eV, the electronic charge to be $1{\cdot}6 \times 10^{-19}$ C, Planck's constant h to be $6{\cdot}5 \times 10^{-34}$ J s and the velocity of light *in vacuo* to be 3×10^8 m s^{-1}, calculate the kinetic energy with which an electron leaves a caesium surface exposed to light of wavelength 0·56 μm. [*O. Special*]

9. Describe the essential features of Millikan's photoelectric apparatus. What is the importance of Millikan's work?

Light of wavelength 0·6 μm from a sodium lamp falls on a photocell and causes the emission of photoelectrons for which the stopping potential is 0·5 volt. With light of wavelength 0.40 μm from a mercury vapour lamp the stopping potential is 1·5 volts. Find (*a*) h/e, (*b*) h if $e = 1{\cdot}6 \times 10^{-19}$ C, (*c*) the work function in electron-volts of the photocell surface.

10. In an experiment on the photoelectric effect using radiation of wavelength $4{\cdot}00 \times 10^{-7}$ m the maximum electron energy was observed to be $1{\cdot}40 \times 10^{-19}$ joule. With radiation of wavelength $3{\cdot}00 \times 10^{-7}$ m the maximum energy was $3{\cdot}06 \times 10^{-19}$ joule. Derive a value for Planck's constant.

Mention one other physical phenomenon involving Planck's constant. (Velocity of light = $3{\cdot}00 \times 10^8$ m s^{-1}.) [*J.*]

8 X-rays

X-rays, so named because their nature was at first unknown, were discovered in 1895 by Röntgen; they are produced by bombarding a target, usually made of a heavy metal, with high-energy electrons.

Modern X-ray tube

The modern X-ray tube, designed originally by Coolidge in 1913, is highly evacuated and contains an anode and a tungsten filament connected to a cathode, Fig. 8.1. Electrons are obtained from the filament by thermionic emission and are accelerated to the anode

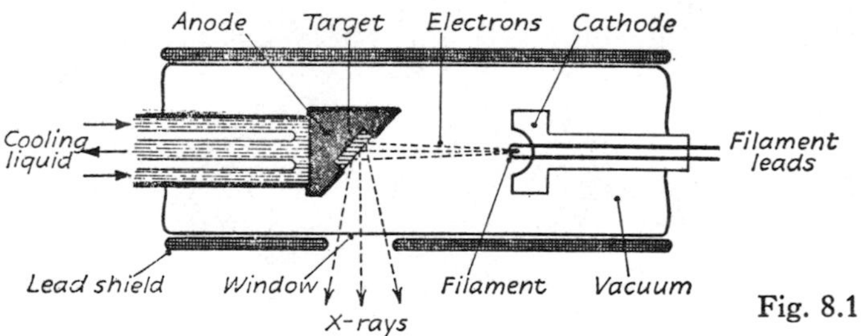

Fig. 8.1

by a p.d., frequently of several hundred kilovolts. The anode is a copper block inclined to the electron stream and having a small target of tungsten, or another high melting point metal, on which electrons are focused by the concave cathode. The tube has a lead shield with a small window to allow the passage of the X-ray beam.

Less than $\frac{1}{2}$ per cent of the kinetic energy of the electrons is converted into X-rays, the rest being changed into heat in the anode. The heat is dissipated by cooling fins or by circulating oil or water through channels in the anode.

The Coolidge tube permits separate adjustment of X-ray quantity and quality, a facility not provided by earlier tubes. The *quantity* emitted per second, i.e., the intensity, increases with the number of electrons hitting the target and this depends on the filament temperature which in turn is controlled by the heating

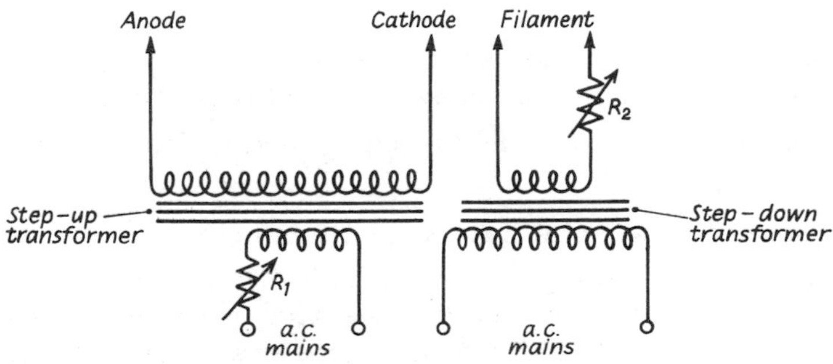

current. The *quality* or penetrating power of the X-rays is determined by the velocity attained by the electrons and increases with the voltage across the tube. 'Soft' X-rays only penetrate soft objects such as flesh, 'hard' X-rays can penetrate much more solid matter.

The voltage needed to operate the tube may be obtained from a half-wave rectifying circuit containing a step-up transformer, and in which the X-ray tube itself is the rectifier, Fig. 8.2. The X-ray hardness is controlled by variable resistor R_1 in the primary of the step-up transformer; R_2 controls the intensity.

Properties of X-rays

Most of the properties of X-rays were known shortly after Röntgen's discovery. They may be summarized as follows.

(*i*) They travel in straight lines.

(*ii*) They readily penetrate matter; penetration is least in materials containing elements of high density and high atomic weight. Thus while sheets of cardboard, wood and some metals fail to stop them, all but the most penetrating are absorbed by a sheet of lead 1 mm thick. Lead glass is a much better absorber than ordinary soda glass.

(*iii*) They cause certain substances to fluoresce. Barium platino-cyanide is an example.

(*iv*) They affect a photographic emulsion in a similar manner to light. X-ray photography is therefore possible.

(*v*) They ionize a gas increasing its conductivity. An electrified body such as a charged electroscope is thus discharged when irradiated by X-rays.

(*vi*) They cause photoelectric emission.

(*vii*) They are not deflected by electric or magnetic fields.

Properties of (*iii*), (*iv*) and (*v*) can be used to detect X-rays.

Nature of X-rays: von Laue's experiment

X-rays cannot be charged particles since they are not deflected by electric or magnetic fields. The vital experiment which established their electromagnetic nature was initiated by von

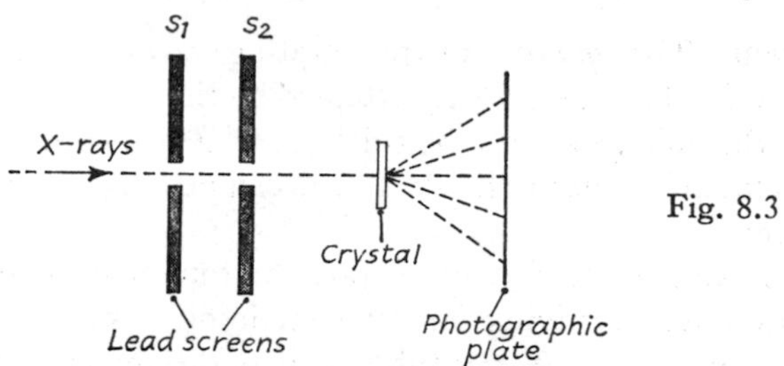

Fig. 8.3

Laue in 1912. After unsuccessful attempts had been made to obtain X-ray diffraction patterns with apparatus similar to that used for light, it was realized that the failure might be due to X-rays having much smaller wavelengths.

Von Laue's suggestion was that if the regular spacing of atoms in a crystal is of the same order as the wavelength of X-rays, the crystal should act as a three-dimensional diffraction grating. This idea was put to the test with conspicuous success by Friedrich and Knipping, two of von Laue's colleagues. The arrangement of their apparatus is shown in Fig. 8.3. A narrow beam of X-rays was collimated by two slits S_1 and S_2 and fell on a thin crystal in front of a photographic plate. After a long exposure the plate (on development) revealed that most of the radiation was undeflected, giving a large central spot, but some of it was deflected and

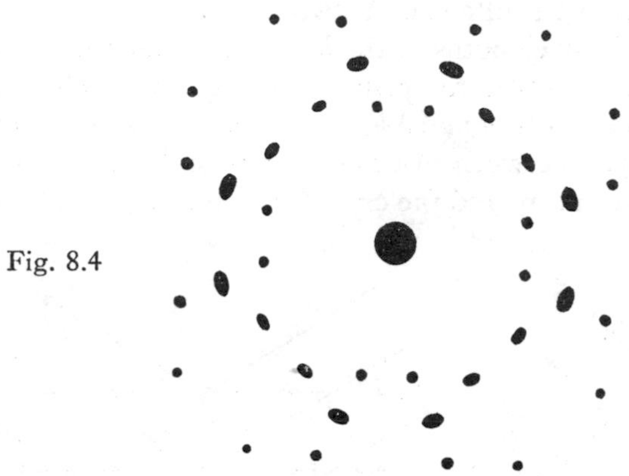
Fig. 8.4

produced a distinct pattern of fainter spots around the central one; Fig. 8.4 shows a Laue diffraction pattern.

The electromagnetic wave behaviour of X-rays was thus demonstrated and analysis of the diffraction patterns confirmed they had wavelengths of about 1×10^{-10} m (0·1 nm) as compared with 4000×10^{-10} m (0·40 μm) to 7500×10^{-10} m (0·75 μm) for light.

X-ray diffraction and Bragg's law

In the Laue technique the crystal is used as a transmission diffraction grating and interpretation of the patterns is difficult. Sir William Bragg and his son Sir Lawrence Bragg developed a simpler method in which the crystal acts as a reflecting diffraction grating.

When X-rays fall on a crystal, each atom scatters a small fraction of the incident beam and, by analogy with the optical case, may be regarded as the source of a weak secondary wavelet. Considering the crystal to consist of planes of atoms, the combined effect of all the atoms in, for example, the top plane is the production of a weak reflected beam such that the angle of incidence equals the angle of reflection, as occurs with the reflection of light by a mirror, Fig. 8.5*a*.

Lower planes of atoms, such as *p*, *q*, *r*, in Fig. 8.5*b* to which the X-rays penetrate, behave similarly. The reflected beams from all the planes involved, interfere and the resultant reflected beam is only strong if the path difference between successive planes is a whole number of wavelengths of the incident X-radiation. Thus reinforcement only occurs for planes *p* and *q* when $AB + BC = n\lambda$, where n is an integer and λ is the wavelength of the X-rays. If d is the distance between planes of atoms and θ is the angle between the X-ray beam and the crystal surface, i.e., the *glancing*

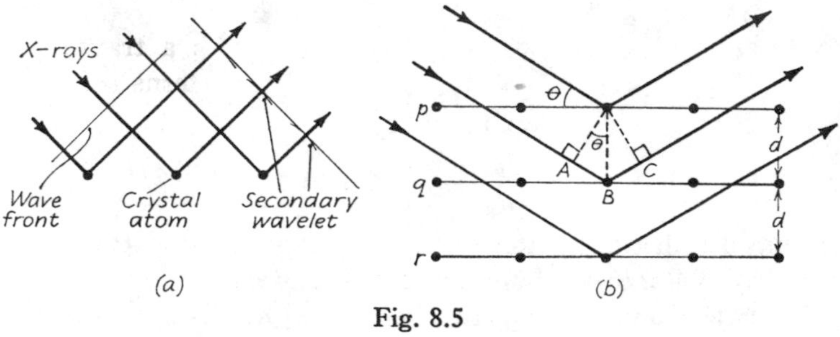

Fig. 8.5

angle, then $AB + BC = 2d \sin\theta$ and the reflected beam has maximum intensity when

$$2d \sin\theta = n\lambda$$

This relation is called *Bragg's Law*. Intensity maxima occur for several glancing angles. The smallest angle is given by $n = 1$ and is called the first-order reflection; $n = 2$ gives the second order and so on.

This process is often termed X-ray reflection and although it may appear that reflection occurs, it is in fact a diffraction effect since interference takes place between X-rays from secondary sources, i.e., crystal atoms, on the same wavefront.

X-ray spectrometer

The Bragg X-ray spectrometer was developed for the measurement of X-ray wavelengths or crystal lattice spacing; the principle of the instrument is shown in Fig. 8.6. X-rays from the target of an X-ray tube are collimated by two slits S_1 and S_2 (made in lead sheets) and the narrow beam so formed falls on a crystal C set on the table T of the spectrometer. The reflected beam passes through a third slit S_3 into an ionization chamber I where it causes an ionization current which is a measure of the intensity of the reflected radiation (p. 140).

As the crystal and ionization chamber are rotated, the angle of

Fig. 8.6

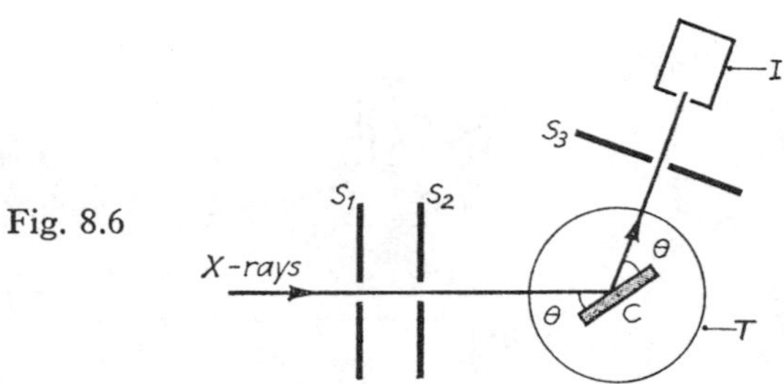

reflection always being kept equal to the angle of incidence, the ionization current is determined. Strong reflection occurs for glancing angles satisfying Bragg's law $2d \sin \theta = n\lambda$. Knowing either d or λ the other can be found.

X-ray wavelengths can now be measured directly using mechanically ruled diffraction gratings (similar to optical gratings) provided the X-rays strike the grating at a glancing angle less than 1°. X-ray analysis can then provide information about the structure of many complex substances.

X-ray spectra and the quantum theory

The radiation from an X-ray tube can be analysed with a spectrometer and an intensity-wavelength graph obtained to show the spectral distribution. A typical X-ray spectrum is given in Fig. 8.7. It has two parts:

1. A *continuous spectrum* which has a definite lower wavelength limit, increases to a maximum and then decreases gradually in the longer wavelengths. All targets emit this type of radiation.

2. A *line* or *characteristic spectrum* consisting of groups or series of two or three peaks of high-intensity radiation superimposed on

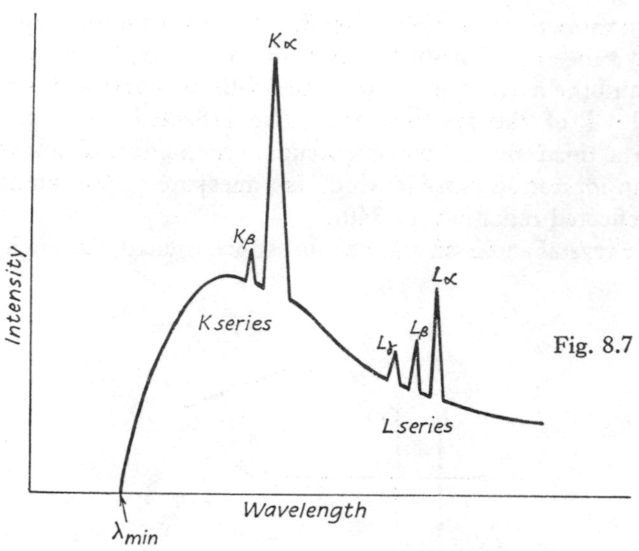

Fig. 8.7

the continuous spectrum. The series are denoted by the letters *K*, *L*, *M*, etc., in order of increasing wavelength, and the peaks by α, β, γ. The wavelengths of the peaks are characteristic of the target element; all the series are not normally given by one element.

The continuous spectrum is due to electrical interaction between the bombarding electrons and nuclei of the target atoms. An electron approaching a positively charged nucleus is accelerated and according to electromagnetic theory will then emit radiation, in this case X-rays. As a result the electron loses energy, slows down and the radiation is also appropriately known as 'bremsstrahlung' (German for 'braking radiation').

Certain features of the continuous spectrum are readily explained by the quantum theory. Thus the existence of a definite minimum wavelength can be justified if we assume that this radiation consists of X-ray photons produced by electrons which have given up all their kinetic energy in a single encounter with a target nucleus. If such an electron has mass m and velocity v on striking the target, the energy hf of the photon is given by

$$hf = \tfrac{1}{2}mv^2 \qquad (1)$$

h being Planck's constant and f the frequency of the radiation.

With a potential difference V across the X-ray tube, an electron of charge e gains kinetic energy eV and hence

$$\tfrac{1}{2}mv^2 = eV \tag{2}$$

From (1) and (2)

$$hf = eV \tag{3}$$

The value of f given by (3) is the maximum frequency of the X-rays emitted at voltage V, since all the energy of the electron is converted to the photon. The corresponding wavelength will have a minimum value, and if this is λ_{min} then $c = f\lambda_{min}$, where c is the velocity of propagation of X-rays. It follows that

$$\lambda_{min} = \frac{hc}{eV} \tag{4}$$

As V increases we see from (4) that λ_{min} decreases, i.e., X-rays of higher frequency and greater penetrating power are emitted. The values of λ_{min} calculated from this equation agree with those found experimentally.

In practice an electron usually has more than one encounter before losing all its energy. Several photons are produced with smaller frequencies than f and therefore with greater wavelengths than λ_{min}. Different electrons lose different amounts of energy and so a continuous spectrum covering a range of wavelengths is obtained. The great majority of electrons, however, lose their kinetic energy too gradually for X-rays to be emitted and merely heat the target.

The explanation of line spectra will be considered in Chapter 12 in connection with the structure of the atom.

Worked example

An X-ray tube operates at 30,000 *volts and the current through it is* 2 *mA. Calculate*

(*a*) *The electrical power input and the rate at which heat must be removed from the target.*

(*b*) *The number of electrons striking the target per second.*

(*c*) *The velocity of the electrons when they hit the target.*

(*d*) *The lower wavelength limit of the X-rays emitted.*

(*a*) Power input $= VI$, where V is the tube voltage and I the tube current

$$= 30{,}000 \text{ volts} \times 0{\cdot}002 \text{ ampere}$$
$$= 60 \text{ watts.}$$

Neglecting the small conversion of energy into X-rays, the rate of production of heat at the target = 60 watts = 60 joules per second.

$\therefore$ Rate at which heat must be removed from the target = 60 J s^{-1}.

(*b*) Current through tube is given by $I = n \times e$, where n is the number of electrons striking the target per second and e is the electronic charge, i.e., $1{\cdot}6 \times 10^{-19}$ coulomb.

$$\therefore n = \frac{I}{e} = \frac{0{\cdot}002 \text{ ampere}}{1{\cdot}6 \times 10^{-19} \text{ coulomb}}$$

Number of electrons striking target per second $= 1{\cdot}25 \times 10^{16}$.

(*c*) If m is the mass of an electron and v its velocity at the target, then from equation (2) above

$$\tfrac{1}{2}mv^2 = eV$$
$$\therefore v = \sqrt{\frac{2eV}{m}}$$

$$e = 1{\cdot}6 \times 10^{-19} \text{ coulomb}$$
$$m = 9 \times 10^{-31} \text{ kg}$$
$$V = 30{,}000 \text{ volts}$$
$$\therefore v = \sqrt{\frac{2 \times 1{\cdot}6 \times 10^{-19} \times 30{,}000}{9 \times 10^{-31}}}$$

Velocity of electrons $= 1{\cdot}0 \times 10^8 \text{ m s}^{-1}$.

(*d*) From equation (4) above, the lowest X-ray wavelength emitted is given by

$$\lambda_{min} = \frac{hc}{eV}$$

where h and c have their usual meaning.

$$h = 6{\cdot}6 \times 10^{-34} \text{ J s}$$
$$c = 3 \times 10^8 \text{ m s}^{-1}$$
$$\therefore \lambda_{min} = \frac{6{\cdot}6 \times 10^{-34} \times 3 \times 10^8}{1{\cdot}6 \times 10^{-19} \times 30{,}000}$$
$$= 0{\cdot}41 \times 10^{-10} \text{ m}$$

Lower wavelength limit of X-rays emitted $= 0{\cdot}41 \times 10^{-10}$ m.

Uses of X-rays

The usefulness of X-rays is largely due to their penetrating power, those of shortest wavelength being least easily absorbed.

(*a*) MEDICINE. Here, radiographs or X-ray photographs are used for a variety of purposes. Since X-rays can damage healthy cells of the human body, great care is taken to avoid unnecessary exposure. In radiography the X-ray film is sandwiched between two screens which fluoresce when subjected to a small amount of X-radiation. The film is affected by the fluorescent light rather than the X-rays; formerly X-rays were used to sensitize the film directly and much longer exposures were required.

Suspected bone fractures can be investigated since X-rays of a certain hardness can penetrate flesh but not bone. In the detection of lung tuberculosis by mass radiography use is made of the fact that diseased tissue is denser than healthy lung tissue which consists of air sacs and so the former absorbs X-rays more strongly. When an organ is being X-rayed whose absorptive power is similar to that of the surrounding tissue a 'contrast medium' is given to the patient, orally or by injection. This is less easily penetrated by X-rays and enables a shadow of the organ to be obtained on a radiograph. Thus in the diagnosis of stomach ulcers the patient swallows a cupful of a barium sulphate 'feed' some time before the radiograph is taken.

In the treatment of cancer by radiotherapy, very hard X-rays are used to destroy the cancer cells whose rapid multiplication causes malignant growth.

(*b*) INDUSTRY. Castings and welded joints can be inspected for internal imperfections using X-rays A complete machine may also be examined from a radiograph without having to be dismantled.

(*c*) X-RAY CRYSTALLOGRAPHY. The study of crystal structure by X-rays, initiated by von Laue and the Braggs, is now a powerful method of scientific research. The first crystals to be analysed were of simple compounds such as sodium chloride but in recent years the structure of organic molecules as complex as penicillin has been unravelled.

(*d*) ART. When a painting is being examined, for example to see if it is genuine or an imitation, an X-ray photograph can reveal restoration, alterations and even the type of paint. The early artists used paints with pigments of mineral origin which absorb X-rays more strongly than modern pigments.

QUESTIONS

1. Draw a labelled diagram to illustrate the construction of a hot cathode X-ray tube. How may the intensity and the penetrating power of the rays be varied with such a tube? If the potential difference applied to the tube is 20 kV, what would be the velocity with which the electrons strike their target? The specific charge of the electron is $1{\cdot}8 \times 10^{11}$ C kg^{-1}. Discuss what becomes of the kinetic energy of the electrons. [*W.*]

2. Describe the modern hot cathode X-ray tube, and give a diagram of a circuit suitable for its operation.

Discuss briefly the energy conversions that take place in the tube.

If the p.d. across the tube is 1500 volts, and the current 10^{-3} ampere, find (*a*) the number of electrons crossing the tube per second, (*b*) the kinetic energy gained by an electron traversing the tube without collisions. (Take the electronic charge e to be $1{\cdot}6 \times 10^{-19}$ coulomb.) [*O.*]

3. An X-ray tube works at a potential difference of 100,000 volts. Only 0·1 per cent of the energy of the cathode rays is converted into X-radiation and heat is generated in the target (anticathode) at a rate of 504 joules per second. What current does the tube pass and what is the energy and velocity of an electron when it reaches the target? (Electron charge = $1{\cdot}6 \times 10^{-19}$ coulomb; electron mass = $9{\cdot}1 \times 10^{-31}$ kg.) [*S. part qn.*]

4. Write a short account of the production and properties of X-rays. Include details of the detection and uses of this radiation. [*A.E.B.*]

5. Outline the evidence for believing (*a*) that X-rays are an electromagnetic radiation, (*b*) that wavelengths in the X-ray region are of the order of 10^{-3} times those of visible light. [*O. part qn.*]

6. What is the minimum wavelength of the X-rays produced when electrons are accelerated through a potential difference of 10,000 volts in an X-ray tube? Why is there a minimum wavelength?
($e = 1{\cdot}60 \times 10^{-19}$ C; $h = 6{\cdot}6 \times 10^{-34}$ J s; $c = 3 \times 10^{8}$ m s^{-1}.)

7. In a television cathode ray tube electrons are accelerated by a voltage of 16 kV. Calculate the highest frequency of the electromagnetic radiation emitted when the electrons are stopped by the screen of the tube. Also find the nature of the radiation from Fig. 6.2 on p. 94. (Use data at end of question 6.)

8. Gamma rays available for detecting flaws in a casting have a wavelength of $1{\cdot}6 \times 10^{-12}$ m. Calculate the target voltage that would have to be applied to a suitable X-ray tube to produce radiation having the same maximum penetrating power as these gamma rays.
(Planck's constant $h = 6{\cdot}63 \times 10^{-34}$ J s; the electron charge $= 1{\cdot}6 \times 10^{-19}$ C; velocity of light $c = 3 \times 10^{8}$ m s^{-1}.)

[*A.E.B. Special part qn.*]

9 Conduction in gases: positive rays: isotopes

The conduction of electricity by gases, generally known as *gas discharge*, has been a profitable subject for scientific investigation. It led to the discovery of the electron and provided evidence for the existence of isotopes. Among the devices depending on gas discharge are advertising signs and certain types of street lighting.

Ionization in gases

Dry gases at N.T.P. are very good insulators and normally only conduct if they are subjected to large potential differences. For example, about 30,000 volts are required to produce a spark discharge between two rounded electrodes one centimetre apart in air; the corresponding value for pointed electrodes one centimetre apart is 12,000 volts. An ionized gas is a much better conductor.

Ionization occurs when an electron is removed from an atom (or molecule) by supplying a certain amount of energy to overcome the attractive force securing the electron to the atom. The two resulting charged particles form an *ion-pair*, the electron being a negative ion and the atom, now deficient of an electron, a positive ion. When a p.d. is applied between two electrodes in the ionized gas, positive ions move towards the cathode and electrons towards the anode. The ions thus act as charge carriers and current flows in the gas. If an atom gains an electron it becomes a heavy negative ion but these are generally few in number and not important in gaseous conduction.

Various agents can ionize a gas including a flame, sufficiently energetic electrons, ultraviolet, X-rays and the radiation from radioactive substances, i.e., alpha, beta and gamma rays. The ionizing action of a flame may be shown by charging a polythene rod, holding it for a few seconds above a flame and then testing it with an electroscope. No charge is detected since in the flame gas molecules are in rapid motion and some, as a result of frequent collisions, lose electrons to create ion-pairs. Positive ions so formed are attracted to the negative charge on the polythene and neutralize it.

The few ions always present in the atmosphere are caused by cosmic rays from outer space and radioactive minerals in the earth. They are responsible for a charged, insulated body such as an electroscope, gradually discharging.

Current-voltage relation for an ionized gas

The air between two parallel plates *P* and *Q*, Fig. 9.1*a*, is ionized by a beam of ionizing radiation. When a p.d. is applied the resulting ionization current is recorded by a sensitive current

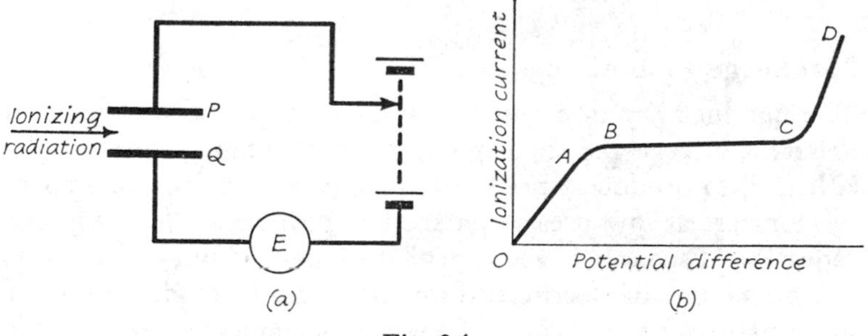

Fig. 9.1

detector *E*. (This may be a pulse electroscope or a d.c. amplifier as described in Chapter 11.) If the p.d. is varied while the intensity of the radiation remains constant, the current variation is shown by the curve *OABCD* in Fig. 9.1*b*.

The shape of the curve is explained in the following manner.

Small potential differences cause the electrons and positive ions to move slowly to the anode P and the cathode Q respectively. On the way some ions recombine to form neutral atoms. As the p.d. increases, the ions travel more quickly and there is less opportunity for recombination; the ionization current increases. At B all the ions produced by the radiation reach the electrodes, no recombination occurs and further increase of p.d. between B and C does not affect the current. Along BC the current has its *saturation value* and is independent of the applied voltage.

Beyond C the current rises rapidly with p.d. and indicates that a new source of ion-pairs has become operative. The original ions due to the radiation are now accelerated sufficiently by the large p.d. to form new electrons and new positive ions by collision with neutral air molecules between the plates. Thus along CD each original ion-pair creates several other ion-pairs, the process being known as *ionization by collision.* It can be shown that electrons are mainly responsible for this, although the positive ions make a contribution.

Two points should be noted:

(*i*) Ohm's law is obeyed between O and A.

(*ii*) The saturation current is proportional to the rate of production of ions by the radiation and so measures the intensity of the radiation.

Discharge tube effects

The conductivity of a gas increases as its pressure is reduced. Whereas a large p.d. is required at atmospheric pressure (100 kN m^{-2}) to produce a brief current flow in the form of a spark, by contrast at low pressure a smaller p.d. causes a steady current. The discharge is accompanied by certain luminous effects.

The passage of electricity through air can be studied at different pressures using a glass tube which is connected to a vacuum pump by a side tube, Fig. 9.2. A p.d. of several thousand volts d.c. is applied between two electrodes at opposite ends of the tube, from an E.H.T. power supply or from the secondary of an induction coil. The appearance of the discharge as air is removed is shown in Fig. 9.3; other gases give the same stages but different colours.

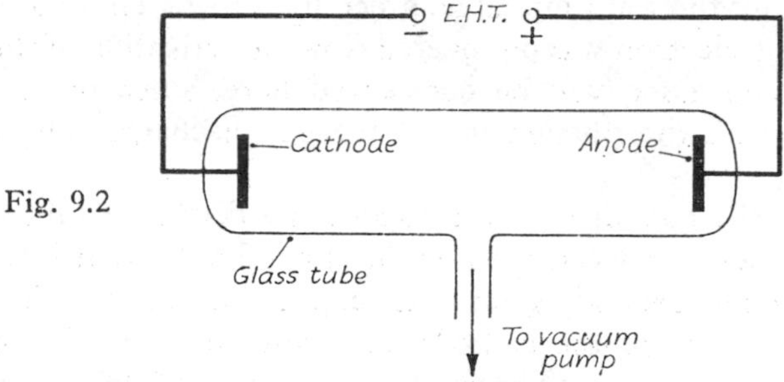

Fig. 9.2

Luminous effects do not occur until the pressure is about 2·5 kN m^{-2} and take the form of wavy violet streamers. The stage at which the pink positive column almost fills the tube is used in advertising signs, neon gives a red discharge and argon pale blue. At pressures below 10 N m^{-2} the Crookes dark space

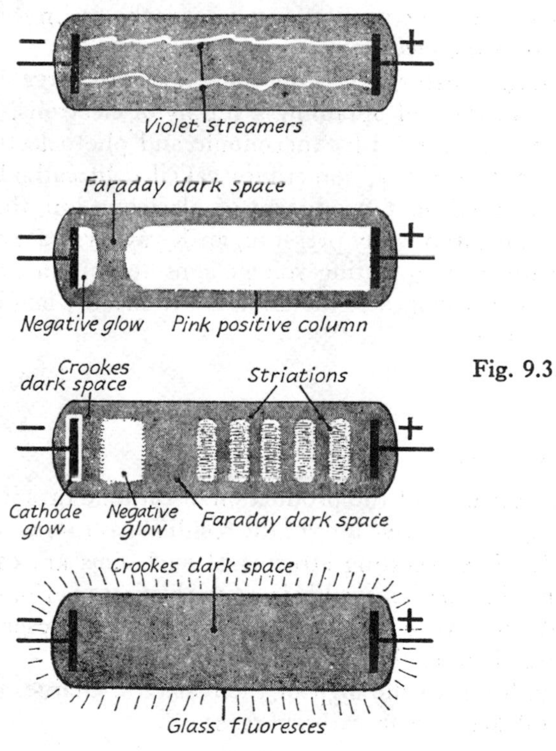

Fig. 9.3

fills the tube but the walls fluoresce, green light being emitted by soda glass. The electron was discovered from investigation of this last stage which alone will be considered here, since the full explanation of all the phenomena of the gas-discharge tube is complex.

A gas normally contains a few ions and in a discharge tube at low pressure these are accelerated by the applied p.d. towards the anode or cathode depending on their signs. The positive ions bombard the atoms of the cathode and cause the emission of electrons. In their journey towards the anode some of the ejected electrons produce further positive ions by collision with neutral gas molecules they encounter. In this way fresh ions are made available for carrying the current and the discharge is maintained so long as residual gas is present. A beam of high-speed electrons, i.e., cathode rays, travels towards the anode and those striking the walls of the tube cause fluorescence. The cathode rays have the same properties whatever the gas in the tube or the material of the electrodes.

Although historically important, gas discharge is now little used as a means of obtaining a supply of electrons. The process has been superseded by thermionic and photoelectric emission. Gas-discharge tubes, sometimes called cold cathode tubes, are not only inefficient producers of electrons but they may also present (at cathode ray pressure) an X-ray hazard. In many cases they require an operating voltage considerably in excess of 5 kV and at such voltages X-radiation is produced when cathode rays strike matter.

Positive rays

The explanation of the production of cathode rays in a discharge tube requires positive ions of the residual gas to travel towards the cathode. The resulting streams of such ions are called *positive rays* and their path is visible in a tube having a perforated cathode. A faint glow, whose colour depends on the gas present, appears in the space behind the cathode, Fig. 9.4.

In addition to the sign of their electric charge, positive rays differ markedly from cathode rays:

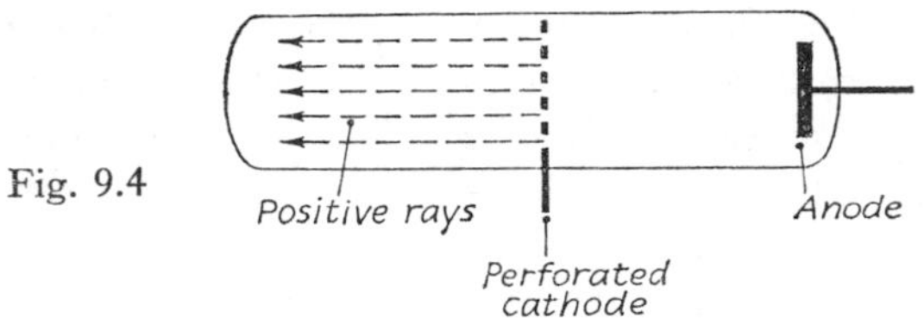

Fig. 9.4

(1) They are deflected to a much smaller extent than cathode rays by electric and magnetic fields. This is not surprising since, being ionized atoms and molecules, they are much more massive.

(2) Whereas most of the electrons in a beam of cathode rays have the same velocity, positive rays exhibit a range of velocities. This arises from the fact that the positive ions comprising the rays are formed at various points between the anode and cathode and so are accelerated to different velocities before reaching the cathode.

(3) The properties of positive rays are related to the gas in the tube.

Thomson's positive rays experiment

J. J. Thomson determined the charge to mass ratio of positive rays from their deflections in *parallel* electric and magnetic fields. His apparatus consisted of a special form of gas-discharge tube, Fig. 9.5*a*; *A* is the anode, *C* the cathode and *B* a large bulb containing the gas under study at a suitable low pressure. When a

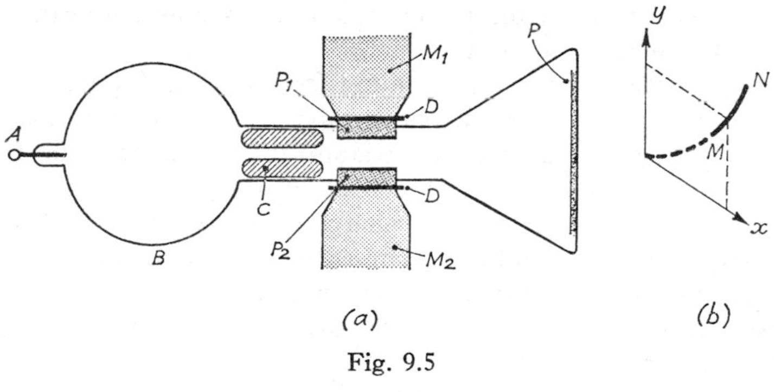

Fig. 9.5

high p.d. is applied a narrow stream of positive rays emerges from the cathode, traverses the electric and magnetic fields and then falls on a photographic plate P. The magnetic field is produced by an electromagnet M_1M_2 whose pole pieces P_1 and P_2 are insulated from the rest of the core of the magnet by thin mica sheets D. P_1 and P_2 are connected to a source of p.d. thus creating an electric field parallel to the magnetic field.

In the absence of the fields the positive rays produce one central spot on P directly in line with the channel through the cathode. When the fields are applied, each deflects the particles but in directions at right angles. In Fig. 9.5*b* the electric deflection, y, will be in the plane of the paper and the magnetic deflection, x, in a direction perpendicular to the plane of the paper. It can be shown (see next section) that particles having the same charge to mass ratio but different velocities strike P at different points which lie on a parabola such as MN. Particles with a different specific charge lie on a different parabola. By making measurements on the parabolas Thomson obtained charge to mass values for various atoms.

Although certain factors such as traces of impurities and the formation of abnormal ions cause difficulties in interpreting positive ray parabolas, further useful information about atoms may be deduced. Thus if an atom contains more than one electron it can form more than one ion and each produces a corresponding parabola. Helium gives two parabolas, one due to singly charged ions and the other to doubly charged ions. It may therefore be inferred that the helium atom has two electrons to lose in ionization; similarly from the behaviour of hydrogen we can say it has one electron per atom.

Atomic weights can also be found from the relative positions of the parabolas on a set of photographs. Thomson did this by assuming that for a particular atom the parabola with the smallest charge to mass ratio related to singly charged ions. Knowing the charge and the charge to mass ratio, the mass could be calculated. The determination of atomic weights by positive ray analysis really involves weighing single atoms; by contrast chemical methods give the average atomic weight for a large number of atoms.

Deflection of charged particles by parallel electric and magnetic fields

In Fig. 9.6 a beam of positively charged particles, each of mass M and charge Q, is shown moving with velocity v perpendicular to a uniform electric field of intensity E and to a uniform magnetic field of flux density B. If E and B are parallel and act over the

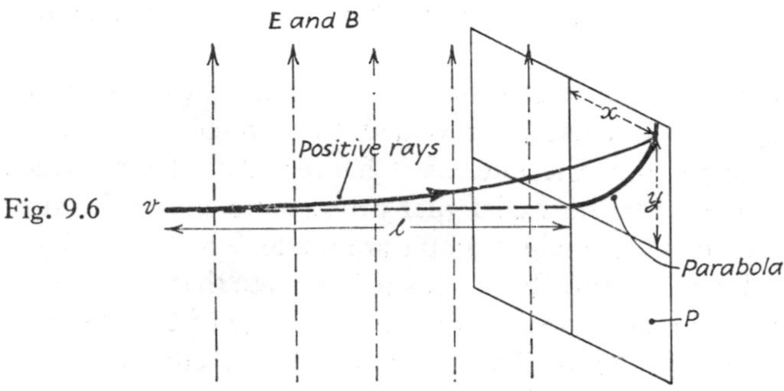

Fig. 9.6

entire length l of the beam from the source to the plane P, the electric force in the y-direction is EQ and the y-deflection is given by

$$y = \frac{1}{2}\cdot\frac{EQ}{M}\cdot\frac{l^2}{v^2} \qquad \text{(p. 26)} \qquad (1)$$

The magnetic force in the x-direction is BQv and the x-deflection is

$$x = \frac{1}{2}\cdot\frac{BQv}{M}\cdot\frac{l^2}{v^2} = \frac{1}{2}\cdot\frac{BQ}{M}\cdot\frac{l^2}{v} \qquad (2)$$

Eliminating v from (1) and (2)

$$y = \frac{2E}{B^2l^2}\cdot\frac{M}{Q}\cdot x^2$$

This is the equation of the curve formed on P by the points of impact of particles having a charge to mass ratio M/Q but different velocities. It is a parabola.

Atomic number

After it had been established that the negatively charged electron was one of the basic constituents of all atoms, the search began for a positively charged counterpart. Positive rays were thoroughly investigated but the lightest particle to be detected was obtained with hydrogen in the discharge tube and its charge to mass ratio clearly indicated that it was a positive hydrogen ion. The latter, being the simplest and lightest positively charged particle then known, was called a *proton* (from the Greek *protos* meaning first).

Subsequently, experiments on the bombardment of atoms by suitable high-speed particles revealed that in certain cases a proton is ejected from the nucleus (Chapter 13). This provided further evidence for the belief that protons are one of the fundamental particles from which atoms are made. The proton has a charge equal in magnitude but opposite in sign to that on the electron and its rest mass is 1836 times the rest mass of the electron.

Reference was made in Chapter 1 to the periodicity of properties which appears when the elements are arranged in order of increasing atomic masses. Originally a few elements were obviously out of place, for example, argon had a higher atomic mass than potassium, but on physical and chemical grounds it clearly had to precede potassium. Such anomalies implied that the atomic mass only gave the approximate position of an element in the periodic table. For a time, the difficulty was overlooked and the elements were arranged in the order required by their properties. They were numbered accordingly, beginning with hydrogen as 1, helium as 2, lithium as 3 and so on to uranium as 92. The number allotted to an element was called its *atomic number*.

The significance of atomic number did not become clear until the nuclear theory of the atom had been proposed. Evidence will be given later to support the view, now accepted, that

the atomic number Z of an element equals the number of protons in the nucleus.

An atom is normally electrically neutral, and since the proton carries the same charge as the electron, it follows that the atomic number is also the number of extranuclear electrons in the neutral atom. Hydrogen with atomic number 1 thus has one proton and one electron while uranium with atomic number 92 has 92 protons and 92 electrons. Atomic number is a more fundamental property than atomic mass.

Nuclear constituents: mass number

Since the atomic number of an element (i.e., the number of protons in the nucleus) is about half its atomic mass, it follows that if (as the nuclear theory supposes) the mass of an atom is due to its nucleus then there must be other constituents besides protons in the nucleus. The possibility of the existence of an electrically neutral particle, having a similar mass to that of the proton, was suggested in 1920. This particle, named the *neutron*, remained undiscovered until 1932 (p. 230) partly on account of the difficulty of detecting a particle which, being uncharged, is not deflected by electric or magnetic fields and produces no appreciable ionization in its path. Neutrons, like protons, can be expelled from certain nuclei by bombardment, and there is now no doubt that they must be considered basic constituents of matter. Each does not consist of a proton in close association with an electron but is an entity in itself. The rest mass of the neutron is 1839 times that of the electron.

The mass number A of an atom is defined as the sum of the number of protons and neutrons in the nucleus. Protons and neutrons are sometimes called *nucleons.*

The simplest nucleus is that of hydrogen which consists of one proton; in symbolic notation it is written ${}^{1}_{1}\text{H}$, where the superscript gives the mass number and the subscript the atomic number. Helium has two protons and two neutrons, giving mass number 4, atomic number 2 and symbol ${}^{4}_{2}\text{He}$. Lithium, ${}^{7}_{3}\text{Li}$, has mass number 7, atomic number 3 and its atom has three protons and four neutrons. The neutron is represented by ${}^{1}_{0}n$ since it has mass number 1 and zero charge, i.e., atomic number 0. The electron can be written ${}^{0}_{-1}e$.

In an alternative representation the mass number is written after the symbol, e.g., ${}_{3}\text{Li}^{7}$. Sometimes the atomic number is omitted and the name or symbol of the element is given, followed by the mass number, e.g., lithium 7 or Li 7.

Isotopes and nuclides

If two atoms have the same number of protons but different numbers of neutrons, their atomic numbers are equal but not their mass numbers. Each atom is said to be an *isotope* of the other. Since they have the same number of electrons they are chemically indistinguishable and occupy the same place in the periodic table. (The term isotope is derived from the Greek words *isos*, meaning same, and *topos*, meaning place.)

Few elements consist of identical atoms, most are isotopic mixtures. Thus hydrogen has three forms: ^1_1H with one proton in the nucleus, heavy hydrogen or ***deuterium*** ^2_1D with one proton and one neutron and ***tritium*** ^3_1T with one proton and two neutrons. Ordinary hydrogen contains 99·99 per cent of ^1_1H atoms. Isotopes are not as a rule given separate names and symbols; exception is made in the case of hydrogen because there is an appreciable difference in the physical properties of the three forms due to the ratio of their atomic masses being much larger than usual. Water made from deuterium is called heavy water and is denoted by D_2O; it has a density of 1·108 g cm^{-3}, a freezing point of 3·82°C and a boiling point of 101·42°C. The nucleus of the deuterium atom is called a deuteron (compare proton for the nucleus of the lighter isotope).

Isotopes account for fractional atomic masses. For example, chlorine with atomic mass 35·5 has two forms. One has seventeen protons and eighteen neutrons, giving atomic number 17 and mass number 35; the other has seventeen protons but twenty neutrons so that the atomic number is the same but the mass number is 37. These two isotopes are present in ordinary chlorine in the approximate ratio of three atoms of $^{35}_{17}Cl$ to one atom of $^{37}_{17}Cl$, making the average atomic mass 35·5. Chemically they are identical but one is slightly denser than the other.

Isotopes were discovered among the radioactive elements in 1906 but their nature was not understood. The first hint of their existence among non-radioactive elements was obtained in 1912 by Thomson. With neon in his positive rays apparatus two parabolas appeared, corresponding, in the light of modern knowledge, to isotopes of masses 20 and 22. The proportions were

TABLE 9.1

Atomic number	*Element*	*Nucleons*		*Electrons*	*Percentage abundance*
		Protons	*Neutrons*		
1	Hydrogen	1	0	1	99·99
	Deuterium	1	1	1	0·01
	Tritium[1]	1	2	1	—
2	Helium	2	1	2	10^{-4}
		2	2	2	100
3	Lithium	3	3	3	7·4
		3	4	3	92·6
4	Beryllium	4	5	4	100
5	Boron	5	5	5	19·6
		5	6	5	80·4
6	Carbon	6	6	6	98·9
		6	7	6	1·1

[1] Tritium is formed by several different nuclear reactions between cosmic rays and stable nuclei. It is radioactive with a half-life of 12·4 years and a very low natural abundance.

such as to give an average atomic mass of 20·2, the chemical atomic mass of neon.

Isotopes have the same number of protons (i.e. same atomic number Z) but different numbers of neutrons (i.e., different mass numbers A); they are the *same* element. On the other hand *different* elements have different numbers of protons but can have the same number of neutrons. The composition of the nucleus determines the species of atom and the term *nuclide* has been introduced to be used when we specify an atom with a particular proton-neutron combination. Table 9.1 shows the constituents of some naturally occurring nuclides. $^{6}_{3}$Li and $^{7}_{3}$Li are isotopes, $^{9}_{4}$Be and $^{10}_{5}$B have the same number of neutrons but different numbers of protons. All four are nuclides.

Although there are only 103 elements (89 in nature and 14 man-made), each one has isotopes and the total number of different nuclides at present exceeds 1300. Of these about 300 occur naturally and the rest are made artificially (see p. 165). All the artificial nuclides and some of the natural ones are radioactive and are called radionuclides.

Atomic mass: Aston's work

The *atomic mass* was formerly referred to as the atomic weight. Is is now defined as *the mass of an atom taking the mass of the atom of the carbon nuclide* $^{12}_{6}$C *as being* 12 *atomic mass units* (a.m.u.). One a.m.u. is thus one-twelfth of the mass of the carbon 12 atom and equals $1{\cdot}66 \times 10^{-24}$ g.

Formerly atomic masses (weights) were referred to the hydrogen atom as 1 and then to the oxygen isotope $^{16}_{8}$O as 16 but, in 1960, physicists and chemists agreed to adopt the carbon 12 scale. This scale was chosen because in the determination of atomic mass by the methods of mass spectroscopy (to be explained shortly), carbon 12 is a convenient standard for comparison since it forms many compounds. Furthermore, there are only two isotopes of carbon and their proportions vary very little in naturally-occurring carbon.

Atomic masses were first measured to a high degree of accuracy by F. W. Aston who modified Thomson's positive rays apparatus and established by the work he did between 1919 and 1927 that

(*i*) most elements exhibit isotopy

(*ii*) most isotopic masses are very nearly but not quite whole numbers.

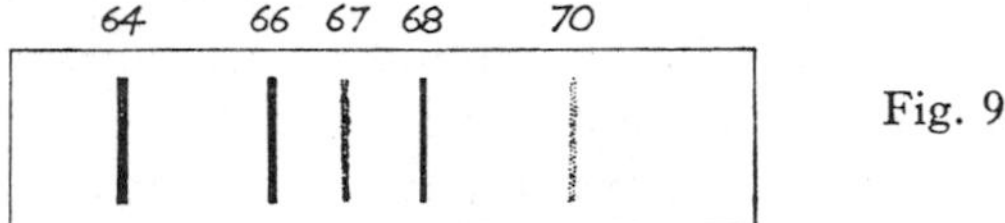

Fig. 9.7

In Aston's apparatus the deflecting electric and magnetic fields were arranged so that all particles of the same mass, irrespective of their velocity, were brought to a line focus rather than spread out along a parabola. When ions of different masses were present, a series of lines, i.e., a mass spectrum, Fig. 9.7, was obtained on a photographic plate. The relative intensities of the lines enabled an estimate to be made of the relative amounts of isotopes. Aston called his instrument a mass spectrograph.

Bainbridge's mass spectrograph

Many types of mass spectrograph have been constructed for the accurate determination of atomic mass but only that devised by Bainbridge in 1933 will be described here. The essential features of his instrument are shown in Fig. 9.8.

Positive rays from a discharge tube (not shown) pass through slits S_1 and S_2 and emerge as a narrow beam with a range of velocities and charge to mass ratios. In the region between S_2 and S_3 crossed uniform electric and magnetic fields are applied. The electric field maintained between P_1 and P_2 exerts a force acting

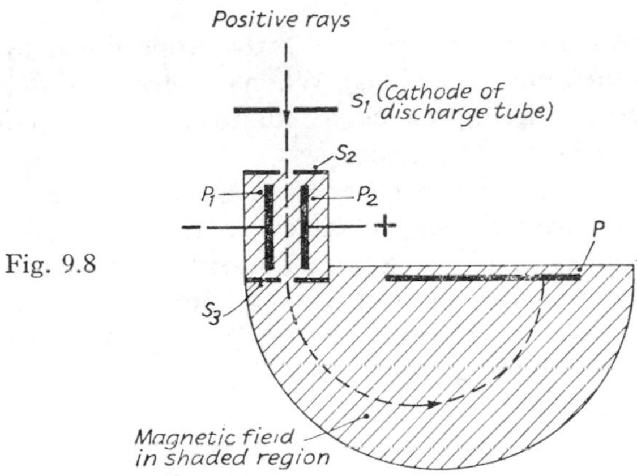

Fig. 9.8

to the left on the positive ions. The magnetic field, which acts normal to and into the plane of the diagram, tends to deflect the ions to the right. If Q is the charge of an ion and E the intensity of the electric field, the electric force is EQ. The magnetic force is BQv, where v is the velocity of the ion and B the flux density. If the forces are equal

$$BQv = EQ$$

$$\therefore \quad v = E/B \tag{1}$$

The ion will be undeflected and will emerge from the selector system, as S_2–S_3 is called, if its velocity equals the ratio E/B. All ions leaving S_3 thus have the same velocity v whatever their charge to mass ratio and *velocity selection* is said to have occurred.

Beyond S_3 only the magnetic field acts, the ions describe circular arcs and strike the photographic plate P. For particles of mass M, the radius r of the path is given by

$$BQv = \frac{Mv^2}{r}$$

or

$$r = \frac{Mv}{BQ} \qquad (2)$$

From (1) and (2)

$$r = \frac{M}{Q} \cdot \frac{E}{B^2}$$

If B and E are constant then r is directly proportional to M (assuming Q is the same for all ions). When ions having different masses are present each set produces a definite line and from their positions the masses can be found.

The mass spectrograph, apart from its great importance in physics, is now a powerful tool in chemical analysis. It can detect one part of impurity in 10^9 parts. In a modern instrument such as the Nier spectrograph positive ions are created by firing electrons into a gas at low pressure.

QUESTIONS

1. Give a short account of the conduction of electricity through gases, discussing both ionized gases at ordinary pressures, and also discharge-tube conditions. [*O. part qn.*]

2. What are positive rays? How have their properties been investigated? [*J. part qn.*]

3. 'Chlorine is an element of *atomic number* 17 and *atomic weight* 35·46. It has two naturally occurring *isotopes* of *mass number* 35 and 37.'

Comment on this statement and explain the meanings of the terms given in italics. Calculate the relative abundance of the two isotopes. [*L. part qn.*]

4. The *atomic number* and the *atomic mass* of aluminium are 13 and 27 respectively. What is the significance of these statements in relation to the structure of the aluminium atom?

A solid aluminium sphere has a radius of 0·1 m. Find (*a*) the total number of electrons in the sphere, (*b*) the fraction of these which are removed when the sphere is raised to a positive potential of 100 V. (Avogadro's constant = $6{\cdot}0 \times 10^{23}$ mol^{-1}; density of aluminium = $2{\cdot}7 \times 10^3$ kg m^{-3}; electronic charge = $1{\cdot}6 \times 10^{-19}$ C; permittivity of free space $\epsilon_0 = 1/(4\pi \times 9 \times 10^9)$ F m^{-1}.) [*J.*]

(*Note.* The mole is based on the gram. See page 6.)

5. Define atomic number and mass number, and explain the term isotope.

Explain the principle of one form of mass spectrometer and describe how the instrument is used for the identification of isotopes. [*O. part qn.*]

6. Describe and account for the form of the path of a charged particle which enters (*a*) a uniform magnetic field, (*b*) a uniform electric field, travelling initially with constant velocity perpendicular to the lines of force.

A fine collimated beam of positive ions from a discharge tube passes through a short region where exist a uniform magnetic and a uniform electric field superimposed and acting in the same direction perpendicular to the axis of the beam. After leaving the fields the beam traverses a field-free evacuated space and impinges upon a photographic plate whose plane is perpendicular to the undisplaced beam. Deduce expressions for the deflection of the beam produced by either field acting alone, assuming the deflection to be small and the length of the path in the field to be much less than the distance from the field region to the plate. Hence show that the action of the combined fields is to cause all ions having the same value of mass per unit charge m/e, but different velocities, to strike the plate along a parabola whose position depends on the value of m/e.

In certain experiments of this nature using oxygen parabolas were observed corresponding to values of m/e both 8 and 16 times the value for the proton; while using neon parabolas were observed corresponding to values 20 and 22. Comment briefly on these two sets of results. [*L. Special*]

10 Radioactivity

In 1896 Henri Becquerel, Professor of Physics at the University of Paris, found that uranium compounds emitted a penetrating radiation which affected a photographic plate wrapped in black paper and, like X-rays, ionized a gas. His discovery aroused great interest and the search for similar substances was taken up by others, including Madame Curie who in 1898 named this remarkable phenomenon radioactivity. In collaboration with her husband she extracted from the ore pitchblende two new radioactive elements, polonium and radium, both previously missing from the periodic table.

Three types of radiation

Radioactive substances emit three types of radiation called alpha, beta and gamma rays which may be identified by their different penetrating ability, ionizing power and behaviour in a magnetic field.

Alpha rays are the least penetrating, having a range of only a few centimetres in air and being readily stopped by the skin or a sheet of thick paper. They do however produce marked ionization in any gas through which they pass. A strong magnetic field deflects them and the direction and size of the deflection suggest that they are positively charged, relatively heavy, particles. They are more appropriately termed alpha particles.

Beta rays are more penetrating, having a range of several

metres in air and a few millimetres in aluminium. They are much less strongly ionizing than alpha particles but more easily deviated by a magnetic field. The deflection and the direction indicate that the rays are negatively charged particles of small mass.

Gamma rays are highly penetrating, several centimetres of lead often failing to absorb them completely. They ionize a gas weakly and are not deflected in a magnetic field. Their behaviour is not that of charged particles.

The different electrical properties of the three types of radiation are summarized in Fig. 10.1 which shows the deflections produced by a magnetic field acting into the plane of the paper. In the figure the deflection of the alpha particles is exaggerated since, if the magnetic field was strong enough to deflect the alpha particles, the beta particles would describe circles of extremely small radii.

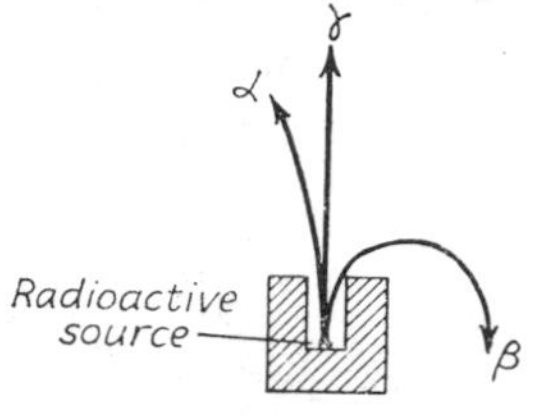

Fig. 10.1

Alpha, beta and gamma rays are termed 'nuclear radiation' (to distinguish them from electromagnetic radiation) since, as we see shortly, they originate in atomic nuclei.

Nature of alpha, beta and gamma rays

The charge to mass ratio, i.e., the specific charge, of alpha and beta particles can be deduced from measurements of the deflection of the particles in electric and magnetic fields. The values obtained provide information about their nature.

Alpha particles have a specific charge which is half the value for the hydrogen ion in electrolysis. If the charge on an alpha particle is $+e$ (where e is the electronic charge) its mass is twice that of the hydrogen atom, but if the charge is $+2e$, the mass of the alpha particle is four times that of the hydrogen atom, i.e., equal to the mass of the helium atom. To settle this point, Rutherford and Geiger measured the total charge carried by a known number of alpha particles using a counting device from which the modern Geiger–Müller tube was developed. They found that the alpha particle carried a charge $+2e$ and was a helium ion with a double positive charge, i.e., a helium atom which has lost two electrons—a helium nucleus, $^4_2$He.

Direct proof of the connection between alpha particles and helium was provided by the Rutherford–Royds experiment in 1909. A large quantity of the gas, radon, was compressed into the tube *A*, Fig. 10.2, whose walls were thin enough to allow the alpha particles emitted by radon to escape into the evacuated space enclosed by the thicker-walled tube *B*. After about a week the mercury level was raised so that any gas which had collected in *B* was forced into *C*. On passing an electric discharge through *C* the characteristic spectrum of helium was observed. Each alpha particle penetrating *A* collected two electrons when it was slowed down in *B* and became a neutral helium atom.

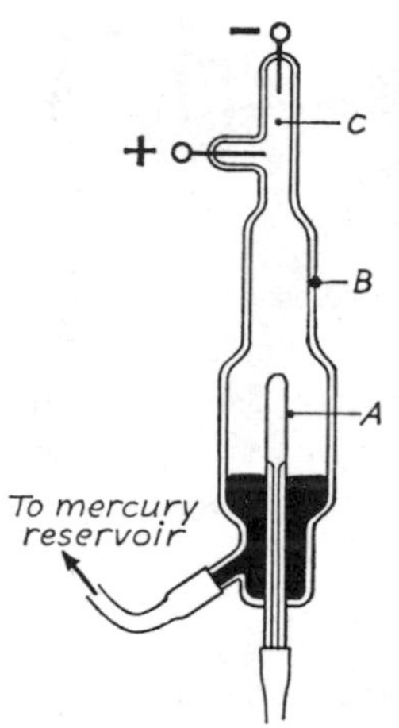

Fig. 10.2

Beta particles were shown by Becquerel to have a specific charge of the same order as that of cathode rays. Later workers confirmed that they were in fact electrons moving with high velocity. In calculating the specific charge for beta particles allowance has to be made for the increase of mass with velocity as predicted by relativity. If m_0 is the rest mass of the electron (i.e., the mass at ordinary velocities) and c the velocity of light, the mass m at velocity v is given by $m = m_0(1 - v^2/c^2)^{-1/2}$. In some cases beta particles are emitted with velocities very close to that of light and if the relativistic mass m is not used, the specific charge decreases with increasing velocity of the particle. When $v = 0{\cdot}5c$, $m = 1{\cdot}15m_0$; when $v = 0{\cdot}9c$, $m = 2{\cdot}3m_0$.

Gamma rays were the subject of controversy in view of their indifference to electric and magnetic fields but notable penetrating power. Definite proof of their wave nature was not obtained until 1914 when Rutherford and Andrade caused them to be diffracted by a crystal. Their wavelengths correspond to those of very short X-rays, and like X-rays they are a form of electromagnetic radiation travelling with the velocity of light but having a different origin.

Energy spectra

The nature of alpha, beta and gamma rays is always the same but their energies of emission vary from one nuclide to another. The energies of alpha and beta particles are determined from measurements of their paths in a magnetic field. The energy of gamma rays is found by measuring their wavelength using a crystal as a diffraction grating and then treating them as photons whose energy is given by the quantum theory equation $E = hf = hc/\lambda$, where h is Planck's constant, f the frequency and λ the wavelength of the rays and c the velocity of light.

The results of these determinations will now be summarized:

Alpha particles. In many cases the alpha particles emitted by a particular nuclide all have the same energy and are said to be monoenergetic. For example, all alpha particles from uranium 238, the most abundant isotope of uranium, have energy 4·2 MeV. Depending on the source, alpha-particle energies vary from 4 to 10 MeV corresponding to emission velocities of 5 to 7 per cent of the velocity of light.

Precise measurements show that some nuclides emit two or more monoenergetic groups of alpha particles, each group having a definite but different energy. In such cases the alpha particles are said to have a 'line spectrum', each line corresponding to one of the monoenergetic alpha particle groups. Thus bismuth 212 (formerly thorium C) emits six groups of alpha particles with energies 6·08. 6·05, 5·77, 5·62, 5·60 and 5·49 MeV respectively, the first two groups account for 97 per cent of the total.

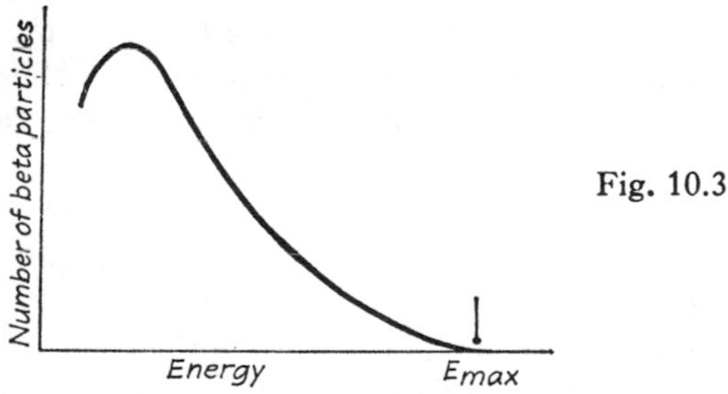

Fig. 10.3

Beta particles. With a few exceptions beta particles exhibit quite a different behaviour. Their energy spectrum is a continuous one in which all energies are present from quite small values up to a certain maximum as shown in Fig. 10.3. The maxima are characteristic of the source and vary from 0·025 to 3·15 MeV for natural radionuclides.

Gamma rays. Gamma-ray energies fall into several distinct monoenergetic groups, giving a line spectrum similar to that of some of the alpha emitters. The gamma rays from the artificial radionuclide cobalt 60 consist mainly of two different quanta of energies 1·17 and 1·33 MeV.

Absorption of alpha, beta and gamma rays

When an alpha particle comes close to an atom of the medium through which it is passing, strong electrostatic forces are exerted between it and the extranuclear electrons, one of which may acquire sufficient energy to escape from the atom. An ion-pair consisting of an electron and a positively charged ion are formed in the encounter and ionization has occurred. In the process the alpha particle loses kinetic energy and, after a certain distance called the *range*, it has insufficient energy to cause further ionization and captures two electrons to form a neutral helium atom. It is then considered to have been absorbed. An alpha particle can also have an encounter with a nucleus. The study of these events has profoundly influenced modern atomic theory and will be considered later.

In their passage through matter beta particles are also absorbed by losing kinetic energy in ionizing encounters. In addition, by reason of their small mass, they are readily scattered by atoms of the medium. A considerable proportion of those incident on a sheet of material are back-scattered to emerge from the incident surface.

A measure of the intensity of the ionization produced when a charged particle passes through a gas is given by the *specific ionization*. This is defined as the number of ion-pairs formed per centimetre of path. It increases with the size of the charge on the particle and decreases as the speed of the particle increases. A fast-moving particle spends less time near an atom of the gas through which it is travelling and so there is less chance of an ion-pair being formed. An alpha particle may produce 100,000 ion-pairs per centimetre in air at atmospheric pressure while a beta particle of similar energy only produces a few hundred ion-pairs per centimetre on account of its higher velocity (on average it is about ten times greater) and smaller charge. It should however be noted that for an alpha particle and a beta particle of the same energy the total number of ion-pairs formed would be of the same order since a beta particle travels about one hundred times further in air than an alpha particle. The formation of one ion-pair in air at N.T.P. always involves the loss of about the same amount of energy (34 eV) by the ionizing particle.

Gamma rays are absorbed appreciably only by metals of high atomic weight such as lead, and the absorption process is complex and differs from that occurring with charged particles. Whereas an alpha or beta particle gradually loses kinetic energy by a series of ionizing encounters with electrons belonging to atoms of the absorber, a gamma-ray photon may interact with either an electron or, if it has enough energy, with a nucleus in several ways. The energy given up by the photon produces one or more high-speed 'secondary' electrons and it is these which are responsible for the ionization created in a gas by gamma rays. They enable gamma radiation to be detected by a device such as the Geiger-Müller tube. The specific ionization of gamma rays therefore depends on the energy of the secondary electrons.

Radioactive disintegration

The changes accompanying the emission of radiation from radioactive substances are unlike ordinary chemical changes in certain fundamental respects. They are spontaneous, they cannot be controlled and are unaffected by chemical combination and physical conditions. Thus they proceed in the same way whether the temperature is $-200°C$ or $2000°C$. Energy considerations too suggest they are different. The energy released as radiation by a radioactive substance emitting alpha particles is several million electron-volts per atom compared with a few electron-volts per atom in any chemical change.

In 1902 Rutherford and Soddy created consternation in the scientific world by proposing that the atoms of radioactive elements are *unstable* and that in a radioactive change they break up to form completely different atoms, the disintegration of each atom being accompanied by the emission of one alpha or one beta particle. The transformation process proceeds at a definite rate through a certain number of stages until ultimately a stable end product is formed. When first advanced the theory conflicted with current views about the permanency of the atom but its ability to account satisfactorily for all the known facts of radioactivity has left no doubt about its validity.

The example of radium is represented in Fig. 10.4. Radium decays very slowly with the expulsion of alpha particles to give the inert gas, radon, which in turn disintegrates, by emitting alpha particles. After another seven disintegrations a stable isotope of lead is produced.

Since an alpha particle is a helium nucleus consisting of two protons and two neutrons, in alpha decay the mass number of the nucleus decreases by 4 and the atomic number by 2. The resultant atom has two fewer protons in its nucleus and rearrangement of the extranuclear electrons is necessary to dispose of the two electrons now surplus to requirements. Most alpha emitters have high atomic numbers and occur in nature, but one of importance, plutonium 239, is made in nuclear reactors.

When beta decay occurs a neutron changes into a proton, and at the same time an electron is created which usually moves away

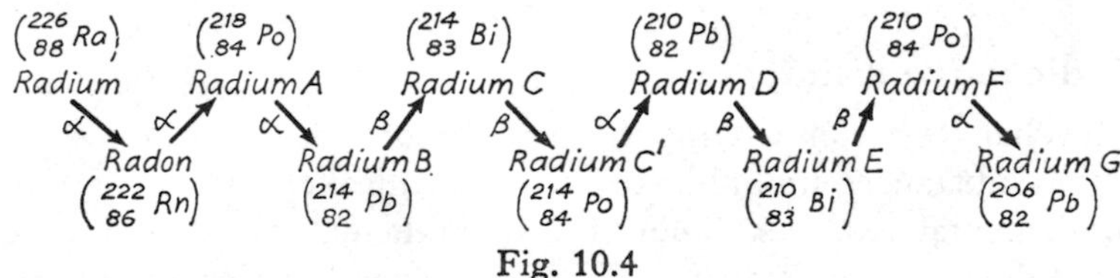

Fig. 10.4

from the nucleus at high speed. The new nucleus has the same mass number but its atomic number increases by one since it has one more proton. Beta emitters have a higher proportion of neutrons; few occur naturally in appreciable quantities but many are obtained artificially by irradiating matter with neutrons.

In Fig. 10.4 in addition to the original but rather unsystematic names of the members of the radium family, the symbol is also given for the familiar element of which the member is an isotope.

Thus radium A is an isotope of polonium 218 and is represented by the symbol $^{218}_{84}Po$ where, as previously stated, the superscript indicates the mass number and the subscript the atomic number. The older names are now becoming obsolete.

The natural radionuclides can be grouped into three series known as the thorium series, the uranium series and the actinium series. The radium family is part of the uranium series.

Law of radioactive decay

Experiments show that all radioactive substances decay exponentially with time. In mathematical terms

$$N = N_0 e^{-\lambda t} \qquad (1)$$

where N_0 is the number of atoms of a certain radioactive nuclide present at some arbitrary zero of time, N the number of undecayed atoms at time t later, e the base of natural logarithms and λ a constant, called the *decay constant*. The negative sign is necessary since N decreases as t increases.

Differentiating equation (1) it follows that

$$\frac{dN}{dt} = -\lambda N_0 e^{-\lambda}$$

$$\therefore \quad \frac{dN}{dt} = -\lambda N \qquad (2)$$

We may therefore say, since dN is the number of atoms decaying in the small time interval dt, that *the rate of disintegration dN/dt, of a given nuclide at any time is directly proportional to the number of atoms N of the nuclide present at that time.* This is the usual way of stating the law of radioactive decay. Rearranging equation (2), $\lambda = dN/(N.dt)$ and we see that the decay constant λ, is the fraction of the total number of atoms present which decay in unit time, provided the unit of time is small.

The decay law is a statistical one which can be derived mathematically from probability considerations. It is impossible to say when a particular atom will decay, we can only say that after a certain time interval a certain fraction of the atoms originally present will have decayed. On the microscopic scale the process is purely random as is evident from the variations which occur when particles from a source are counted. On the macroscopic scale however, where large numbers of particles are concerned, a definite law is followed.

The rate of disintegration of a source is called the *activity* and is measured in curies. *The curie is defined as the quantity of any radioactive material which undergoes* $3{\cdot}70 \times 10^{10}$ *disintegrations per second.* Submultiples are the millicurie (mc) and the microcurie (μc). One gram of pure radium has an activity of one curie.

Half-life

It is often difficult to know when a substance has lost *all* its activity but it is easy to find out how long it takes for the activity to fall to *half* the value it has at some instant. Hence a more convenient alternative to the decay constant λ is the *half-life* $t_{1/2}$, defined as *the time required for the radioactivity of a given amount of a nuclide to decay to half its initial value.* Radium has a half-life of 1622 years; therefore, starting with 1 g of radium, 0·5 g remains as radium after 1622 years, 0·25 g after 3244 years and so on. Half-lives vary from millionths of a second to millions of years. An exponential decay curve illustrating the principle of half-lives is shown in Fig. 10.5.

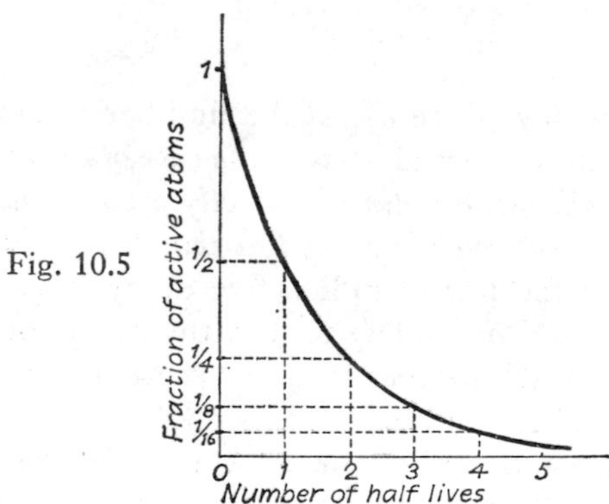

Fig. 10.5

The relationship between λ and $t_{1/2}$ can be derived from the exponential decay equation by taking logs to base e, thus

$$N = N_0 e^{-\lambda t}$$

$$\therefore \log_e N = \log_e N_0 - \lambda t$$

and since $\log_e N = 2{\cdot}303 \log_{10} N$ then

$$\log_{10} N = \log_{10} N_0 - \frac{\lambda . t}{2{\cdot}303}$$

Rearranging

$$\log_{10}\left(\frac{N_0}{N}\right) = \frac{\lambda}{2{\cdot}303}\cdot t$$

When $N = N_0/2$, $t = t_{1/2}$

$$\therefore \log_{10} 2 = \frac{\lambda}{2{\cdot}303}\cdot t_{1/2}$$

$$\therefore \lambda = \frac{0{\cdot}693}{t_{1/2}}$$

The decay constant λ is measured in units of reciprocal time; thus if $t_{1/2}$ is in seconds, λ is in seconds^{-1}. The half-life and consequently the decay constant, is characteristic for each radionuclide and is an important means of identification.

Worked example

Polonium has atomic mass 210 *and a decay constant equal to* $5{\cdot}8 \times 10^{-8}\ s^{-1}$. *Find the number of alpha particles emitted per second by* 1 *mg. Avogadro's constant* $= 6{\cdot}0 \times 10^{23}\ mol^{-1}$.

From the definition of Avogadro's constant

210 g of polonium contains $6{\cdot}0 \times 10^{23}$ atoms

$\therefore$ 10^{-3} g of polonium contains $6{\cdot}0 \times 10^{23} \times 10^{-3}/210$ atoms

$\therefore$ Number of atoms N present in 1 mg of polonium $= 6{\cdot}0 \times 10^{20}/210$

By the law of radioactive decay we have

$$\frac{dN}{dt} = \lambda N$$

where $\lambda = 5{\cdot}8 \times 10^{-8}\ \mathrm{s}^{-1}$ and dN/dt equals the number of particles emitted per second when N atoms are present.

$$\therefore \frac{dN}{dt} = \frac{5{\cdot}8 \times 10^{-8} \times 6{\cdot}0 \times 10^{20}}{210} = 1{\cdot}7 \times 10^{11}$$

$\therefore$ Rate of emission $= 1{\cdot}7 \times 10^{11}$ alpha particles per second.

Radioactivity and nuclear stability

Whilst the chemical properties of an atom are governed entirely by the number of protons in the nucleus (i.e., the atomic number

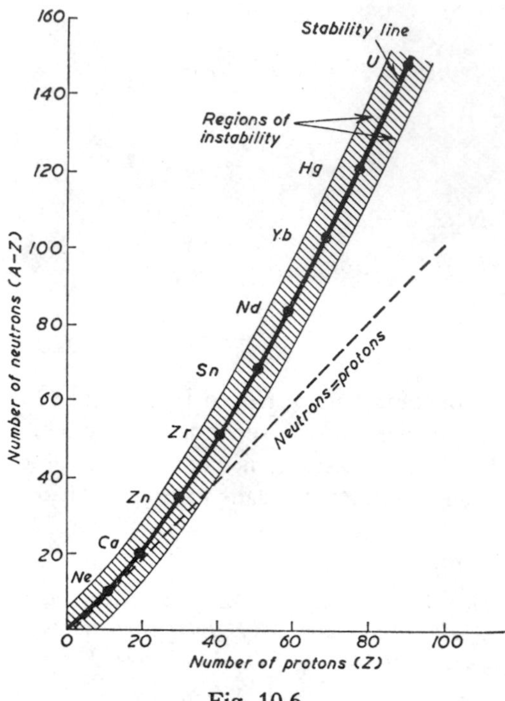

Fig. 10.6

Z), the stability of an atom appears to depend on both the number of protons and the number of neutrons. In Fig. 10.6 the number of neutrons ($A - Z$, where A is the mass number) has been plotted against the number of protons (Z) for all known nuclides, stable and unstable, natural and man-made. A continuous line has been drawn approximately through the *stable* nuclides (only a few of which are labelled) and the shading on either side of this line shows the region of *unstable* nuclides.

For *stable* nuclides the following points emerge.

(1) The lightest nuclides have almost equal numbers of protons and neutrons.

(2) The heavier nuclides require more neutrons than protons, the heaviest having about 50 per cent more.

(3) Most nuclides have both an even number of protons and an even number of neutrons. The implication is that two protons

and two neutrons i.e. an alpha particle, form a particularly stable combination and in this connection it is worth noting that oxygen (O^{16}_{8}), silicon ($^{28}_{14}Si$) and iron ($^{56}_{26}Fe$) together account for over three-quarters of the earth's crust.

For *unstable* nuclides the following points can be made.

(1) Disintegrations tend to produce new nuclides nearer the 'stability' line and continue until a stable nuclide is formed.

(2) A nuclide above the line decays so as to give an increase of atomic number i.e., by beta emission (in which a neutron changes to a proton and an electron). Its neutron to proton ratio is thereby decreased.

(3) A nuclide below the line disintegrates in such a way that its atomic number decreases and its neutron to proton ratio increases. In heavy nuclides this can occur by alpha emission.

Radioisotopes and their uses

The first artificial radioisotope was produced in 1934 by Irene Joliot-Curie, daughter of the discoverer of radium, and her husband. They bombarded aluminium with alpha particles and obtained an unstable isotope of phosphorus:

$$^{27}_{13}Al + ^{4}_{2}He = ^{30}_{15}P + ^{1}_{0}n$$

Since then at least one radionuclide of every element has been made by subjecting the element to neutrons in a nuclear reactor or to protons, deuterons or alpha particles in a particle accelerating machine such as the cyclotron. The use of radioisotopes in industry, research and medicine is rapidly expanding; only a few examples will be given here.

Some applications use the absorption or scattering of radiation in its passage through matter. Thus in the manufacture of paper, plastic or linoleum the thickness of the material can be checked by having a beta source below the material and a Geiger–Müller detector above it. The count-rate depends on the thickness of material the rays have to penetrate and the counter can be calibrated to read thickness directly. A thickness gauge of this type may even be adapted for automatic control of the manufacturing process. Level indicators also depend on absorption and are used to check the filling of toothpaste tubes and packets of soap powders.

The ionizing effect of radiation is useful for removing static electricity which develops on machinery in the textile and paper industries. Static can be a great nuisance, attracting dust and creating a fire hazard. The presence of a radionuclide ionizes the air and allows the charge to leak away.

The use of radioisotopes as 'tracers' when it is required to follow the movement of some object or substance is possible for two reasons. First, their presence even in minute quantities can be detected by the radiation they emit and second, a radioisotope of an element can participate in the same chemical, physical and biological processes as the ordinary element since it is chemically identical and only slightly different physically. Processes in which tracers have been used include the mixing of the ingredients of gramophone records, chocolate and animal foods. The movement of sand and mud in rivers may be followed. In research into friction in machinery a small amount of radioactive iron is introduced into the bearings and the rate of wear found from the resulting radioactivity of the lubricating oil. The use of phosphorus 32 as a tracer in griculture has provided information about the best type of phosphate fertilizer to supply to a given crop and soil.

Gamma rays from high-intensity cobalt 60 sources have many applications. In radiotherapy they are replacing X-rays from expensive X-ray machines in the treatment of cancer. The rapidly growing cells which cause this malignant disease are very sensitive to radiation. Medical instruments and bandages may be sterilized after packing by brief exposure to gamma rays. Food may be similarly treated, the shelf life of meat may be increased from 3 to 15 days. This is perfectly safe since no radioactivity is produced in material irradiated by gamma rays. Rubber can be hardened, removing the need for vulcanizing, and lubricating oils thickened by gamma ray treatment.

Carbon 14 dating

A natural radioisotope interesting from an archaeological point of view is carbon 14, formed when cosmic ray neutrons collide with atmospheric nitrogen.

$$^{14}_{7}\mathrm{N} + ^{1}_{0}n = ^{14}_{6}\mathrm{C} + ^{1}_{1}\mathrm{H}$$

Subsequently carbon 14 forms radioactive carbon dioxide and may be taken in by plants and trees for the manufacture of carbohydrates by photosynthesis. The normal activity of living carbonaceous material is 15·3 counts per minute per gramme of carbon, but once life processes cease, carbon 14 starts to decay by beta emission with a half-life of about 5600 years. By measuring the residual activity, the age of any ancient carbon-containing material such as wood, linen or charcoal may be estimated within the range of 1000 to 50,000 years.

Radiation hazards

The radiation hazards to human beings arise from:

(*i*) Exposure of the body to external radiation.
(*ii*) Ingestion or inhalation of radioactive matter.

The effect of radiation depends on the nature of the radiation, the part of the body irradiated and the dose received. The hazard from alpha particles is slight (unless the source enters the body) since alpha particles cannot penetrate the outer layers of skin. Beta particles are more penetrating, most of their energy is absorbed by surface tissues and adequate protection is afforded by a sheet of Perspex or aluminium a few millimetres thick. Gamma rays present the main external radiation hazard since they penetrate deeply into the body and may require substantial concrete or lead shielding.

Radiation can cause immediate damage to tissue and, according to the dose, is accompanied by radiation burns (i.e., redness of the skin followed by blistering and sores which are slow to heal), radiation sickness and in extremely severe cases by death. Delayed effects such as cancer, leukemia and eye cataracts may appear many years later. Hereditary defects may also occur in succeeding generations due to genetic damage. The most susceptible parts are the reproductive organs, blood-forming organs such as the liver, and to a smaller extent the eyes. The hands, forearms, feet and ankles are less vulnerable. Damage to human cells is thought to be due to the ionizing effect of the radiation.

Three units have been defined for radiation dose:

(*a*) The *röntgen* (*r*) is the quantity of X- or gamma radiation which produces ion-pairs corresponding to $1/(3 \times 10^9)$ C of charge of either sign in 1 cm^3 of air at N.T.P. In terms of energy it can be shown that this quantity of radiation will lose $8{\cdot}77 \times 10^{-3}$ J per kg of air at N.T.P.

(*b*) The ***rad*** is defined as the amount of any type of radiation (not just X- or gamma) which transfers 10^{-2} J to a kg of a specified absorbing medium. Thus for air, 1 röntgen equals 1 rad approximately. The rad is intended to replace the röntgen.

(*c*) The ***rem***. Equal doses of different ionizing radiations provide the same amount of energy in a given absorber but they may not have the same biological effect on the human body. In view of this, the rem (*r*öntgen *e*quivalent *m*an) has been introduced and is defined by the relation

$$\text{Dose in rems} = \text{Dose in rads} \times \text{R.B.E.}$$

where R.B.E. is the relative biological effectiveness. For beta particles, X- and gamma rays the R.B.E. is 1 and 1 rad = 1 rem; for alpha particles, protons and fast neutrons the R.B.E. is 10.

The rem is a biological unit and is important when biological changes are concerned. The rad is a physical unit of absorbed radiation which can be measured.

All human beings receive about 150 millirems per year due to natural background radiation from cosmic rays, radioactive minerals, radon in the atmosphere and potassium 40 in the body. The maximum permissible dose for personnel in nuclear power stations and those doing work involving radiation is 5 rems per year. A dose of 500 rems to every part of the body would be lethal for at least 50 per cent of those receiving it.

The dose rate from one of the weak sources used for experimental work in physics is very small. At a distance of 25 cm from a 5 μc cobalt 60 source it is less than 0·1 millirem per hour.

QUESTIONS

1. Write brief notes on (*a*) the nature, (*b*) the properties and (*c*) the energy spectra, of alpha, beta and gamma radiation.

2. The original names of the members of the first part of the uranium series and the particles they emit at each decay are given in Fig. 10.7.

Uranium I $\xrightarrow{\alpha}$ Uranium X_1 $\xrightarrow{\beta}$ Uranium X_2 $\xrightarrow{\beta}$ Uranium II $\xrightarrow{\alpha}$ Ionium $\xrightarrow{\alpha}$ Radium

Fig. 10.7

Rewrite this part of the series in modern symbolic notation using the table of the elements in Appendix 1. Uranium I is written $^{238}_{92}U$.

If an alpha particle and two beta particles are emitted in three consecutive decays, what can be said about the initial and final nuclei? What changes occur in the mass number and the atomic number in such cases?

3. A radioisotope of silver has a half-life of 20 minutes. (*a*) How many half-lives does it have in 1 hour? (*b*) What fraction of the original mass would remain after 1 hour? (*c*) What fraction would have decayed after 2 hours?

4. (*a*) The half-life of radium is 1622 years. How long will it take for seven-eighths of a given amount of radium to decay?

(*b*) After 50 hours 6·25 per cent of a sample of the radionuclide $^{42}_{19}K$ remains undecayed. What is the half-life?

5. State the law governing the rate of decay of a radioactive substance, and explain the terms decay constant (λ) and half-life (T). Show that these two quantities are related by the equation

$$\lambda T = \log_e 2$$

Two radioactive sources A and B initially contain equal numbers of radioactive atoms. Source A has a half-life of one hour, and source B a half-life of two hours. What is the ratio of the rate of disintegration of source A to that of source B (*a*) initially, (*b*) after two hours, (*c*) after ten hours? [*O. and C. part qn.*]

6. What is meant by the *half-value period* (*half-life*) of a radioactive material?

Describe how the nature of alpha particles has been established experimentally.

The half-value period of the body polonium 210 is about 140 days. During this period the average number of alpha emissions per day from a mass of polonium initially equal to 1 microgram is about 12×10^{12}. Assuming that one emission takes place per atom and that the approximate density of polonium is 10 g cm^{-3}, estimate the number of atoms in 1 cm^3 of polonium. [*J.*]

7. Outline the main facts of radioactivity and briefly describe the properties of the radioactive radiations.

Radon is a monatomic gas of atomic mass 222 and with a radioactive constant equal to $2{\cdot}1 \times 10^{-6}\ s^{-1}$. Calculate the number of alpha particles emitted per second by 1 g of radon at N.T.P. when free from disintegration products.
(Avogadro's constant = $6{\cdot}0 \times 10^{23}\ mol^{-1}$.) [*S.*]

8. '$^{24}_{11}Na$ is a *radioactive isotope* of sodium which has a *half-life period* of 15 hours and disintegrates with the emission of *beta particles* and *gamma rays*. It emits beta particles that have energies of 4·2 *MeV*.'

Explain the meanings of the five terms that are italicized in the statement above. [*L.*]

9. Describe and explain simple experiments which demonstrate the distinctive properties of the radiations emitted by radioactive substances.

Write brief accounts of TWO *industrial* (*not medical*) uses to which radioactive substances may be put. [*J.*]

10. Explain what is meant by the *transformation constant* (radioactive decay constant) of a radioactive material. Deduce a relationship between this constant and the half-life period.

The half-life period of a radioactive element is 10 days. Calculate how long it takes for 90 per cent of a given mass of this element to disintegrate. [*A.E.B. Schol.*]

11. Give an account of the types of radioactive emissions found in nature and explain how you would distinguish between them.

A piece of timber has been recovered from an archaeological excavation and it is required to find its approximate age by measuring the radioactivity of the carbon 14 contained therein. For this purpose it may be assumed that the proportion of carbon 14 in the natural carbon of living wood is everywhere and at all times the same and that it begins to decay at death. If the number of disintegrations observed from 5 g of carbon prepared from the specimen is 21 per minute, how old is the specimen? (The proportion of carbon 14 to natural carbon in living wood is 1·25 in 10^{12} and the half-value period of carbon 14 may be taken to be 5600 years. The mass number of natural carbon is 12.)
Avogadro's constant = $6{\cdot}0 \times 10^{23}\ mol^{-1}$. [*J. Special*]

12. (*a*) Account for the fact that when a very heavy nucleus (e.g. that of a uranium isotope) fissions (i.e. splits) it gives two nuclei of medium mass which are *beta* emitters.

(*b*) Explain why the number of neutrons in a nucleus must be increased (by irradiating it with neutrons in a nuclear reactor) to manufacture a beta emitting nuclide.

(*c*) If carbon 12 ($^{12}_{6}C$) is stable what would you guess about boron 12 ($^{12}_{5}B$)? Justify your answer.

11 Radioactivity measurements

In a nuclear radiation detector energy is transferred from the radiation to atoms of the detector and in most cases this is achieved by one of the following effects:

(*i*) The ionization of gases as in ionization chambers, Geiger–Müller tubes and cloud chambers.

(*ii*) The blackening of photographic emulsions.

(*iii*) The scintillation of phosphors as in scintillation counters.

Before considering the various detecting devices and giving an outline of measurements which may be performed with them, some radioactive sources used for instructional purposes in physics will be discussed.

Radioactive sources

Closed sources (previously called sealed sources) are frequently supplied mounted in a holder with a 4 mm plug. The active material is sealed in metal foil to prevent the escape of any radioactive daughter elements and protection of the foil against mechanical damage is provided by a wire gauze cover, Fig. 11.1*a*. When not in use the source is stored in a small lead castle, Fig. 11.1*b*, in a wooden box.

Approved closed sources have low activities, of the order of 5 μc, and include:

(*i*) RADIUM 226 FOR ALPHA, BETA AND GAMMA RAYS. Although radium 226 is itself an alpha and gamma emitter, the decay

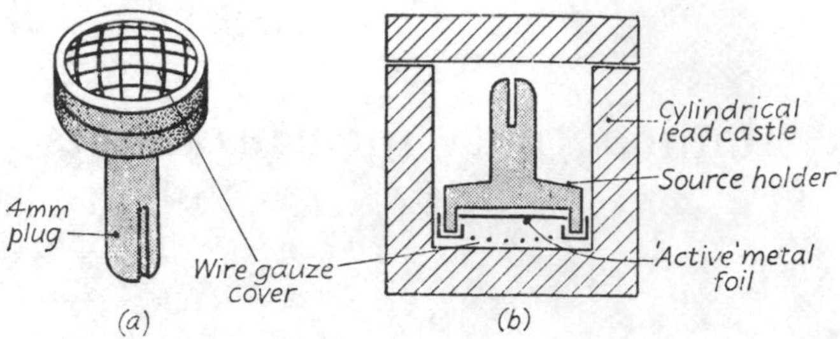

Fig. 11.1

products retained in the source contribute beta particles (as well as alpha and gamma radiation). The half-life of radium 226 is 1622 years.

(*ii*) AMERICIUM 241 AND PLUTONIUM 239 FOR ALPHA PARTICLES ONLY. Gamma rays are also emitted by americium but are negligible in quantity and of very low energy. Americium 241 has a half-life of 470 years and plutonium 24,400 years.

(*iii*) STRONTIUM 90 FOR BETA PARTICLES ONLY. Yttrium 90 is also present as a daughter product and emits beta particles with a maximum energy appreciably higher than those from strontium. Strontium 90 has a half-life of 28 years and yttrium 90 of 64 hours.

(*iv*) COBALT 60 FOR GAMMA RAYS ONLY. An aluminium cover disc absorbs the beta particles emitted by this radionuclide but allows the gamma rays to pass. The half-life of cobalt 60 is 5·27 years.

Some other very weak sources with activities of the order of 0·1 μc or less are not completely enclosed but the radioactive material, usually uranium, radium or thorium, is firmly secured to an inactive support. Such sources are used in cloud chambers.

Sources should always be lifted with forceps or a handling tool, never with bare hands. They should be held so that the open window is directed away from the body and never brought close to the eyes for inspection.

Ionization chamber

An ionization chamber in its simplest form comprises two electrodes between which ion-pairs, i.e., electrons and positive ions, can be produced from neutral gas atoms and molecules by ionizing radiation. One electrode of the chamber is often a cylindrical can and the other a metal rod situated along the axis of the cylinder. Under the influence of an electric field between the electrodes, electrons move to the anode and positive gas ions to the cathode so forming an ionization current. Some means of detecting this current is necessary. Fig. 11.2 shows the basic arrangement required.

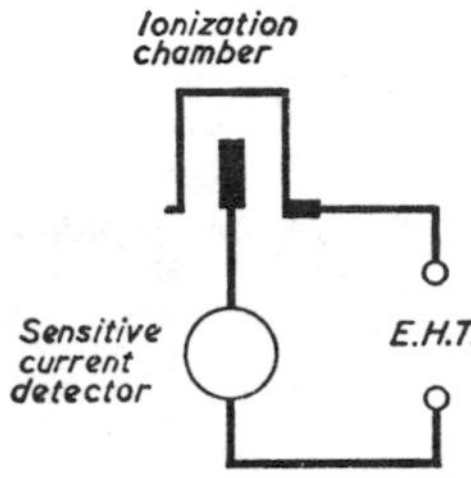

Fig. 11.2

The magnitude of the ionization current depends on the nature and intensity of the ionizing radiation and the volume of the chamber. A 5 μc alpha source creates a current of about 10^{-9} ampere in a small chamber. Beta particles and particularly gamma rays have much smaller specific ionization (they form a smaller number of ion-pairs per centimetre of path length) and so cause smaller currents.

Instruments which are sufficiently sensitive to be used in conjunction with a small ionization chamber for the detection of alpha particles are the pocket dosemeter, the pulse electroscope and the d.c. amplifier. The first two are modifications of the gold-leaf electroscope.

Pocket dosemeter

The pocket dosemeter has a metallized quartz fibre instead of a gold leaf and is normally used as a monitor to measure the dose received by personnel engaged in radiation work, hence the name dosemeter.

In Fig. 11.3*a* the dosemeter is shown mounted on an ionization chamber. The quartz fibre is attached to a conducting support,

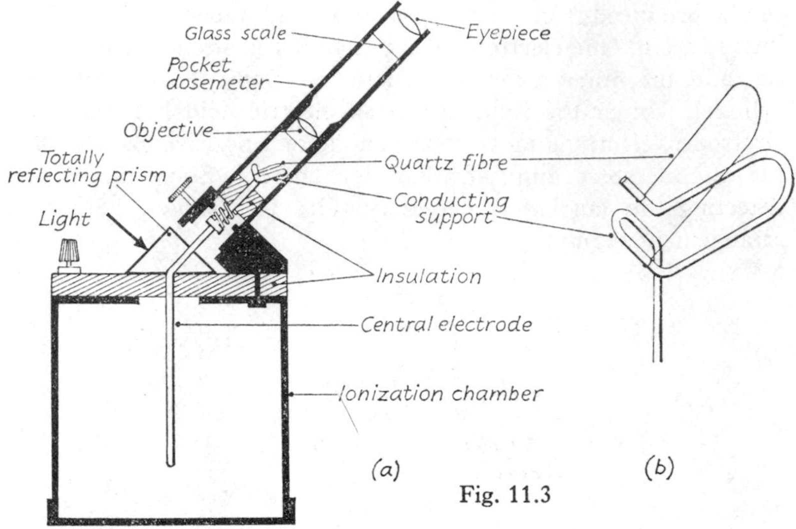

Fig. 11.3

Fig. 11.3*b*, from which it is repelled when the electroscope is charged. An image of the fibre alone is obtained on a scale in the eyepiece of the microscope, and adjustment of the charging voltage (150 to 250 volts) applied between the fibre and case of the dosemeter allows the fibre to be set on the zero of the scale. The ionization chamber has a well insulated central electrode in contact with the fibre and this too becomes charged. The wall of the chamber and the electroscope case are also connected.

A radioactive source inside the chamber creates ion-pairs which discharge the dosemeter, causing the quartz fibre to return to its support under the restoring force of its own elasticity. The rate of movement of the fibre across the scale is a measure of the intensity of the ionizing radiation.

Pulse electroscope

The pulse electroscope is available in different forms and is usually designed for use with a cylindrical ionization chamber.

In the leaf type, Fig. 11.4, the sensitive system is a narrow aluminium foil strip or leaf fixed to the electroscope support at both ends, directly at the top and by a quartz glass fibre or other flexible wire at the bottom. The electroscope support is extended

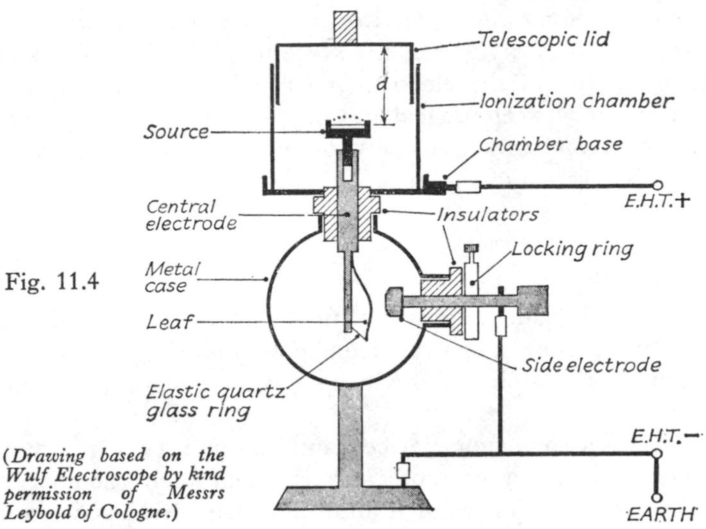

Fig. 11.4

(Drawing based on the Wulf Electroscope by kind permission of Messrs Leybold of Cologne.)

upwards to act as the central electrode of the ionization chamber. E.H.T. + is applied to the outer electrode, i.e., the cylindrical metal vessel, and E.H.T. −, which is at earth potential, to the side electrode and electroscope case. The E.H.T. voltage thus acts across the chamber and electroscope in series.

When a radioactive source is mounted in the socket in the central electrode, ionization current flows in the chamber between the central and outer electrodes and the electroscope becomes charged. The leaf is repelled from its support and arches outwards. At a certain charge it touches and discharges on the side electrode and is then restored to its undeflected position ready for another charge. The whole action constitutes a pulse and it will now be shown that the pulse rate is a measure of the ionization current.

The leaf and central electrode may be regarded as forming one plate of a capacitor having capacitance C, the side electrode and metal case of the electroscope being the other plate. If V is the p.d. between the leaf and side electrode just before discharge, the charge Q delivered is given by $Q = VC$. The ionization current $I = Q/t$, where t is the time between successive pulses, hence $I = VC/t$. The pulse rate equals $1/t$ and since VC is constant to a first approximation, I is proportional to $1/t$. *If the current in the chamber has its saturation value the pulse rate gives a measure of the intensity of the ionizing radiation* (see p. 140).

The sensitivity of the electroscope can be increased by reducing the gap between the leaf and the side electrode. An image of the sensitive system is usually projected on to a screen to facilitate observation of the pulses.

d.c. amplifier

This is a high gain amplifier which acts as a micro-micro ammeter and creates from a very small d.c. input (e.g. the current in an ionization chamber) a d.c. output large enough to operate a milliammeter.

It uses semi-conductor devices and has a very high input resistance. The input current from the ionization chamber is applied to a very high resistor R and the voltage developed across it is applied to the input of the amplifier, Fig. 11.5. When for example, $R = 10^{11}$ ohms (100 kMΩ) a reading of 1 mA may be obtained on the output milliammeter from an input current of 10^{-11} ampere.

The d.c. amplifier is not only more sensitive than the pulse electroscope but also allows readings to be obtained more quickly. Once again if the current in the ionization chamber has its saturation value the milliammeter reading gives a measure of the intensity of the ionizing radiation in the chamber (see p. 140).

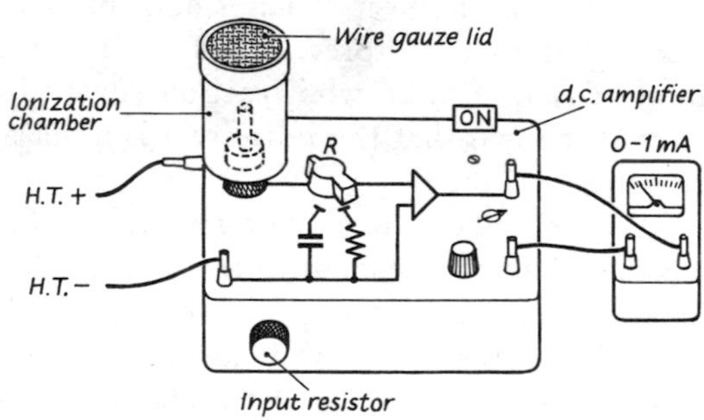

Measurement of the range of alpha particles in air

The range of alpha particles in air may be determined using an ionization chamber with either a pulse electroscope or a d.c. amplifier. In the arrangement shown in Fig. 11.4 the ionization chamber has a telescopic lid which can be set at different distances from the source (e.g., 5 μc radium 226 or americium 241). The ionization current in the chamber is small when the lid is close to the source but increases as *d* increases due to the greater volume of air now ionized. The current and therefore the pulse rate attain a maximum value when *d* exceeds the range of the

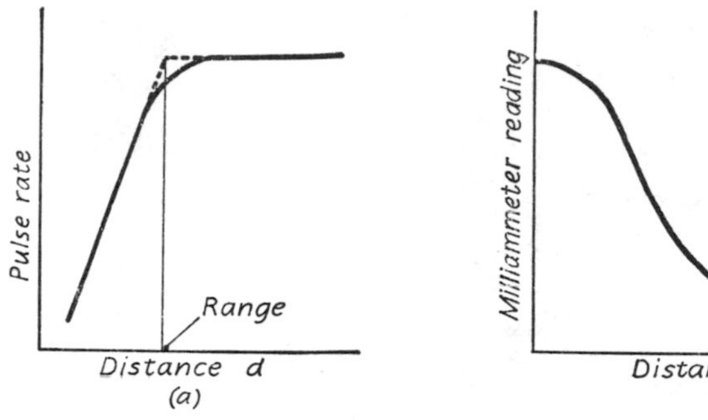

Fig. 11.6

alpha particles in air. The range is extrapolated from a graph as shown in Fig. 11.6*a*.

Using the d.c. amplifier of Fig. 11.5 the source is supported centrally above the gauze on top of the ionization chamber. The milliammeter readings are then noted as the source is raised by 0·5 cm steps. When no alpha particles reach the chamber, the milliammeter reading is zero and the corresponding value of *d*, obtained from a graph like that shown in Fig. 11.6*b*, gives the range in air.

The alpha particles from a monoenergetic source have a fairly well-defined range, and by referring to an energy-range conversion table (see Kaye and Laby's *Physical and Chemical Constants*) or a conversion graph, the energy of the alpha particles can be found.

Measurement of the half-life of thoron

Thoron is an alpha emitting gas which collects above its solid, parent nuclides in an enclosed space and is readily separated from them. If a polythene bottle containing thorium carbonate or thorium hydroxide is connected to an ionization chamber mounted on a pulse electroscope as in Fig. 11.7*a* or on a d.c. amplifier, a small quantity of the gas enters the chamber when the bottle is squeezed. As the thoron decays the ionization current decreases. With a pulse electroscope the interval between successive pulses increases. The time of each pulse is

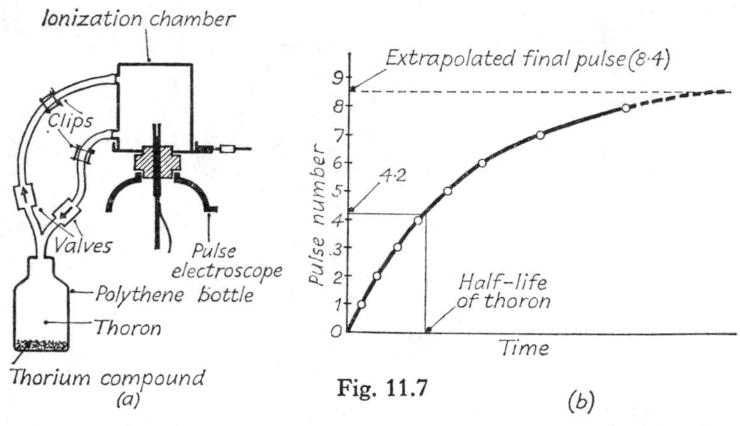

Fig. 11.7

noted up to the last detectable pulse. A graph of pulse number against time is plotted, Fig. 11.7*b* and the final pulse is estimated by extrapolation; in this case it is the 8·4th. The half-life of thoron is then obtained from the graph as the time for 4·2 pulses to occur. After this number of pulses the electroscope has discharged half the total quantity of charge of the ionization chamber. With a d.c. amplifier the time is measured for the milliammeter current to fall to a half (or better still, a quarter) of its value at some instant.

The chief constituent of the source is thorium 232 of half-life $1{\cdot}4 \times 10^{10}$ years. Some of the nuclides present in the thorium series are shown in Fig. 11.8. Those following thoron do not

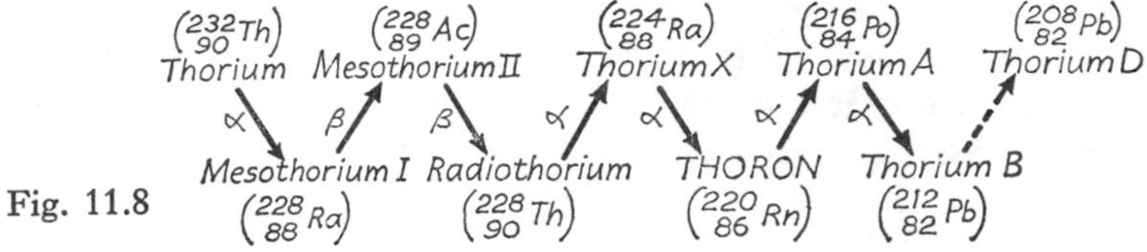

Fig. 11.8

appreciably affect the result of this experiment since their half-lives are so very different from that of thoron (52 second). Thoron is also called thorium emanation and is an isotope of radon ($^{222}_{86}$Rn), a member of the uranium series.

Geiger–Müller tube

The Geiger–Müller tube is a very sensitive type of ionization chamber. It consists of a cathode in the form of a metal cylinder (or layer of graphite on the inside of a glass tube) and a coaxial wire anode usually made of tungsten. The space between the electrodes contains an inert gas such as neon, at a pressure of about 10 cm Hg. While gamma rays readily penetrate the wall of the tube, less penetrating radiation enters through an end-window often made of mica. If alpha particles and slow beta particles are to be detected the window has to be especially thin. A typical tube is shown in Fig. 11.9.

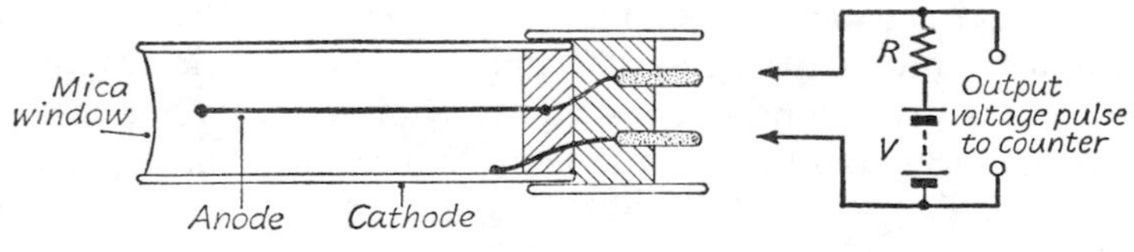

Fig. 11.9

The central wire is maintained at a potential of about 450 volts positive with respect to the cathode, and since the wire is very thin an intense electric field is created near it. If an ionizing particle passing through the gas produces an ion-pair from a neon atom, the resulting electron is rapidly accelerated towards the anode and when close to it has sufficient energy itself to produce ion-pairs in encounters. The electrons freed in these encounters can produce additional ionization and an *avalanche* of electrons spreads along the whole length of the wire, which absorbs them to produce a large pulse of anode current. In this way, a single electron freed in one ionizing event can lead to the release, in a few tenths of a microsecond, of as many as 10^8 electrons. This process is known as *gas amplification* and is responsible for the high sensitivity of the Geiger–Müller tube.

During the electron avalanche the comparatively heavy positive ion members of the ion-pairs have been almost stationary around the anode. After the avalanche has occurred they move towards the cathode under the action of the electric field, taking about 100 microseconds to reach it. They now have appreciable energy and would cause the emission of electrons from the cathode by bombardment. A second avalanche would follow, maintaining the discharge and creating confusion with the effect of a later ionizing particle entering the tube. The presence in the tube of a small amount of a *quenching agent* such as bromine tends to prevent this, since the positive ion energy is used to decompose the molecules of the quencher. In a halogen quenched tube these subsequently recombine and are available for further quenching.

A Geiger–Müller tube has a *dead time* of about 200 microseconds due to the time taken by the positive ions to travel towards the anode. Ionizing particles arriving within this period will not give separate pulses, i.e., are not resolved. If radioactive substances emitted particles at regular intervals a maximum of 5000 pulses per second could be detected, but this is not so and in practice the counting rate is less. Almost every beta particle entering a Geiger–Müller tube is detected. By contrast, the detection efficiency for gamma rays is less than 1 per cent. Gamma photons produce ion-pairs indirectly in the gas of the tube as a result of the secondary electrons they create when absorbed by the tube wall (cathode). The number of such electrons is small since gamma rays interact weakly with matter and this accounts for the low detection efficiency.

If a resistor R is connected in series with a Geiger–Müller tube and its voltage supply V, as in Fig. 11.9, the current pulse creates a voltage pulse (of about a volt for a halogen quenched tube) which is then applied to some form of electronic counter. Two will be considered.

Scaler

A scaler adds up and gives visual indication of the total number of pulses received from the detecting device in a certain time. Frequently it consists of two dekatron counters, the first for recording units and the second for tens, followed by a mechanical register for hundreds. The dekatron is a cold cathode tube containing a central disc-shaped anode surrounded by a ring of 30 equally spaced pins, the whole being enclosed in a glass tube filled with neon at reduced pressure. The pins consist of 10 cathodes, 10 'first guides' and 10 'second guides' arranged in the order cathode, first guide, second guide, as in Fig. 11.10. The cathodes are numbered 0 to 9 and all are connected together except number

Fig. 11.10

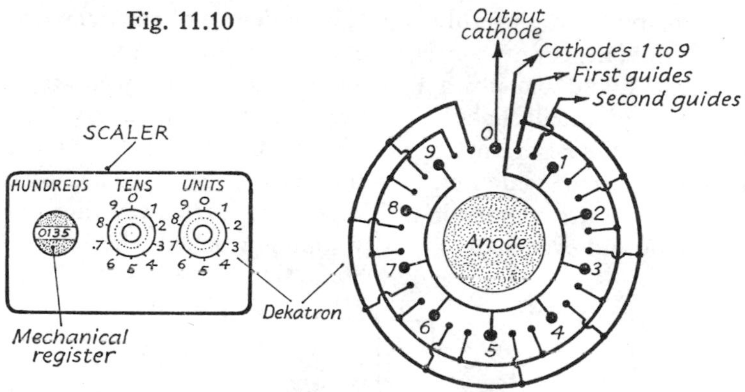

0 which has a separate connection. All the first guide pins are joined as are all the second guides.

Normally the anode is about 400 volts positive, the cathodes are at earth potential and both sets of guide pins 60 volts above earth. Under these conditions a small orange discharge occurs in the neon between the anode and one of the cathodes. By operating the reset control on the scaler all cathodes except number 0 are temporarily made 60 volts positive, and the discharge appears opposite cathode 0 since this is now at the lowest potential with respect to the anode. The first input pulse from the Geiger–Müller tube causes a negative voltage pulse of 120 volts to be applied to the first guides and the discharge moves from cathode 0 to the first guide nearest it, i.e., clockwise. An instant later a similar pulse makes the second guides the most negative part of the system and the discharge moves to the first of the second guides. At the conclusion of this pulse the discharge passes to the nearest cathode, that is, number 1. This sequence is repeated for each input pulse until, on the tenth pulse, cathode 0 is reached and an output pulse is provided to the second dekatron which then records one count of ten. After every 100 pulses the second dekatron sends a pulse to the mechanical register, and since this can usually handle 10 pulses per second a two dekatron scaler has a maximum count-rate of 1000 pulses per second.

Ratemeter

A ratemeter is very useful where a high degree of accuracy is not required. The count-rate is read directly from a meter in the instrument and usually a loudspeaker is also incorporated to register individual clicks. This last facility makes it a valuable monitor in the laboratory. Pulses from a Geiger–Müller tube are fed into a circuit which ensures that each pulse gives a constant small charge to a capacitor *C*. The charge leaks away through a resistor *R* and eventually a steady state is reached when the leak

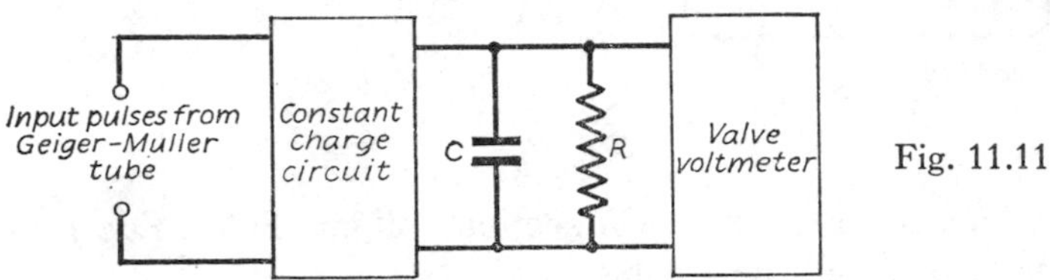

Fig. 11.11

rate is directly proportional to the rate at which pulses are received. The p.d. across *R* is then a measure of the count-rate and is read by a valve voltmeter calibrated in counts per second or counts per minute, Fig. 11.11.

A reading cannot be taken until equilibrium has been attained, and it can be shown that this does not occur until about five time constants (i.e., $5CR$) of the capacitor-resistor network have elapsed. It would seem that a circuit with a small time constant is desirable to reduce waiting time. However, the accuracy of a reading is greater for a large value of *CR* although a given accuracy can be achieved with a smaller time constant when the count-rate is large.

All but the simplest ratemeters have a control, often marked 'time constant' or 'int time' (meaning integrating time), which allows various capacitors to be connected across R to give different time constants. Typical values are 1, 5 and 25 seconds, and in practice the time constant is adjusted according to the extent of the fluctuations on the meter. Considerable variation indicates the use of too small a time constant. Some ratemeters have a very useful arrangement whereby the capacitors are all charged together. The reading can then be allowed to reach equilibrium on a short time constant and switched to a longer one before it is read.

Once the meter reading has been brought into equilibrium there still remains the problem of taking a reading which is varying due to the random nature of radioactive emission. A convenient procedure is to make an estimate of the average reading over a period equal to about twice the time constant.

Characteristic of a Geiger–Müller tube

The characteristic curve of a Geiger–Müller tube shows how its response depends on the applied voltage and enables the best working voltage for the tube to be found. The characteristic is determined by placing a suitable source at a short distance from the tube, as in Fig. 11.12, and noting count-rates on the scaler or ratemeter as the voltage applied to the tube is increased by stages.

Fig. 11.12

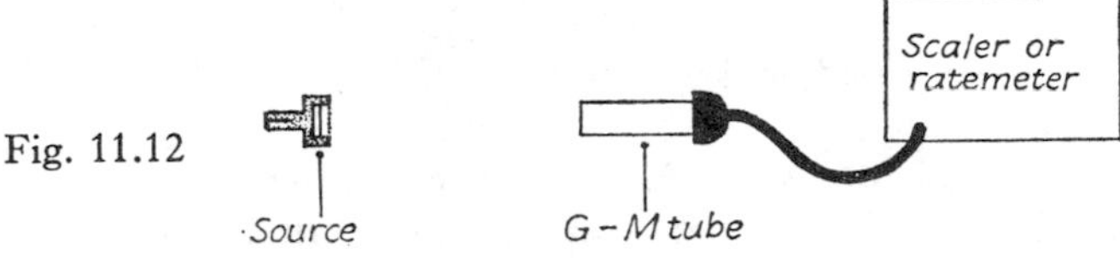

(Most scalers and ratemeters include a variable H.T. supply for the Geiger–Müller tube.) A typical curve is shown in Fig. 11.13. The pulses are too small to be detected until the starting voltage is reached. At this stage a single ionizing event does not produce a full avalanche although some gas amplification does occur; consequently, only those particles which produce a large number of ion-pairs initially are detected. When the voltage reaches the *threshold*, the count-rate remains almost constant over a range, called the *plateau*, of 100 volts or more, as shown by the horizontal part of the curve. A similar plateau effect is obtained with an ionization chamber (p. 139). On the plateau a full avalanche is obtained along the entire length of the anode and all particles whatever their nature and energy produce the same output pulse. Normally a tube is operated about the middle of the plateau; the sensitivity is then greatest and is independent of the supply voltage over an appreciable range. Beyond the plateau the count-rate for the

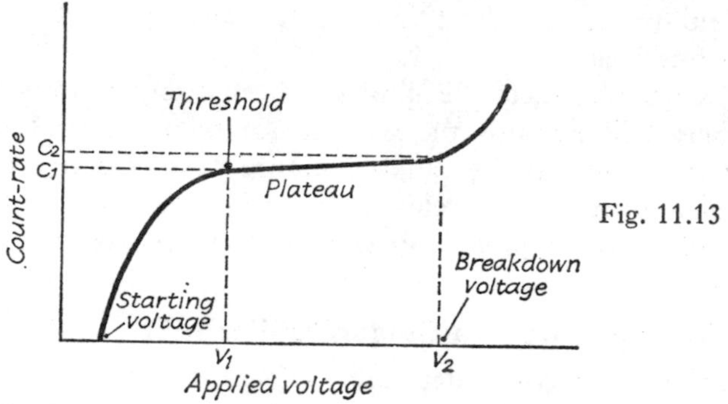

Fig. 11.13

same intensity of radiation increases rapidly with voltage due to incomplete quenching. Continuous discharge sets in and operation of the tube in this region causes damage.

The plateau always has a slight upward slope which is calculated from the expression

$$\text{Percentage slope} = \frac{C_2 - C_1}{V_2 - V_1} \times \frac{100}{C_M}$$

where C_1 = the count-rate at V_1, C_2 = the count-rate at V_2 and $C_M = (C_1 + C_2)/2$. The length and slope of the plateau are useful indications of the condition of a tube, and the latter should always be less than 0·15 per cent per volt.

Measurement of the range of beta particles in aluminium

Beta particles have a continuous energy spectrum and the number emerging from an absorber falls off gradually as the thickness of absorber increases; this behaviour contrasts with the fairly sharp cut-off given by alpha particles. For practical purposes the ***range of beta particles*** is defined as the thickness of aluminium beyond which very few particles can be detected.

The range may be determined by inserting an increasing

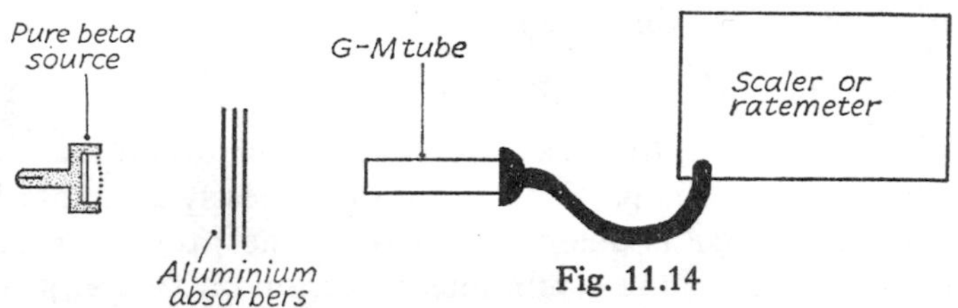

Fig. 11.14

number of aluminium sheets between a pure beta source (e.g., strontium 90) and a beta-sensitive Geiger–Müller tube connected to a scaler or ratemeter as shown in Fig. 11.14. Count-rates are measured and an absorption curve is drawn.

A typical curve is given in Fig. 11.15 in which the wide range of count-rates is accommodated by plotting the logarithm of the

Fig. 11.15

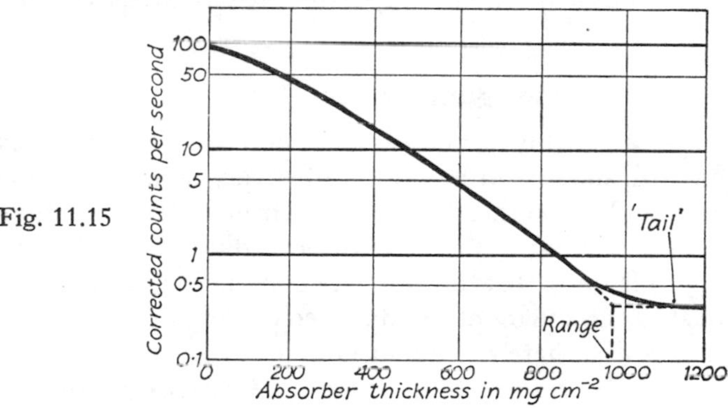

count-rate. This is most conveniently done by plotting the count-rates (after subtraction of the background count-rate, p. 168) directly on the log scale of semi-log graph paper. The absorber thickness can be expressed either in centimetres of aluminium or, as is more common, in terms of the *surface density* of the absorber. This is the mass per unit area and equals the product of the density and the thickness of the absorber. For example, a sheet of aluminium 2 mm thick of density 2·7 g cm^{-3} has a surface density of $2{\cdot}7 \times 0{\cdot}2 = 0{\cdot}54$ g cm^{-2} or 540 mg cm^{-2}. The range in mg cm^{-2} is found by extrapolation from the absorption curve, as shown. The maximum energy of the beta particles may be obtained from a conversion table or graph relating range in aluminium and maximum energy.

Two further points should be noted.

(*i*) The shape of the absorption curve depends on the energy spectrum of the beta particles and is often nearly a straight line. The horizontal tail is due to 'bremsstrahlung'; this is produced in the same way as the continuous spectrum of X-rays (p. 132).

(*ii*) The absorption of beta particles by light materials depends, to a first approximation, on the surface density and is almost independent of the nature of the material. Thus if a beta particle travels successively through a sheet of aluminium, a layer of air and the mica end-window of a Geiger–Müller tube having surface densities of 100, 13 and 4 mg cm^{-2} respectively, the total thickness of absorbing material is 117 mg cm^{-2}. The effectiveness of an absorber is thus conveniently expressed by the surface density.

Inverse square law for gamma rays

Gamma rays are highly penetrating on account of their small interaction with matter. In air they suffer very little absorption or scattering and, like other forms of electromagnetic radiation, their intensity falls off with distance according to the inverse square law. This states that the intensity of radiation I is inversely proportional to the square of the distance d from a point source. That is, $I = k/d^2$, where k is a constant.

The law may be verified by placing a Geiger–Müller tube at various distances from a pure gamma source (e.g., cobalt 60) and measuring the corresponding count-rates, Fig. 11.16. If after correction for background, C is the count-rate, then C is directly proportional to I and we can write $C = k_1/d^2$, where k_1 is another constant. A graph of C against $1/d^2$ should be a straight line through the origin but small errors occur in the measurement of d and become important as d decreases. Non-linearity of the graph results. The errors can be eliminated by an alternative procedure.

Let $d = D + x$, where D = the distance measured from the

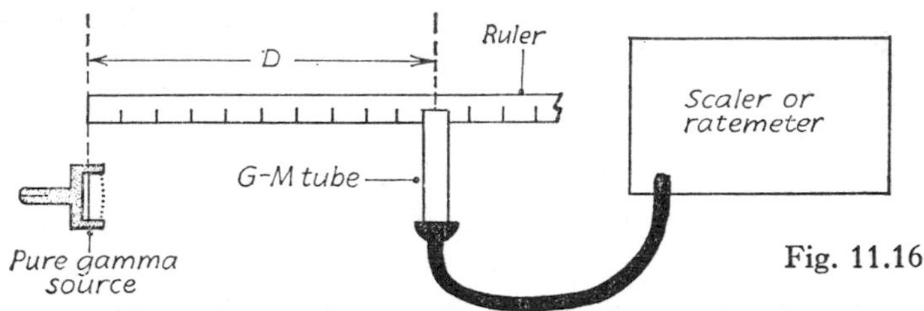

Fig. 11.16

source to any point on the Geiger–Müller tube and x = an unknown correction term which gives the true distance d. The law may then be written

$$C = k_1/(D + x)^2$$

$$\therefore\ D + x = (k_1/C)^{1/2}$$

Hence
$$D = (k_1/C)^{1/2} - x$$

A graph of D against $1/C^{1/2}$ should be a straight line of slope $k_1^{1/2}$ and intercept $-x$ on the D axis, as shown in Fig. 11.17.

Fig. 11.17

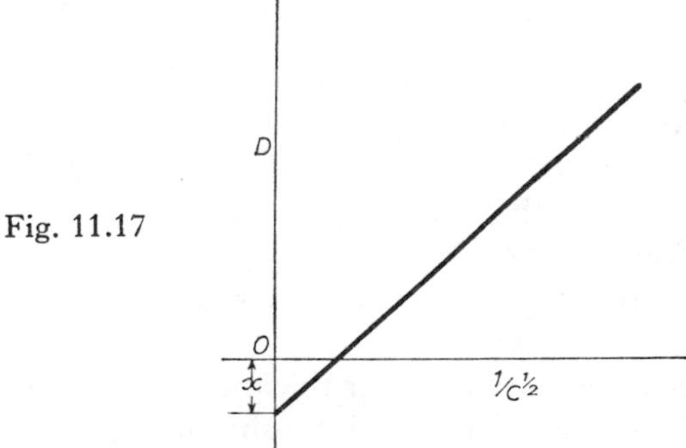

In practice, departure from the law arises because of (*i*) the finite size of the source and (*ii*) counting losses due to the counter dead time when the source is close to the Geiger–Müller tube.

Measurement of the half-thickness of lead for gamma rays

The '*half-thickness*', denoted by $x_{1/2}$, is a convenient term for dealing with the absorption of gamma rays. It is defined as the thickness of absorber, usually lead, which reduces the intensity of the gamma radiation to half its incident value.

The half-thickness can be determined by inserting sheets of lead between a gamma source (e.g., cobalt 60) and a Geiger–Müller tube and counter in a similar manner to that described for beta absorption.

The count-rate C, corrected for background, is directly proportional to the intensity of radiation, and it is again convenient to plot C directly on semi-log graph paper. The thickness of lead is usually expressed in the surface density unit of g cm^{-2}. An absorption curve for monoenergetic gamma rays is shown in Fig. 11.18; by considering two (or more) half-thicknesses, i.e., the

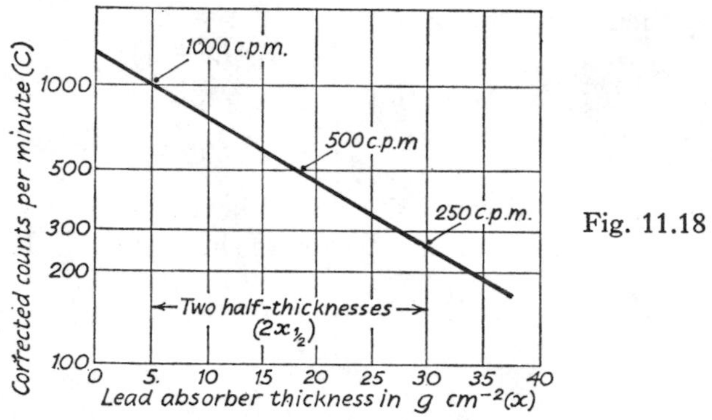

Fig. 11.18

thickness required to halve the count-rate twice, a more accurate result is obtained for $x_{1/2}$. The energy of the gamma rays can be obtained from a conversion graph or table relating half-thickness and energy.

The graph of $\log_{10} C$ against absorber thickness is seen to be a straight line. This implies that the intensity of the gamma radiation decreases exponentially with increasing absorber thickness. Thus, if I_0 is the intensity of the gamma rays from the source in the absence of absorbing material and I is the intensity after passing through a thickness x of absorber, then

$$I = I_0 e^{-\mu x}$$

where e is the base of natural logarithms and μ is a constant called the *linear absorption coefficient.* Taking count-rate as a measure of intensity

$$C = C_0 e^{-\mu x}$$

$$\therefore \log_e C = \log_e C_0 - \mu x$$

and $\log_{10} C = \log_{10} C_0 - \frac{\mu}{2{\cdot}303} \cdot x$ (since $\log_e = 2{\cdot}303 \log_{10}$)

The graph of $\log_{10} C$ against x should thus be a straight line if the absorption is exponential. This is only strictly true for a parallel beam of monochromatic (i.e., of one wavelength and energy) gamma rays. μ, which is an alternative term to $x_{1/2}$, can be found from the slope of the line and is smaller for high energy (more penetrating) rays than for low energy rays.

Cloud chambers

The track of an ionizing particle in a gas can be made visible by a cloud chamber. There are two types.

Expansion cloud chamber. This was invented by C. T. R. Wilson in 1911. Normally if air saturated with vapour is cooled by a sudden expansion, drops condense on dust particles to form a cloud. Wilson found that gas ions can also act as condensation nuclei for the supersaturated vapour. If an ionizing particle passes through dust-free air, saturated with vapour, which is suddenly expanded, drops of liquid form on the ions produced by the particle. With suitable illumination a white trail marking the track can be seen and photographed.

A small cloud chamber is shown in Fig. 11.19, in which the

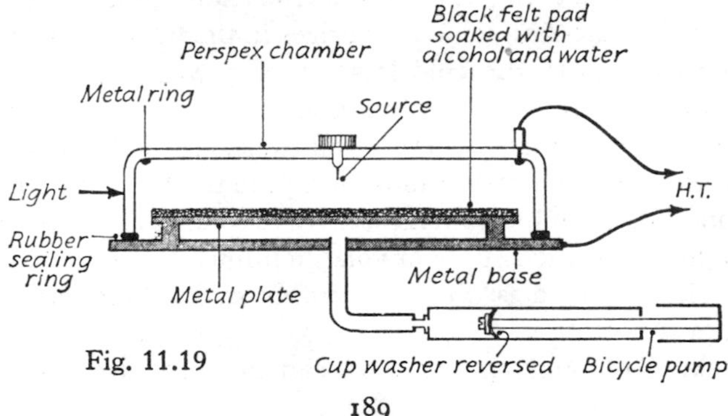

Fig. 11.19

sudden expansion is caused by withdrawing sharply the piston of a bicycle pump having the leather cup washer reversed. Ions are being produced all the time inside the chamber by the radiation and would cause blurred tracks at the instant of expansion. A p.d. of 200 or 300 volts between a metal ring at the top of the chamber and its base creates a clearing field which removes them. As a result only the tracks of particles which have just left the source are observed in an expansion. A mixture of alcohol and water is used to saturate the air since it reduces the expansion necessary for drops to condense on the ions.

Diffusion cloud chamber. This is an improvement on the expansion type in that it works continuously. Basically it consists of a vessel containing air or some other gas which is kept warm at

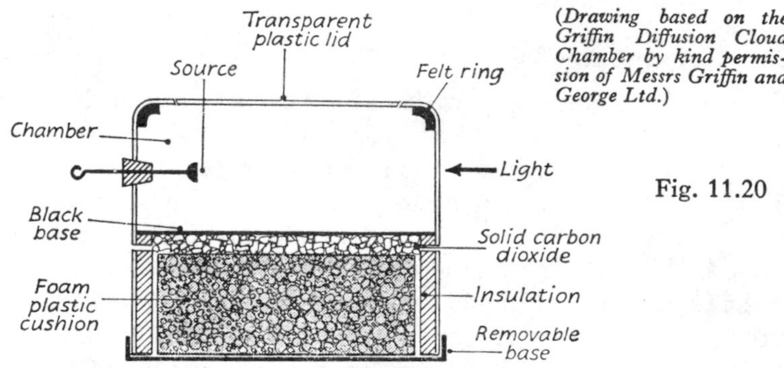

(Drawing based on the Griffin Diffusion Cloud Chamber by kind permission of Messrs Griffin and George Ltd.)

Fig. 11.20

the top and cold at the bottom. Frequently the top is at room temperature and the bottom is in contact with 'dry ice' (solid carbon dioxide) at $-78°C$. A simple arrangement is illustrated in Fig. 11.20. The felt ring at the top of the chamber is soaked with a liquid such as alcohol, which vaporizes in the warm upper region and then diffuses to the cold lower region where condensation occurs. Between the two regions there is a layer of air, supersaturated with vapour, where conditions are suitable for the condensation of droplets on ions along the tracks of the ionizing radiation. The chamber remains sensitive so long as the temperature gradient and the supply of volatile liquid is maintained. The electric clearing field is obtained simply by rubbing the plastic lid with a soft cloth.

Each kind of ionizing radiation can be recognized from the

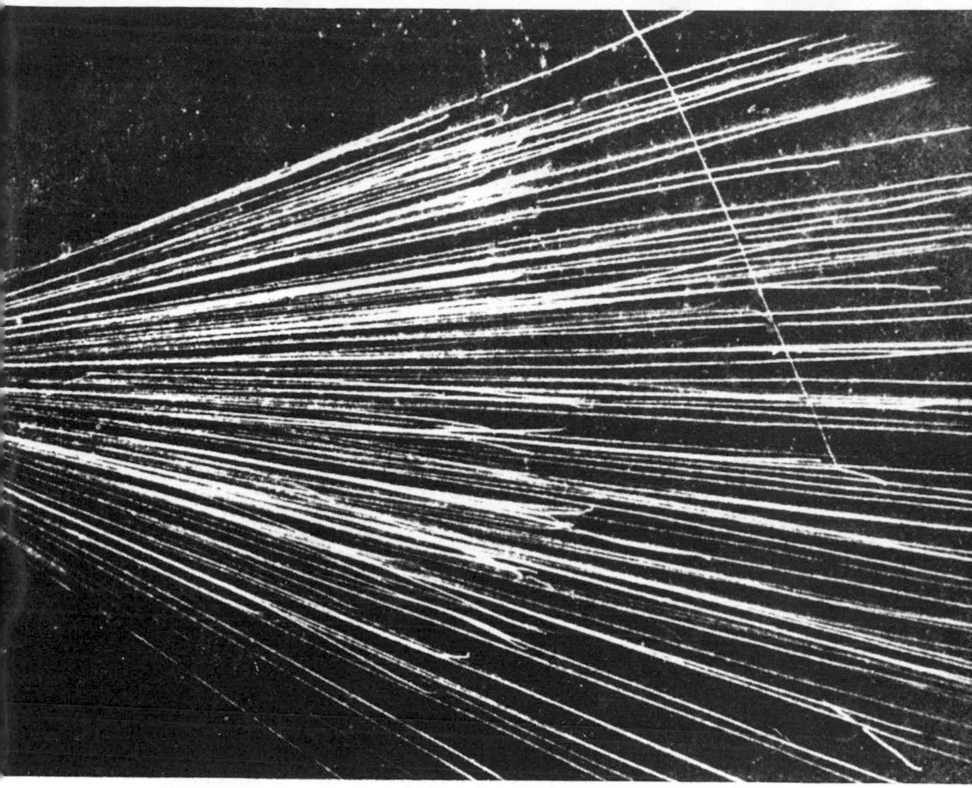

(*Photo by Professor Blackett—first published in the Royal Society 'Proceedings'; print by courtesy of U.K.A.E.A.*)

Plate 3 Cloud chamber tracks of alpha particles showing two different ranges. One alpha particle has caused the disintegration of a nitrogen nucleus (see p. 229); the long track of the resulting proton and the short track of the residual oxygen nucleus can be seen.

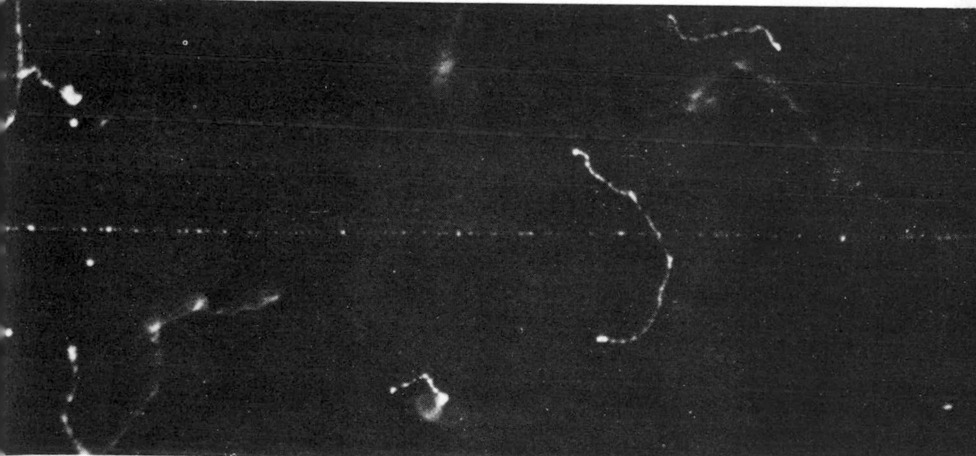

(*Courtesy: The Director, Science Museum*)

Plate 4 Tracks of beta particles. The thin, straight track across the centre of the photograph is due to a fast beta particle and the thicker, tortuous tracks are caused by slow beta particles.

track it produces, and from track length measurements the kinetic energies of particles can be estimated. Typical tracks for alpha and beta particles are shown in Plates 3 and 4.

Bubble chamber

A major disadvantage of both types of cloud chamber is the low stopping power of the gas in the chamber even when it is under pressure. This limits the probability of an ionizing particle, particularly one of high energy, having an encounter with an atom of the detector. The bubble chamber, invented in 1952 by D. A. Glaser in America, overcomes this fault by using a liquid as the detecting medium. Ionizing events then occur more frequently since a liquid is more than one hundred times denser than a gas.

Whereas a cloud chamber uses a supersaturated vapour to show ionizing tracks, a bubble chamber uses a superheated liquid. A liquid normally boils, forming bubbles, when its temperature reaches the boiling point. However if the liquid in a clean, smooth glass vessel is heated under pressure no bubbles are formed. When the pressure is suddenly released, the liquid becomes superheated. If it is exposed to ionizing radiation, the resulting ions act as nuclei for the production of small bubbles which appear as continuous tracks to reveal the path of the radiation. In the absence of particles, bubbles eventually form and the liquid has to be compressed again before it is ready for use.

The bubble chamber is extensively used in high-energy nuclear physics in conjunction with machines which produce bursts of charged particles. The operation of the chamber can then be synchronized with the entry of the particles. Liquid hydrogen is the most popular choice for bubble chamber liquids since collisions with the simplest atom of all are easiest to interpret.

Other detectors

Photographic emulsion

Nuclear radiation acts on a photographic emulsion in much the same way as light, causing the reduction of silver bromide and iodide to free silver. The silver blackens on developing and shows the track of each ionizing particle as a line of grains. In ordinary photographic plates the tracks are ill-defined and special nuclear emulsions are used containing about ten times the usual proportion of silver halide. Due to the relatively high density of the emulsion the tracks are usually fairly short and have to be studied under a high-power microscope. Sometimes stacks of plates are used and the tracks traced from one plate to the next.

Nuclear emulsions are also used in the film badges worn by personnel who are exposed to radiation in research or in industry. The degree of blackening of the film depends on the amount of energy absorbed and can be related to the radiation dose received over a period by comparison with standards.

Scintillation counter

This type of detector makes use of a phosphor, i.e., a substance which, as explained earlier (p. 41), absorbs energy and emits a flash of light or a scintillation when struck by a fast-moving particle. Scintillation screens coated with zinc sulphide were used by Lord Rutherford and others for early experiments with alpha particles. The procedure was simply to observe the screen in a darkened room and count the scintillations, each one being caused by one alpha particle. (The same effect can be seen by viewing the

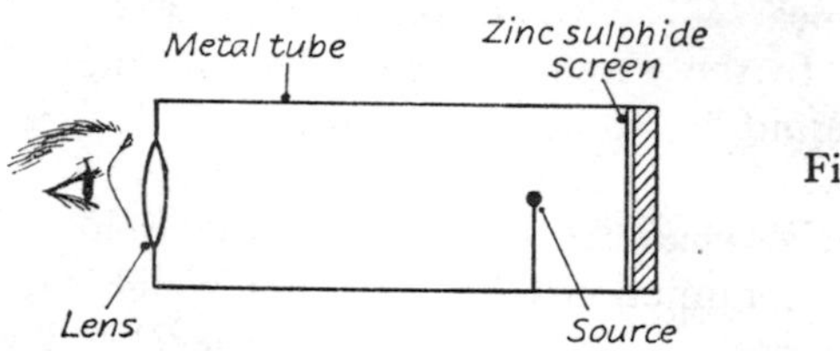

Fig. 11.21

figures on a luminous watch face with a lens in the dark.) This technique was laborious and suitable only for very low count-rates. An instrument called a *spinthariscope* is shown in Fig. 11.21 and illustrates the principle.

After temporary eclipse, scintillation methods have been revived using electronic counting. The choice of phosphor depends on the radiation to be detected. For alpha particles, zinc sulphide activated with silver is commonly used; anthracene is the most efficient phosphor for beta particles; and for gamma counting a large single crystal of sodium iodide activated with thallium is employed. The resolving time for a modern scintillation counter is less than 1 microsecond and therefore much higher counting rates are possible than with a Geiger tube. The detection efficiency for gamma rays can be as high as 50 per cent if the phosphor is large enough to absorb a high proportion of the gamma energy and so yield a good supply of fast secondary electrons for producing scintillations. Scintillation counters are now replacing Geiger–Müller tubes for gamma counting.

Solid state detector

A completely new type of detector, called a solid state detector, has now been developed which can detect alpha, beta, gamma and X-rays, protons and neutrons. Basically it is a silicon diode in which 'holes' and electrons (p. 259), created at the junction by ionizing radiation, are rapidly swept apart to opposite electrodes. An electrical pulse of extremely short duration is produced and after amplification is counted by a ratemeter or scaler.

QUESTIONS

1. Explain how ionizing radiation is detected by an ionization chamber and pulse electroscope. State clearly the part played by each instrument in the process.

If 34 eV is required to create one ion-pair in air, calculate the current produced when one alpha particle per second from a radium source is stopped inside an ionization chamber. Energy of alpha particles from radium = 4·8 MeV; electronic charge = $1{\cdot}60 \times 10^{-19}$ C.

2. Describe how you would measure (*a*) the range in air of alpha particles from a given source, and (*b*) the half-life of thoron.

3. Explain with reference to a Geiger–Müller tube the terms (*a*) avalanche, (*b*) gas amplification, (*c*) quenching and (*d*) dead time.

Draw a typical characteristic curve for a Geiger–Müller tube and explain its shape.

4. Define the terms in italics in the following statements:

(*a*) the absorption of beta particles by an element of low atomic weight depends largely on the ***surface density of the absorber***.

(*b*) The ***range of beta particles*** from strontium 90 is 960 mg cm^{-2}.

(*c*) The *half-thickness of lead for gamma rays* from cobalt 60 is 14·0 g cm^{-2}.

5. A Geiger–Müller tube and scaler are used to measure the decay of a radionuclide and the following count-rates are obtained at the times shown:

Background count = 30 counts per minute (c.p.m.).

Time (hours)	0	1	2	3	4	5	6	7	8	9	10
Count-rate (c.p.m.)	4032	3075	2341	1780	1375	1048	802	619	475	371	287

Plot log C (where C is the count-rate corrected for background) against time and hence determine from the graph the half-life of the nuclide. (*Note:* if semi-log graph paper is used C can be plotted directly on the log scale.)

Why does the linearity of the graph verify the exponential law of radioactive decay?

6. Write an essay on the detection of ionizing radiation.

7. What is gamma radiation? Explain *one* way in which it originates.

An experiment was conducted to investigate the absorption by aluminium of the radiation from a radioactive source by inserting aluminium plates of different thicknesses between the source and a Geiger tube connected to a ratemeter (or scaler). The observations are summarized in the following table:

Thickness of aluminium (cm)	*Corrected mean count rate (min^{-1})*
2·3	1,326
6·9	802
11·4	496
16·0	300

Use these data to plot a graph (using the graph paper available) and hence determine for this radiation in aluminium the *linear absorption coefficient*, μ (defined by $\mu = -(dI/I)(1/dx)$ where I is the intensity of the incident radiation and dI is the part of the incident radiation absorbed in thickness dx).

Draw a diagram to illustrate the arrangement of the apparatus used in the experiment and describe its preliminary adjustment.

What significance do you attach to the words 'corrected' and 'mean' printed in italics in the table? [*J.*]

12 Structure of the atom

The discovery and investigation of cathode rays, positive rays and radioactivity revealed the existence of sub-atomic particles and led to speculation about the structure of the atom. It has been said that 'the latest word in science is never the last'. The growth of ideas concerning atomic structure provides a good illustration of how theories emerge and are discarded when they are no longer useful.

One of the earliest theories, favoured by J. J. Thomson and known as the 'plum pudding' model, regarded the atom as a uniform sphere of positively charged matter with a sufficient number of negative electrons distributed throughout it (like currants in a pudding) to maintain electrical neutrality. This picture of the atom soon proved to be unsatisfactory.

Rutherford's nuclear atom

The nuclear atom is the basis of the modern theory of atomic structure and was proposed by Rutherford in 1911. While working in Canada in 1906 he had observed that the passage of alpha particles through a very thin metal foil was accompanied by some scattering of the particles from their original direction. Shortly afterwards he became Professor of Physics at the University of Manchester and in 1909 two of his assistants, Geiger and Marsden, made a more detailed study of this effect.

They directed a narrow beam of alpha particles on to gold foil about 10^{-6} m thick and found that while most of the particles passed straight through, some were scattered appreciably, while a very few, about 1 in 8000, suffered deflections of more than 90° and were in effect reflected back towards the radioactive source, Fig. 12.1. This last result was surprising and in Rutherford's words: 'It was about as credible as if you had fired a 15-inch shell at a piece of tissue paper and it came back and hit you.'

Rutherford realized that if electrostatic repulsion between the positive charge on the alpha particle and that on the gold atom was responsible for the scattering, the electric field produced by the all-over distribution of positive charge in the 'plum pudding atom' was too weak to account for large deflections. Furthermore

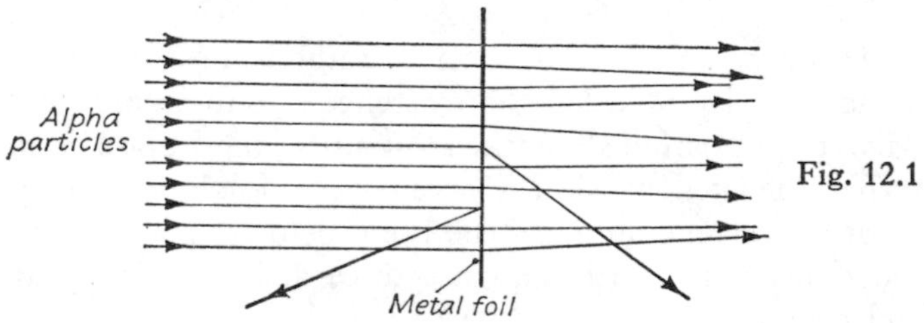

Fig. 12.1

these could not be due to a succession of small deflections on account of the thinness of the foil. Rutherford suggested that *all the positive charge and all the mass were concentrated in a very small volume or nucleus at the centre of the atom.* The large-angle scattering of alpha particles would then be explained by the strong electrostatic repulsion to which the particles are subjected on approaching closely enough to the tiny nucleus; the closer the approach the greater the scattering. We now believe, as explained earlier, that protons are responsible for the positive charge on the nucleus and protons and neutrons together for the nuclear mass.

The electrons were imagined to be outside the nucleus (hence the term extranuclear electrons) and at relatively large distances from it so that their negative charge did not act as a shield to the positive nuclear charge when an alpha particle penetrated the atom. The stability of such an arrangement was explained by supposing that the electrons moved in circular orbits round the nucleus (like planets round the sun), the electrostatic attraction between the two opposite charges providing the centripetal force which circular motion requires.

On this planetary model it would be reasonable to expect that many physical and chemical properties of atoms could be explained in terms of the number and arrangement of the extranuclear electrons on account of their greater accessibility. We shall see presently how they can account for optical and X-ray spectra.

Geiger–Marsden scattering experiment

To test his theory Rutherford derived a mathematical expression for the number of alpha particles deflected through various angles. The derivation was complex but involved, among other factors, the charge on the nucleus of the scattering atom, the thickness of the foil, the charge, mass and velocity of the bombarding alpha particles, and was based on the assumption that the

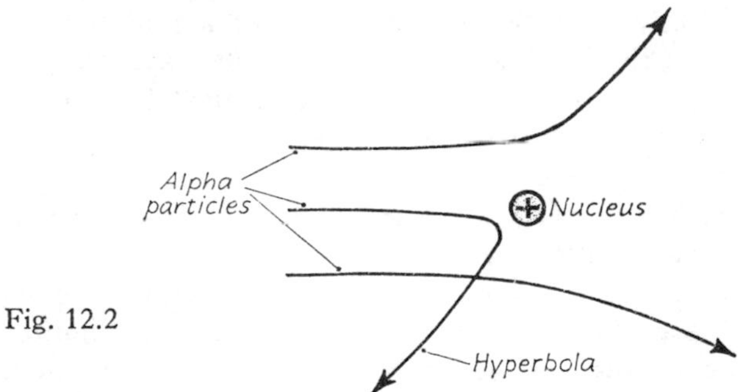

Fig. 12.2

repulsive force between the two positive charges obeys an inverse square law. The path predicted for the scattered alpha particle was a hyperbola, Fig. 12.2.

The test was carried out by Geiger and Marsden using the apparatus shown in Fig. 12.3. A fine beam of alpha particles from a radioactive source fell on a thin foil of gold, platinum or other metal in an evacuated metal box. The angular deflection of the alpha particles was measured by using a microscope to observe the scintillations on a glass screen coated with zinc sulphide. The screen and microscope could be rotated together relative to the

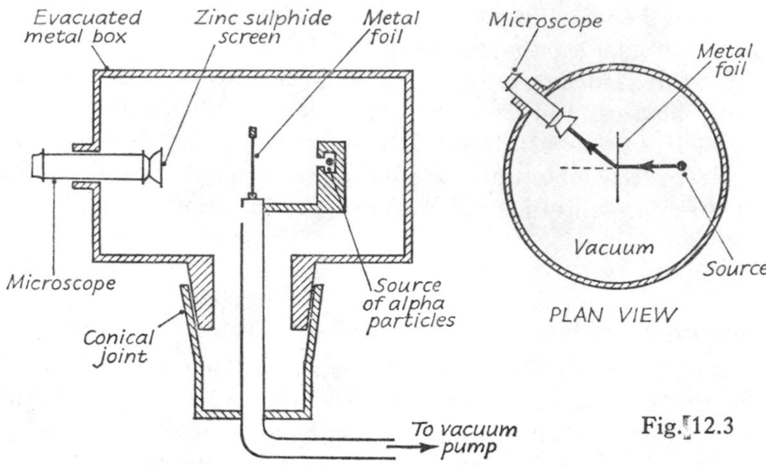

Fig. 12.3

foil and source which were fixed in position. Geiger and Marsden spent many hours in a darkened room counting the scintillations for a wide range of angles. In 1913 they reported that their results completely confirmed Rutherford's deductions and vindicated the use of the inverse square law. We shall see later, however (p. 230), that in certain cases where the alpha particle approaches extremely close to the nucleus the inverse square law no longer holds.

This experiment represents one of the great landmarks in physics. As well as causing a complete and permanent change in our picture of atoms, it inaugurated the technique of using high-speed particles as atomic probes. The subsequent exploitation of the technique was responsible for profound discoveries in nuclear physics.

Nuclear charge and size

Scattering experiments provide a means of estimating (*a*) the charge on the nucleus and (*b*) the size of the nucleus.

(*a*) *Charge on the nucleus*

This was a vital problem in the development of the theory of atomic structure. It was felt that the position of an element in the periodic table, i.e., its atomic number, was equal to the positive nuclear charge and so also to the number of extranuclear electrons. The measurements made by Geiger and Marsden showed that this was very approximately true. However in 1913 Moseley, a young physicist who was also working with Rutherford, obtained convincing evidence using a different technique to be described shortly.

The scattering experiment was improved and repeated in 1920 by Chadwick. For the three elements copper, silver and platinum he obtained nuclear charge values of 29·3, 46·3 and 77·4 respectively. These figures are in good agreement with the corresponding atomic numbers of 29, 47 and 78. In the light of more recent knowledge we can say, as indicated in Chapter 9, that an element of atomic number Z has Z protons in the nucleus and Z extranuclear electrons.

(*b*) *Size of the nucleus*

The maximum angle of scattering occurs when the distance between the centres of an alpha particle and the atomic nucleus involved in the encounter is a minimum. This distance will give an optimum value for the sum of the radii of an alpha particle and the nucleus. It turns out to be about 10^{-14} m, therefore the radius of the nucleus must be of the order 10^{-14} to 10^{-15} m.

It should, however, be remembered, as was pointed out in Chapter 2 when discussing the size of the electron, that size on the atomic scale does not have the exact meaning it does in the everyday world of macroscopic bodies. Atomic particles do not appear to resemble anything we can detect with our senses and we cannot picture the nucleus as a body with a definite surface since its boundary depends on the method of investigation. With this reservation, if the size of the nucleus is compared with the size of the atom (radius of the order 10^{-10} m) it is evident, since electrons are similar in size to nuclei, that most of the atom is empty. The actual volume of the nucleus and electrons in an atom is roughly one billionth (10^{-12}) of the total volume of the atom. The penetration of thin foil, with negligible deflection, by most alpha particles is not surprising; close approaches to the nucleus are rare events.

Moseley and X-ray spectra

Moseley was the first to determine atomic numbers accurately and his method is of theoretical and historical importance. He carried out a detailed study of X-ray spectra using a Bragg X-ray spectrograph, i.e., a spectrometer having a photographic plate in place of an ionization chamber to detect the X-rays. It was explained in Chapter 8 that in the production of X-rays two types of radiation are emitted, a characteristic line spectrum superimposed on a continuous spectrum. Moseley measured the frequencies (or wavelengths) of the lines in the characteristic

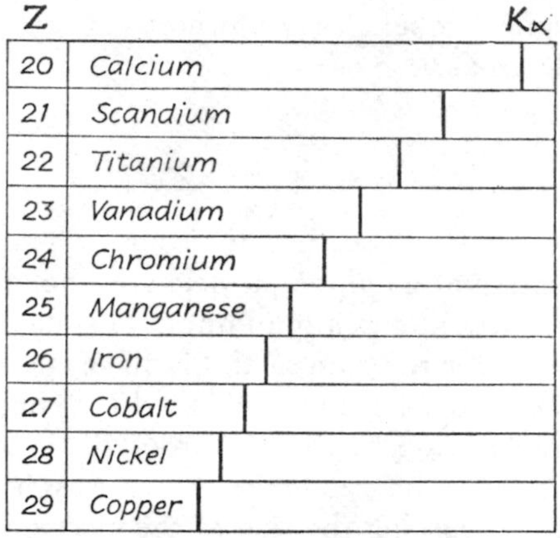

Z		$K\alpha$
20	Calcium	
21	Scandium	
22	Titanium	
23	Vanadium	
24	Chromium	
25	Manganese	
26	Iron	
27	Cobalt	
28	Nickel	
29	Copper	

Fig. 12.4

spectra of nearly 40 elements and found that the frequency of any particular line, such as the $K\alpha$ of Fig. 8.7, increased progressively from one element to the next in the periodic table, Fig. 12.4. If f is the frequency of this line for a certain element, it is related to a number Z, which always works out to be the atomic number, by the expression

$$\sqrt{f} = a(Z - b)$$

where a and b are constants for this particular line.

Moseley wrote, 'We have here a proof that there is in the atom a fundamental quantity which increases by regular steps from one element to the next'. He supported his belief that this fundamental quantity was the positive charge on the nucleus by reasoning based on Bohr's theory of the atom. The foundations of the periodic table were made secure and the elements finally placed in their correct order.

Types of optical spectra

So far we have mainly considered the small central nucleus which carries the positive charge and almost all the mass of the atom. Another aspect of atomic structure is concerned with the arrangement of the extranuclear electrons in the relatively large space they inhabit outside the nucleus. Insight into this problem is provided by optical spectra.

Spectroscopic examination of the light from luminous sources shows that optical *emission spectra* form three groups.

(*i*) *Continuous spectra* are emitted by hot solids and liquids and also hot gases at high pressures. All wavelengths are present but maximum emission occurs at one wavelength which decreases as the temperature of the source increases. These are 'black body type' spectra.

(*ii*) *Band spectra* are those with several well-defined groups or bands of lines. The lines are close together at one side of each band and make this side sharper and brighter than the other. The molecules of glowing gases or vapours, heated or excited electrically, form band spectra.

(*iii*) *Line spectra* consist of quite separate bright lines on a dark background, each line being light of practically one wavelength. No two elements give the same line spectrum; that due to neon gas has, among others, red lines; sodium vapour gives yellow lines and so on. Line spectra are due to the atoms of gases or vapours and are often called atomic spectra.

Some emission spectra are illustrated in Fig. 12.5. Of the three types, line spectra alone can be expected to be characteristic of the individual atoms concerned since only in a gas (especially at low pressure) are the atoms far enough apart not to interact. In molecular spectra the bands result from interaction between atoms in each molecule. In solids, liquids, and gases at high pressure atoms are so close that interaction is inevitable and the combined effect of many atoms gives a continuous spectrum.

Absorption spectra are a second class of spectra and also form three groups. A line spectrum may be obtained when white light passes through a cooler gas or vapour. Dark lines occur, against the continuous spectrum of white light, at exactly those frequencies which are present in the line emission spectrum of the gas or vapour. The absorption spectrum of an element is thus the same as its emission spectrum except that the latter consists of

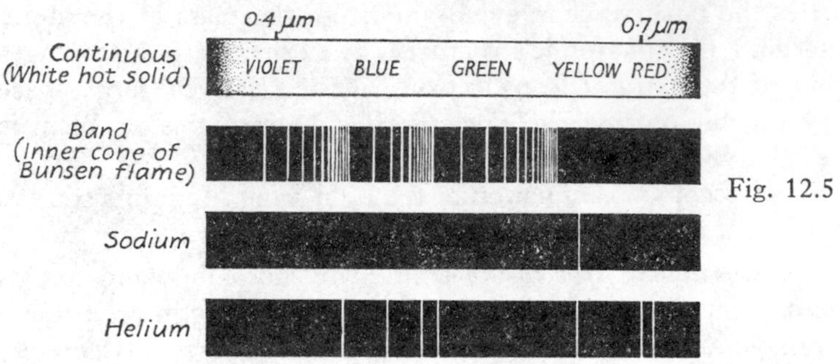

Fig. 12.5

bright lines on a dark background and the former of dark lines on a bright background. The formation of this type of spectrum will be discussed later (p. 212); for the present it suffices to say that the atoms of the cooler gas absorb light of the frequencies which they can emit, and then re-radiate the same frequencies almost immediately but in all directions. Consequently the parts

Fig. 12.6

of the spectrum corresponding to those frequencies appear dark by comparison with other frequencies not absorbed. The presence of a layer of relatively cooler gas round the sun causes the so-called Fraunhofer lines, Fig. 12.6, in the solar spectrum. They indicate the presence of hydrogen, helium, sodium, etc., in the sun's atmosphere.

Balmer's formula

The line spectra of the lighter elements such as hydrogen are fairly simple compared with those of the heavier elements which may comprise hundreds of lines. In an effort to bring some order to spectroscopy attempts were made in the late nineteenth century to find numerical relationships between the wavelengths of the lines in the spectra of certain elements.

One of the most successful of these empirical expressions was derived for the wavelengths of the lines in the hydrogen spectrum by the Swiss schoolmaster, Johann Balmer, in 1885. His formula can be written

$$\frac{1}{\lambda} = R_h\left(\frac{1}{2^2} - \frac{1}{n^2}\right) \tag{1}$$

where n has values 3, 4, 5, etc., and R_h is a constant, called the *Rydberg constant*, for hydrogen: $R_h = 1{\cdot}10 \times 10^7\ \text{m}^{-1}$. The reciprocal of the wavelength, $1/\lambda$, is called the *wave number* and is often used by spectroscopists in preference to wavelength or frequency. The wavelength λ of the $H\alpha$ line in the hydrogen spectrum, Fig. 12.7, is given by $n = 3$, the $H\beta$ line by $n = 4$ and so on. The line of minimum wavelength in the *Balmer series*

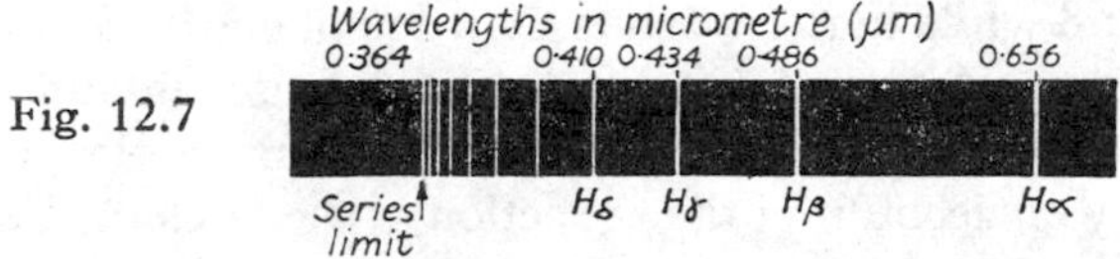

Fig. 12.7

corresponds to $n = \infty$ and has a wavelength of $4/R_h$, i.e., $3{\cdot}64 \times 10^{-7}$ m (0·364 μm).

Other series were found in the ultraviolet and infrared regions of the hydrogen spectrum. Each obeyed an equation similar to (1) with 2^2 replaced by 1^2, 3^2 or 4^2 etc. The lines of the *Lyman series* are in the ultraviolet and are given by

$$\frac{1}{\lambda} = R_h\left(\frac{1}{1^2} - \frac{1}{n^2}\right)$$

where $n = 2, 3, 4$, etc. The *Paschen series* is in the infrared with wavelengths obeying

$$\frac{1}{\lambda} = R_h\left(\frac{1}{3^2} - \frac{1}{n^2}\right)$$

where $n = 4, 5, 6$, etc. Any theory of atomic structure must be able to account for these series.

The Bohr atom

Rutherford's model of the atom, although strongly supported by evidence for the nucleus, is inconsistent with classical physics. An electron moving in a circular orbit round a nucleus is accelerating because the direction of its velocity is always changing. According to electromagnetic theory it should therefore emit radiation continuously and thereby lose energy. If this happened the radius of the orbit would decrease and the electron would spiral into the nucleus. Clearly, either the extranuclear atom or the classical theory of radiation requires modification.

In 1913, in an effort to overcome this paradox, the Danish physicist Niels Bohr, drawing inspiration from the success of the quantum theory in solving other problems involving radiation and atoms, made two revolutionary suggestions for amending electromagnetic theory. The first proposal was:

(*i*) Electrons can revolve round the nucleus only in certain *allowed orbits* and while in these orbits they do not emit radiation.

An electron in a particular orbit has a definite amount of energy. It possesses kinetic energy because of its motion and potential energy on account of the attraction of the nucleus. Each allowed orbit can therefore be associated with a certain quantity of energy, called the energy of the orbit, which equals the total energy of an electron in it. This brings us to Bohr's second proposal:

(*ii*) An electron can 'jump' from one orbit of energy E_2 to another of lower energy E_1 and the energy difference is emitted as one quantum of radiation of frequency f given by Planck's equation

$$E_2 - E_1 = hf \tag{2}$$

The orbits are numbered 1, 2, 3, etc., from the nucleus outwards and are also lettered K, L, M, etc. The K-orbit has the lowest energy value.

In the Bohr model of the hydrogen atom, Fig. 12.8, the single extranuclear electron normally exists in the K-orbit and represents the most stable or *ground state* of the atom. If the atom is excited by some means, energy is absorbed and the electron is assumed to jump to a higher orbit of greater energy which represents an *excited state* of the atom. Very soon afterwards the electron returns to the K-orbit, either directly or by stages, and the excess energy liberated by each transition is emitted as a quantum of radiation. Since certain orbits only are allowed, only quanta of certain energies are produced, corresponding to the frequencies found in the line spectrum of hydrogen. The return transitions which cause the various spectral series in hydrogen are shown in Fig. 12.8. The lines of the Lyman series are formed by return electronic jumps to the K-orbit, the energy differences

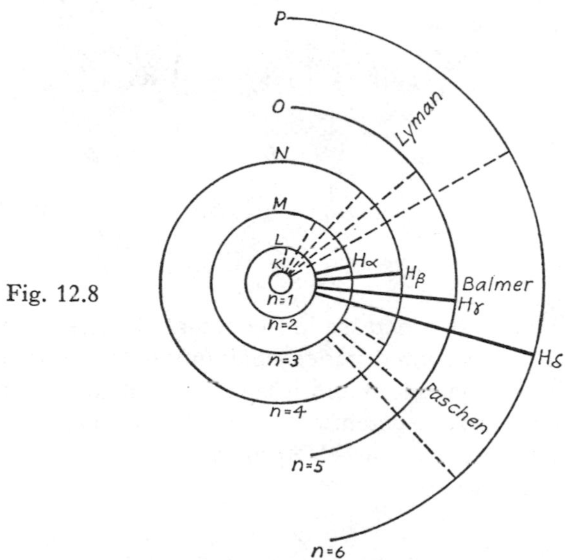

Fig. 12.8

being such as to give ultraviolet radiation. Quanta having smaller energies are emitted in transitions to the L-orbit from orbits of greater radius and the visible lines of the Balmer series occur.

Bohr assumed that the allowed orbits had circumferences which were integral multiples of h/mv, where m is the mass of an electron and v is its orbital velocity. This assumption was necessary if the energy differences between orbits were to give quanta of the observed frequencies.

Energy of an orbit

To make quantitative predictions from Bohr's theory an expression must be obtained for the energy of an orbit.

Consider first an electron at rest at a distance x from the nucleus of an atom having atomic number Z. The attractive force on it is, by the inverse square law, $e \times Ze/4\pi\epsilon_0 x^2$, i.e. $Ze^2/4\pi\epsilon_0 x^2$, where e is the electronic charge and ϵ_0 is the permittivity of free space. To move it away from the nucleus by a small distance dx work dW has to be done, where $dW = (Ze^2/4\pi\epsilon_0 x^2).dx$. The total work, W, required to move it from a distance r from the nucleus to infinity (i.e., outside the atom where it is not under the influence of the nucleus), is given by

$$W = \int_r^\infty dW = \int_r^\infty \left(\frac{Ze^2}{4\pi\epsilon_0 x^2}\right) \cdot dx$$

$$= \left(-\frac{Ze^2}{4\pi\epsilon_0 x}\right)_r^\infty$$

$$= \frac{Ze^2}{4\pi\epsilon_0 r}$$

By definition W gives the increase in the potential energy of the electron when it moves from distance r to infinity. At infinity the potential energy is a maximum and it is convenient to take it as the reference level of zero potential energy. Inside the atom at distance r from the nucleus the electron therefore has negative potential energy E_P, where

$$E_P = -\frac{Ze^2}{4\pi\epsilon_0 r}$$

The kinetic energy, E_K, of an electron of mass m moving with speed v in a circular orbit is $\frac{1}{2}mv^2$. The centripetal force required is provided by the electrostatic attraction of the nucleus and for an orbit of radius r the equation of circular motion gives

$$\frac{mv^2}{r} = \frac{Ze^2}{4\pi\epsilon_0 r^2}$$

$$\therefore\ mv^2 = \frac{Ze^2}{4\pi\epsilon_0 r} \tag{3}$$

Hence,
$$E_K = \frac{1}{2}\cdot mv^2 = \frac{1}{2}\cdot\frac{Ze^2}{4\pi\epsilon_0 r}$$

The total energy E of an electron moving in an orbit is thus

$$E = E_K + E_P = \frac{1}{2}\cdot\frac{Ze^2}{4\pi\epsilon_0 r} - \frac{Ze^2}{4\pi\epsilon_0 r}$$

$$\therefore\ E = -\frac{1}{2}\cdot\frac{Ze^2}{4\pi\epsilon_0 r}$$

E depends on r and to obtain values of E whose differences give radiation of the frequencies actually observed, the values of r must be correctly chosen. Bohr found that his allowed orbits had to have a circumference given by

$$2\pi r = n\cdot\frac{h}{mv} \qquad (4)$$

where n is the orbit number and h is Planck's constant. Eliminating v between (3) and (4) gives

$$r = \frac{n^2h^2\epsilon_0}{\pi Ze^2m} \qquad (5)$$

Hence from (5)

$$E = -\frac{Z^2e^4m}{8\epsilon_0^2h^2}\cdot\frac{1}{n^2} \qquad (6)$$

If two orbits have total energies E_1 and E_2 and orbit numbers n_1 and n_2 then from (6) we have

$$E_2 - E_1 = \frac{Z^2e^4m}{8\epsilon_0^2h^2}\left(\frac{1}{n_1^2} - \frac{1}{n_2^2}\right) \qquad (7)$$

In an electronic transition involving the emission of radiation, E_2 must be greater than E_1 and n_2 greater than n_1. If f is the frequency and λ the wavelength of this radiation

$$E_2 - E_1 = hf = \frac{hc}{\lambda} = \frac{Z^2e^4m}{8\epsilon_0^2h^2}\left(\frac{1}{n_1^2} - \frac{1}{n_2^2}\right)$$

Hence
$$\frac{1}{\lambda} = \frac{Z^2e^4m}{8\epsilon_0^2h^3c}\left(\frac{1}{n_1^2} - \frac{1}{n_2^2}\right) \qquad (8)$$

Equation (8) has the same form as Balmer's formula if $n_1 = 2$ and $n_2 = 3, 4, 5$, etc. Further, substitution of the accepted values for e, m, h, c and $Z = 1$ for hydrogen in the constant term outside the brackets gives excellent agreement with the experimental value of R_h, the Rydberg constant for hydrogen. This provides striking evidence in support of Bohr's ideas concerning the origin of spectra.

In equation (7) if $n_1 = 1$ and $n_2 = \infty$ the energy needed to remove an electron completely from an atom, i.e., the ionization energy, can be calculated.

Objections to the Bohr atom

Despite its outstanding achievements, particularly in explaining the hydrogen spectrum, the Bohr atom had certain shortcomings. First, it could not interpret the details of the spectra of atoms containing more than one electron. Second, the very arbitrary method of selecting allowed orbits had no theoretical basis and third, it involved quantities, such as the radius of an orbit, which could not be checked experimentally.

Nevertheless great credit is due to Bohr for linking spectroscopy and atomic structure and for introducing quantum ideas into atomic theory. Bohr's model of the atom has been superseded by a new theory, based on *wave mechanics* or *quantum mechanics*. In this theory, which is sometimes called the 'new quantum theory' to distinguish it from the 'old quantum theory' of Planck and Bohr, there is no need to make assumptions because they give correct results. But whereas the Bohr atom was easily visualized and involved fairly simple mathemetics, its successor is highly abstract and the mathematics are more difficult.

For the present it is sufficient to say that while wave mechanics preserves the general idea of a hollow, nuclear atom, it discards the Bohr picture of electrons moving in allowed orbits. Nevertheless the essential characteristic of Bohr orbits, i.e., definite energy values, is retained.

Energy levels in atoms

Wave mechanics permits the electrons in an atom to have only certain energy values. These values are called the *energy levels* of the atom and the way in which they arise will be considered later (p. 221). Their existence is supported by their ability to explain atomic spectra but more direct experimental evidence is also available and will be discussed shortly.

Energy level diagrams can be drawn for different atoms and are useful when dealing with properties depending on the extra-nuclear electrons. The levels, both occupied and vacant, are each allotted (as were the Bohr orbits) a ***principal quantum number n***, where $n = 1, 2, 3$, etc., and are also lettered K, L, M, etc.,

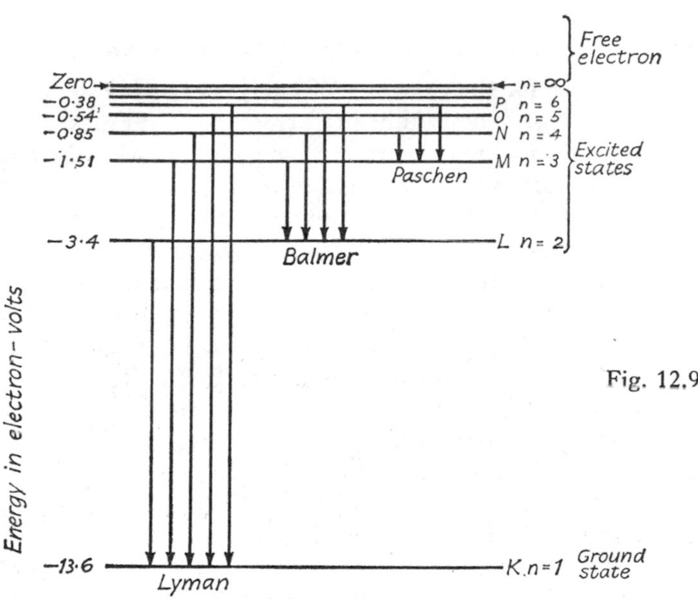

Fig. 12.9

respectively. All levels have negative energy values because the energy of an electron at rest outside an atom is taken as zero and when the electron enters the atom, energy is lost as radiation. The K-level, with the largest negative value, is the lowest level. Other levels have less negative values, i.e., more positive values, and represent higher energy states.

The energy level diagram for hydrogen is shown in Fig. 12.9. In this case the K-level has energy $-13{\cdot}6$ eV and is the one normally occupied by the single electron of a hydrogen atom in its most stable or ***ground state***. Above this state are the ***excited*** *states* to which the atom may be raised by absorbing the correct amount of energy.

The emission of a spectral line by an excited atom is considered to be due to an electronic transition, occurring directly or by stages, from a higher to a lower energy level. The frequency f of the quantum of radiation emitted in any transition is given by Planck's equation $E_2 - E_1 = hf$, where E_1 and E_2 are the energies of the levels concerned. The transitions for three of the series in the hydrogen spectrum are shown in Fig. 12.9.

Energy levels and electron impact experiments

Direct evidence for the existence of energy levels is provided by experiments, first successfully performed by J. Franck and G. Hertz in 1914, in which electrons have collisions with the atoms (or molecules) of a gas at low pressure.

When an electron has an encounter with a gas atom one of three things is possible: (*i*) the electron shoots straight through the atom or is scattered, without loss of kinetic energy, (*ii*) excitation occurs, i.e., an electron in the gas atom is raised to a higher energy level, (*iii*) ionization occurs, i.e., an electron is completely removed from the gas atom. In (*i*) the collision is elastic. In (*ii*) and (*iii*) the collisions are inelastic since the kinetic energy lost by the bombarding electron does not reappear as kinetic energy of the gas atom but is emitted as electromagnetic radiation when the gas atom is de-excited or de-ionized.

An arrangement for a Franck–Hertz type of experiment is shown in Fig. 12.10*a*. Electrons emitted by the hot cathode C in a tube containing gas at a suitable pressure are accelerated by a positive potential V_1 on the grid G. When V_1 just exceeds the small negative potential V_2 which the anode A has, with respect to G, electrons reach A and a small current is indicated on the galvanometer. As V_1 is increased the current increases. During this phase, PQ in Fig. 12.10*b*, the bombarding electron energies are small and all collisions between electrons and gas atoms are elastic. At a certain value of V_1, called the *first excitation potential*, some electrons have inelastic collisions with gas atoms near G and raise them to their first excited energy level. The negative potential V_2 ensures that the electrons, having lost their kinetic energy, are carried back to G. The anode current therefore falls abruptly, QR. Further increase of V_1 allows even those electrons which have inelastic collisions to overcome V_2 and reach A. The galvanometer reading increases again, RS.

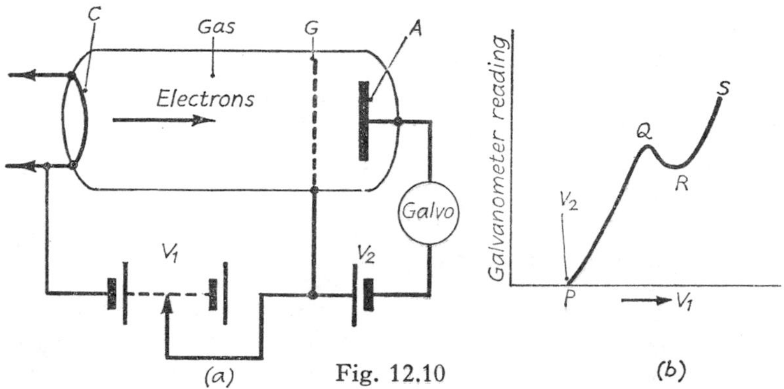

Fig. 12.10

Other effects may be obtained at higher values of V_1 depending on the tube and circuit conditions. Thus it is possible to find the *ionization potential* of the gas, i.e., the potential at which the bombarding electrons have enough energy to cause gas atoms to be ionized.

Collision experiments, as outlined above, indicate that an atom cannot absorb *any* amount of energy. For example, in the case of hydrogen with a first excitation energy of 10·2 eV (corresponding to a first excitation potential of 10·2 volts) the first inelastic collisions do not occur until the bombarding electrons have an energy of 10·2 eV. This is the energy needed to raise an electron from the K- to the L-level. Similarly 12·1 eV is required to excite a hydrogen atom to its M-level from the K-level. It may be asked: 'Can a hydrogen atom which receives 10·2 eV in a collision with one electron, subsequently receive the 1·9 eV it requires to reach the M-level, from a collision with another electron?' In theory this is possible, but in practice improbable, because an atom usually only remains in an excited state for about 10^{-8} s before returning to a lower level. In general then, the energy of an atom can only change by certain distinct amounts, i.e., it is *quantized*, and we conclude that these amounts are determined by its energy levels.

Energy levels for different atoms are numerous but characteristic and are found from collision experiments in gases and from a detailed study of emission and absorption spectra (p. 227, question 6). They may also be calculated using wave mechanics.

Excitation and ionization

These two effects have been discussed on several occasions and it will now be convenient to reconsider them here. In both, absorption of energy by an atom is necessary and may occur in various ways.

(*a*) *Collision with a charged particle*

Inelastic collisions take place in a gas-discharge tube between electrons accelerated by an electric field and atoms of a gas (p. 142). An excited or ionized gas atom emits one or more photons when it returns to the ground state. If the radiation is in the visible region, the gas glows when a sufficiently large number of photons is involved. Sodium street lights and neon advertising signs are two examples of devices in which this occurs.

The scintillations of the phosphor in a cathode ray tube are due to excitation of the phosphor atoms by collisions with energetic electrons. Similarly those in a scintillation counter are caused by alpha particles, electrons, etc. (p. 192). Usually an atom in an excited state returns to the ground state almost at once but in some cases the process is delayed; phosphorescence then occurs (p. 41).

(*b*) *Absorption of a photon*

Excitation of an atom may be induced by the absorption of a photon of electromagnetic radiation whose energy *exactly* equals that required to raise the atom to one of its excited states. Once absorbed the photon disappears. This process accounts for absorption spectra (p. 202). The gas or vapour whose absorption spectrum is obtained absorbs from white light photons with energies which 'fit' its energy levels.

Photoelectric emission is an example of ionization by photons (p. 114). In this case *any* photon whose energy exceeds the ionization energy of the atom will produce the effect since the ejected electron carries off the excess energy as kinetic energy.

(c) *Use of a high temperature*

Inelastic collisions can occur between gas atoms as a result of thermal agitation resulting in one or both becoming excited or ionized. Ions are produced in a flame in this way (p. 139). The necessity for a high temperature is apparent when the kinetic energy of translation of an atom at ordinary temperatures is considered. This can be derived from the kinetic theory of gases and is given by $\frac{3}{2}kT$, where k is Boltzmann's constant (k equals R/N_A, R being the gas constant for one mole and N_A Avogadro's constant) and T is the temperature of the gas or vapour in K. Substitution of numerical values gives about 0·037 eV per atom. Ionization energies of the elements vary between 4 eV and 25 eV and are thus considerably greater.

Arrangement of the extranuclear electrons

This has been worked out from a detailed study of such properties of atoms as chemical behaviour, optical and X-ray spectra and

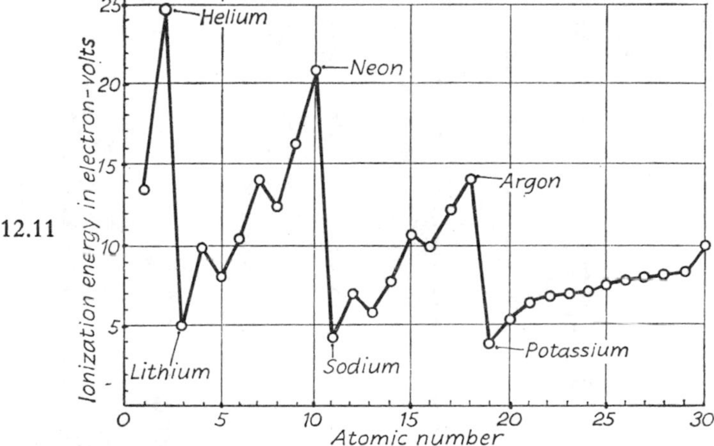

Fig. 12.11

ionization energies. For example, a graph showing the variation of ionization energy with atomic number, Fig. 12.11, displays a periodicity which can be correlated with the arrangement of the electrons. The small ionization energies of the alkali metals suggests they have a loosely held electron in a higher energy level.

TABLE 12.1

Arrangement of electrons

Element	*Atomic number*	*Number of electrons*			
		K	*L*	*M*	*N*
H	1	1			
He	2	2			
Li	3	2	1		
Be	4	2	2		
B	5	2	3		
C	6	2	4		
N	7	2	5		
O	8	2	6		
F	9	2	7		
Ne	10	2	8		
Na	11	2	8	1	
Mg	12	2	8	2	
Al	13	2	8	3	
Si	14	2	8	4	
P	15	2	8	5	
S	16	2	8	6	
Cl	17	2	8	7	
A	18	2	8	8	
K	19	2	8	8	1
Ca	20	2	8	8	2
Sc	21	2	8	9	2
Ti	22	2	8	10	2
V	23	2	8	11	2
Cr	24	2	8	13	1
Mn	25	2	8	13	2
Fe	26	2	8	14	2
Co	27	2	8	15	2
Ni	28	2	8	16	2
Cu	29	2	8	18	1
Zn	30	2	8	18	2

By contrast the inert gases must have very stable electronic structures since they require most energy for ionization.

The electronic configurations for the 30 lightest elements are given in Table 12.1. It will be observed that:

(*i*) The lowest energy levels are occupied first. This is in accordance with the fact that a system is stable when its energy is a minimum.

(*ii*) Each energy level can only accommodate a certain number of electrons. Thus the *K*-level ($n = 1$) has $2(1)^2$, i.e., 2 electrons, the *L*-level ($n = 2$) has a maximum of $2(2)^2$, i.e., 8 electrons, the *M*-level ($n = 3$) has $2(3)^2$, i.e., 18 electrons, and so on. For the first five levels the magic numbers, as they are called, are 2, 8, 18, 32, 50. In a more advanced treatment these particular numbers can be explained.

(*iii*) A new level is started when the highest occupied level contains eight electrons (two for the *K*-level) but subsequently the latter, if incomplete, receives its full quota. For example, in potassium the *N*-level is started even although the *M*-level only has 8 electrons; later *M* builds up to 18.

Each level is sometimes called a 'shell' but this term should not be taken too literally. Electrons in the highest level are known as *valence* electrons since they are concerned with chemical properties.

Origin of X-ray line spectra

The fact that the energy of a light photon is a few electron-volts suggests that optical spectra are due to transitions of loosely held electrons in higher energy levels. As a result this type of spectrum shows a periodicity like most other properties; for example, the spectra of the alkali metals bear close resemblances since they all have one electron in the highest occupied energy level.

Unlike optical spectra, X-ray line spectra do not show a periodic variation. Instead, for a series of elements, they consist of similar lines with a gradual change of frequency from element to element (Fig. 12.4). Energy considerations support the view that X-rays originate from tightly bound electrons in the lowest, closed energy levels. They are only produced when metals are bombarded by high-energy electron beams (of the order of thousands of electron-volts) which are able to penetrate deep into atoms and displace electrons from very deep energy levels. The subsequent fall of an electron from a higher level into one of these gaps in an otherwise complete, but appreciably lower energy level, causes the emission of a high-energy X-ray photon.

The *K*-series of X-ray lines is produced when an electron is knocked out of the lowest or *K*-level. The return of the same or another electron to the gap in the *K*-level causes the emission of a line of the *K*-series. If the electron falls from the *L*-level the $K\alpha$ line occurs, when from the *M*-level we have the $K\beta$ line and so on. Similarly the *L*-series arises when electrons return to

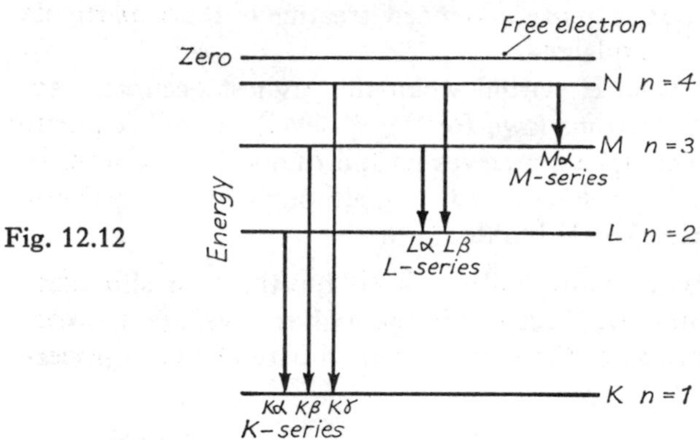

Fig. 12.12

vacancies in the *L*-level. This series is excited by smaller energies than the *K*-series because the *L*-electrons are less strongly held; the X-rays emitted have lower frequencies and longer wavelengths and are less penetrating. An energy level diagram interpreting characteristic X-rays is shown in Fig. 12.12.

The progressive increase of frequency, with increasing atomic number, in say the $K\alpha$ line, is due to small differences in the *K*- and *L*-energy levels of different atoms. This arises from the increasing positive charge on the nucleus and it makes possible the determination of atomic numbers from a study of X-ray spectra.

It is interesting to note that the idea of energy levels in the nucleus is used to explain the line spectrum of gamma radiation (p. 158). Thus if the emission of an alpha or beta particle leaves a radioactive nucleus in an excited state, a gamma ray photon is emitted when the nucleus returns to the ground state. The existence of different nuclear energy levels would account for gamma rays of definite but different energies and frequencies.

Wave aspect of matter

The wave-particle nature of radiation, discussed in Chapter 7, led Louis de Broglie (pronounced de Broy) to suggest in 1923 that matter also might exhibit this duality and have wave properties. His ideas can be expressed quantitatively by first considering radiation. A photon of frequency f and wavelength λ has, according to Planck's quantum theory, energy $E = hf = hc/\lambda$, where c is the velocity of light and h is Planck's constant. By Einstein's energy-mass relation (p. 233) the equivalent mass m of the photon is given by $E = mc^2$.

Hence
$$\frac{hc}{\lambda} = mc^2$$

$$\therefore \lambda = \frac{h}{mc}$$

By analogy, de Broglie suggested that a particle of mass m moving with velocity v behaves in some ways like waves of wavelength λ, given by

$$\lambda = \frac{h}{mv} \qquad (9)$$

Calculation shows that electrons accelerated through a p.d. of about 100 volts should be associated with *de Broglie* or *matter waves*, as they are called, having a wavelength of the order of 10^{-10} m. This is about the same as for X-rays and it was suggested that the conditions required to reveal the wave nature of X-rays might also lead to the detection of electron waves.

In 1927, Davisson and Germer, working in the Bell Telephone Laboratories in New York, diffracted a beam of electrons from the surface of a nickel crystal in a way similar to the diffraction of X-rays in a Bragg spectrometer. Furthermore their results for electron wavelengths agreed closely with calculated values. Shortly afterwards, G. P. Thomson, the son of J. J. Thomson, independently obtained a diffraction pattern by passing electrons through very thin metal foil and allowing the diffracted beam to fall on a photographic plate. The pattern consisted of a number of concentric circles like those shown in Fig. 12.13. Thomson's method corresponded to that used by von Laue for X-rays.

It is evident from equation (9) that for particles heavier than the electron, the de Broglie wavelength is smaller and detection therefore more difficult. However various workers, including Stern and Estermann, have obtained diffraction with beams of protons and alpha particles. The wavelengths of ordinary objects are much too small for present methods of detection.

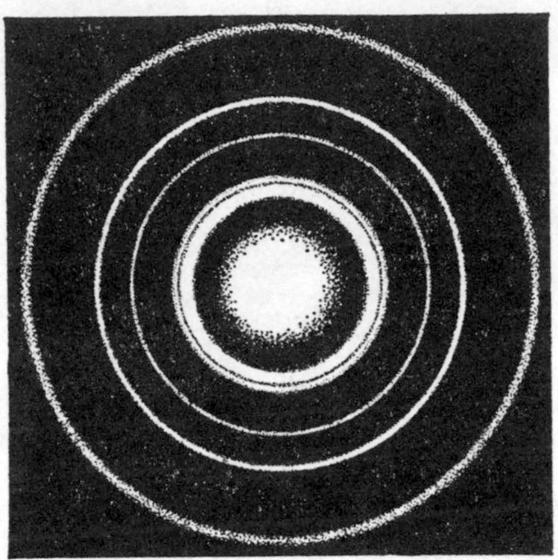

Fig. 12.13

Matter waves are useful in various ways. In the electron microscope, electrons are focused by electric and magnetic fields and the final image formed on a fluorescent screen or a photographic plate. The limit of resolution, which for any microscope is roughly equal to the wavelength of the radiation used to 'illuminate' the object, is considerably greater than in an optical microscope on account of the small wavelength of electron waves compared with light. The field ion microscope gives even greater resolution because the matter waves associated with the helium ions used have an even shorter wavelength.

Wave-particle duality

The display of both wave-like and particle-like properties by matter as well as by radiation appears to be completely contradictory. However, to some extent the dilemma is of man's own making for initially an attempt was made to explain this dual behaviour in terms of analogies of the real waves and real particles of everyday life. It is not unnatural that this should be done but it is not altogether surprising that the laws of classical physics (i.e., physics before 1900), derived for larger scale phenomena, do not apply in the world of photons and electrons. When our real-life analogies are pushed too far they break down. Once it is realized that we are not dealing with particles and waves which are real in the sense that they are like billiard balls or water waves, then the dual behaviour of matter and radiation need not be contradictory. The two aspects are not incompatible so long as we regard the use of the wave and particle ideas as aids to understanding and not true descriptions. A map showing only towns and roads is no more a complete representation of a country than is one showing only physical features; each describes one aspect.

Such arguments help to make the duality dilemma more acceptable but they do not explain the nature of the 'particles' and 'waves'. The present view is that both are to some extent illusions. The 'waves' are not waves of moving matter or varying fields but are considered to be probability waves. Thus the wave-like behaviour of a moving electron is due to the fact that the chance of it being found at any given point depends on the intensity at the point of the electron wave associated with it. Where this is high we are likely to have a high electron density. In the same way an electromagnetic wave, although undoubtedly connected with electric and magnetic fields, is regarded as consisting of photons whose probable locations are given by the intensity of the wave. This outlook forms the basis of wave mechanics, which, as the name implies, considers that the motion of a particle is determined by a wave equation. For microscopic particles it predicts quite a different behaviour from that given by the particle mechanics of Newton but agrees with the latter for macroscopic bodies. It deals in probabilities and not certainties. We may think of wave mechanics as having the same relation to particle mechanics as wave optics to geometrical optics. In the latter, light is considered to travel in straight lines but to understand the details of interference wave optics is required.

The illusory nature of the 'particles' is best understood from an experiment conducted by G. I. Taylor. He enclosed a Young's double slit apparatus in a box with a light source, so weak that only one photon was in the apparatus at a time. After several months he found that a photographic plate was sufficiently affected to reveal the usual dark and bright interference fringes. From this we infer that *individual* photons exhibit a wave behaviour and an interference pattern is not formed just when large numbers of photons are present. The question now arises, 'Through which slit does any single photon pass?' If we attempt to answer this by placing a transparent fluorescent screen behind each slit, we find that two spots are produced, one on the fluorescent screen behind one of the slits and a corresponding one on the photographic plate. But no interference pattern is obtained since the photon loses energy, and therefore frequency in traversing the screen and the waves through the slits are no longer coherent. By detecting the particle aspect of the photon on the fluorescent screen we have destroyed its wave property and are forced to conclude that somehow or other in the double slit experiment each photon passes through both slits. The same conclusion holds for electrons and clearly neither they nor photons behave like real particles.

Whatever the nature of electrons and photons both wave and particle aspects are necessary for an adequate description of their behaviour. Thus we think of electrons as particles when considering valves but a full explanation of the electron microscope requires us to regard them as having wave properties. The two aspects are complementary and not contradictory and in any experiment either one or the other, but not both, is evident. What is revealed to us depends on the method of observation. It was suggested by Eddington that the term 'wavicle' be introduced for entities such as electrons and photons.

Wave mechanics, energy levels and the atom

The fundamental objection to Bohr's theory is that it pin-points an electron in a definite orbit and takes no account of its wave aspect. The modern theory of the atom was developed independently in two forms. In 1925 Heisenberg proposed his quantum mechanics and in 1926 Schrödinger introduced wave mechanics as a development of de Broglie's ideas. Later the two theories were shown to be equivalent mathematically and since wave mechanics is more easily grasped it will be briefly outlined here.

Without the advanced mathematics required, the wave-mechanical theory of the atom can only be explained by analogy with real waves. Thus in a vibrating string fixed at both ends, waves are reflected to and fro and a stationary wave system is set up having nodes and antinodes. In its simplest mode of vibration the string has a node at each end and an antinode in the centre but it can vibrate with two, three or any integral number of loops. The vibration is restricted to those modes having a complete number of loops, i.e., it is 'quantized', and each mode of vibration produces a note of different frequency. Similarly we can imagine an electron, confined to an atom by the attractive force exerted on it by the nucleus, being associated with electron waves which are reflected when they reach the boundary of the atom. A stationary wave system is established inside the atom and can vibrate in various modes. Each mode corresponds to a particular frequency and therefore, by Planck's energy equation, to a particular energy level of the atom. When an electron wave changes its mode of vibration, the energy difference between the levels is emitted (or absorbed) as radiation. This argument by analogy, although much too realistic, enables us to see how wave mechanics can account for the existence of energy levels.

An electron in a particular energy level is represented by a stationary wave equation whose amplitude is called the *wave function* ψ (psi). The value of ψ varies throughout the atom and the volume within which it is not negligible is known as the *orbital* of the electron. The shape of the orbital depends on the energy level concerned. Fig. 12.14 shows the orbitals for the hydrogen electron in its lowest energy level and in one of its higher levels. Orbitals are useful in chemistry when dealing with the covalent bond which is considered to be formed when the orbitals of two electrons overlap.

The probability of finding an electron at a particular point in an atom depends on ψ^2. For a hydrogen atom in the ground state the value of ψ^2 indicates that the electron is somewhere within a sphere, centre the nucleus. Its most probable location at any instant can be shown to be centred on a distance of $0{\cdot}53 \times 10^{-10}$ m from the nucleus (this is also the radius of the first Bohr orbit) but there is a small chance of finding it nearer or farther from the nucleus. In the case of some of the other energy levels in hydrogen and for other atoms, ψ^2 varies with direction as well as with distance from the nucleus. One way in which we now

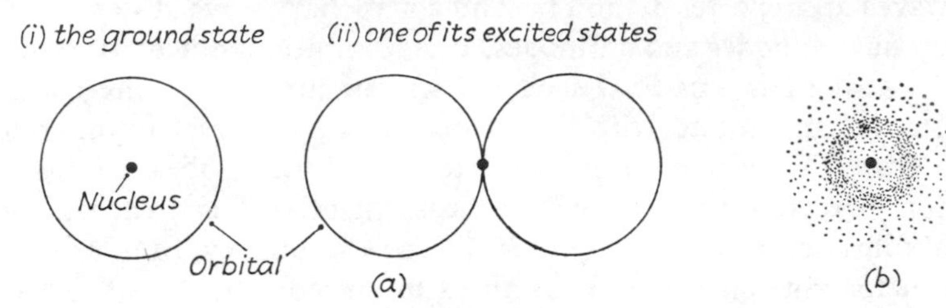

Fig. 12.14

try to 'picture' the atom is to regard it as a positive nucleus surrounded by a cloud of negative charge of varying charge density. The hydrogen atom in its ground state may then be represented as in Fig. 12.14*b*, where the intensity of the shading represents the variation of charge density.

Wave mechanics has been very successful in explaining a wide range of phenomena in physics and chemistry.

Lasers

The *laser*, named from the first letters of *l*ight *a*mplification by the *s*timulated *e*mission of *r*adiation, is a device for producing a very intense beam of light which has the following special properties.

(*i*) It is *monochromatic*, i.e., consists of one wavelength.
(*ii*) It is *coherent*, i.e., all parts are in phase.
(*iii*) It is *collimated*, i.e., all parts travel in the same direction.

The action of a laser can be explained in terms of energy levels.

A material whose atoms are excited emits radiation when electrons in higher energy levels return to lower levels. Normally this occurs randomly, i.e., *spontaneous emission* occurs, Fig. 12.15, and the radiation is emitted in all directions and is incoherent.

The emission of light from ordinary sources is due to this process. However, if a photon of exactly the correct energy approaches an excited atom, an electron in a higher energy level may be induced to fall to a lower level and emit another photon. The remarkable fact is that this photon has the same phase, frequency and direction of travel as the stimulating photon which is itself unaffected. This phenomenon was predicted by Einstein and is called *stimulated emission*; it is illustrated in Fig. 12.16.

In a laser it is arranged that light emission by stimulated

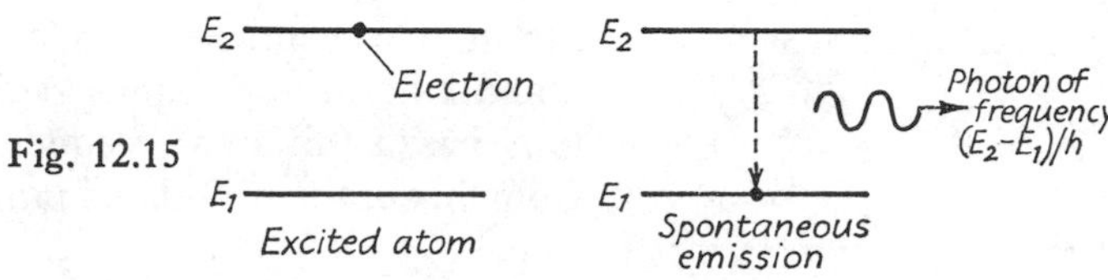

Fig. 12.15

emission exceeds that by spontaneous emission. To achieve this it is necessary to have more electrons in an upper than a lower level. Such a condition, called an 'inverted population', is the reverse of the normal state of affairs but it is essential for light amplification, i.e., for a beam of light to increase in intensity as it passes through a material rather than to decrease as is usually the case.

One method of creating an inverted population is known as

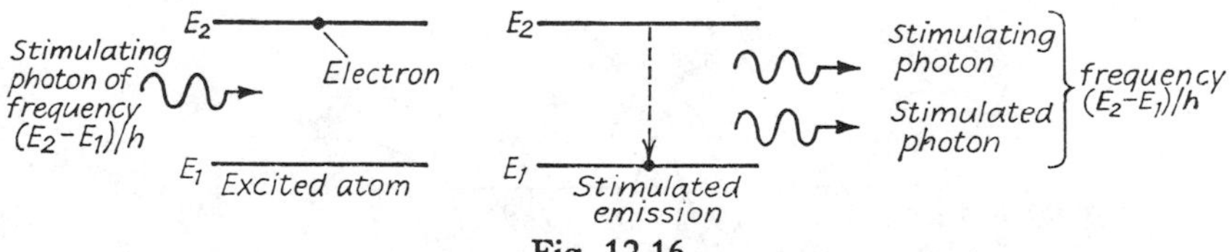

Fig. 12.16

'optical pumping' and consists of illuminating the laser material with light. Consider two levels of energies E_1 and E_2, where $E_2 > E_1$. If the pumping radiation contains photons of frequency $(E_2 - E_1)/h$, electrons will be raised from level 1 to level 2 by photon absorption. Unfortunately, however, as soon as the electron population in level 2 starts to increase, the pumping radiation induces stimulated emission from level 2 to level 1 since it is of the correct frequency and no build-up occurs.

In a three-level system, Fig. 12.17, the pumping radiation of frequency $(E_3 - E_1)/h$ raises electrons from level 1 to level 3 from which they fall by spontaneous emission to level 2. An inverted population can arise between levels 2 and 1 if electrons remain long enough in level 2. The spontaneous emission of a photon due to an electronic fall from level 2 to level 1 may subsequently cause the stimulated emission of a photon which in turn releases more photons from other atoms. The laser action thus occurs between levels 2 and 1 and the pumping radiation has a different frequency from that of the stimulated radiation.

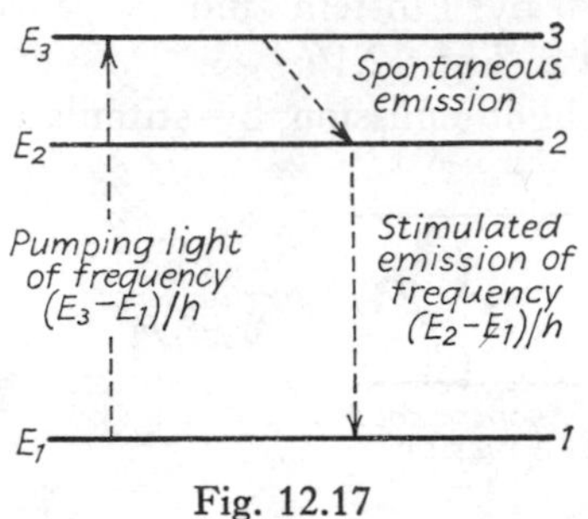

Fig. 12.17

Many materials can be used in lasers. The *ruby rod laser* consists of a synthetic crystal of aluminium oxide containing a small amount of chromium as the laser material. It is a type of three-level laser in which 'level' 3 consists of a band of very close energy levels. The pumping radiation, produced by intense flashes of yellow-green light from a flash tube, Fig. 12.18, raises electrons from level 1 (the ground level) into one of the levels of the band. From there they fall spontaneously to the metastable level

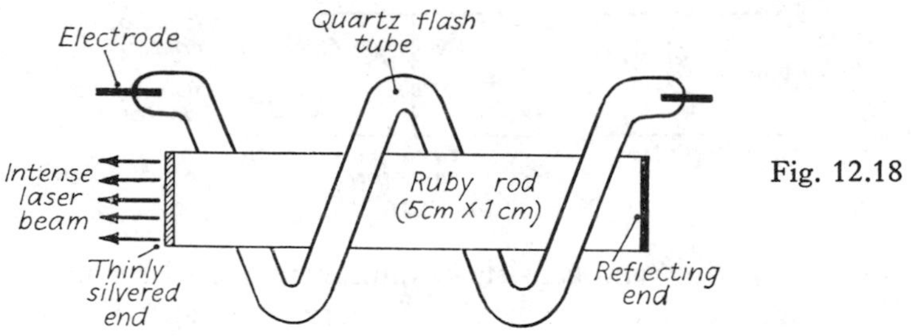

Fig. 12.18

2 where they can remain for approximately 1 millisecond as compared with 10^{-8} second in the energy band. Red laser light is emitted when they are stimulated to fall to level 1 from level 2. One end of the ruby rod is silvered to act as a complete reflector whilst the other is thinly silvered and allows partial transmission.

Stimulated light photons are reflected to and fro along the rod producing an intense beam, part of which emerges from the partially silvered end as the useful output of the laser. The ruby laser emits short pulses of light; another type, the *gas laser*, works continuously and uses a mixture of helium and neon; *semi-conductor lasers* are also being developed.

Lasers have not yet found wide application. The main use to date of solid-state lasers such as the ruby laser has been as a source of energy; a well focused beam can drill through a sheet of steel about three millimetre thick in a thousandth of a second and in medicine they have been used to spot-weld into position a detached retina of the eye. Lasers appear to have a considerable potential as a means of communication since calculations indicate that a laser beam could convey, on account of the high frequency of light, many millions of television channels. Gas and semi-conductor laser beams have been modulated to carry information but, because of their low power, transmission has only been possible over short distances. At the National Physical Laboratory (N.P.L.), Teddington, a machine was completed in 1965, based on a helium-neon laser, which is used to measure automatically lengths up to 1 metre. This enables the otherwise painstaking and time-consuming calibration of precision scales to be completed in 15 minutes.

QUESTIONS

1. Calculate the ratio of the electrostatic force on an alpha particle ($^{4}_{2}He$) to the gravitational force when it is near the nucleus of a gold atom ($^{197}_{79}Au$). What bearing does the answer have on the interpretation of the Geiger–Marsden scattering experiment?

Electronic charge e	$1{\cdot}6 \times 10^{-19}$ C
Atomic mass unit	$1{\cdot}7 \times 10^{-27}$ kg
Gravitational constant G	$6{\cdot}7 \times 10^{-11}$ N m^2 kg^{-2}
Permittivity of free space ϵ_0	$1/(4\pi \times 9 \times 10^9)$ F m^{-1}

2. Outline the evidence for:

(*a*) The nuclear model of the atom.

(*b*) The identification of the atomic number of an atom with its nuclear charge.

(*c*) Energy levels in the atom.

3. Figure 12.19, which represents the lowest energy levels of the electron in the hydrogen atom, specifies the value of the principal quantum number n associated with each state and the corresponding value of the energy of the level, measured in electron-volts. Work out the wavelengths of the lines associated with the transitions A, B, C, D marked in the figure. Show that the other transitions that can occur give rise to lines that are either in the ultraviolet or the infrared regions of the spectrum. (Take 1 eV to be $1{\cdot}6 \times 10^{-19}$ J; Planck's constant h to be $6{\cdot}5 \times 10^{-34}$ J s; and c, the velocity of light *in vacuo*, to be 3×10^{8} m s^{-1}.) [*O. part qn.*]

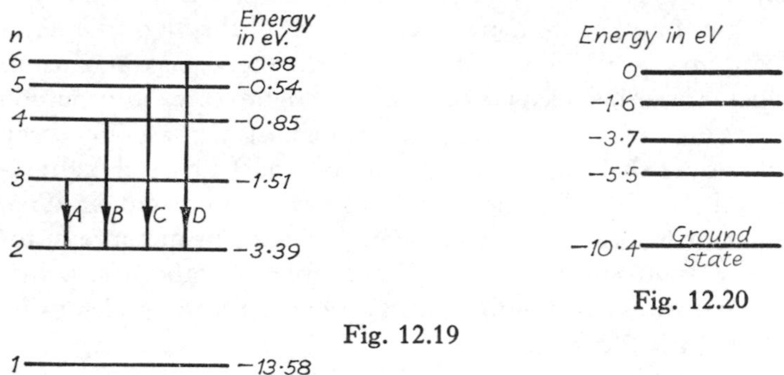

Fig. 12.19

Fig. 12.20

4. Some of the energy levels of the mercury atom are shown in Fig. 12.20.

(*a*) How much energy in electron-volts is required to raise an electron from the ground state to each of the levels shown?

(*b*) What is the ionization energy of mercury?

(*c*) If a mercury vapour atom in the ground state has a collision with an electron of energy (*i*) 5 eV, (*ii*) 10 eV, how much energy might be retained by the electron in each case?

(*d*) What would happen to a photon of energy (*i*) 4·9 eV, (*ii*) 8 eV, which has a collision with a mercury atom?

Energy in eV

0

−1

−4

−6 Ground state

Fig. 12.21

5. Some of the energy levels of an imaginary element are shown in Fig. 12.21. Predict the energies (in electron-volts) of the photons which could be emitted if atoms of the element were bombarded by electrons of energy (*i*) 5 eV, (*ii*) 7 eV. Illustrate each case by a diagram to show how the resulting spectral lines arise.

6. The line spectrum of an element contains the wavelengths 0·75 μm 0·62 μm and 0·34 μm. If a collision experiment with electrons shows that the element has an excited state 1·66 eV above the ground state, what is the minimum number of energy levels that can account for these facts and what are their energies?
(1 eV = $1{\cdot}60 \times 10^{-19}$ J; Planck's constant $h = 6{\cdot}63 \times 10^{-34}$ J s; velocity of light $c = 3 \times 10^{8}$ m s^{-1}.)

7. Find the de Broglie wavelength of (*a*) a car of mass 1000 kg whose speed is 10 m s^{-1}, (*b*) an electron of mass $9{\cdot}1 \times 10^{-31}$ kg accelerated through a p.d. of 100 V.
(Take Planck's constant h to be $6{\cdot}6 \times 10^{-34}$ J s; e/m for the electron as $1{\cdot}8 \times 10^{11}$ C kg^{-1}.)

8. Compare and contrast the properties of the *proton*, *neutron* and *electron*. Explain the role played by each of these particles in the structure of the atom.

How is your account of the arrangement of the electrons in the atom supported by experimental evidence? [*L*.]

9. Discuss briefly: (*a*) the origin of energy levels in atoms, (*b*) the wave-particle duality in nature.

13 Nuclear reactions

A great deal of information concerning the nucleus has been obtained by studying the effects of bombarding atomic nuclei with fast-moving particles. Three historic nuclear reactions will first be considered in which the projectile enters a nucleus, causing rearrangement of the constituent nucleons and the formation of one or more new nuclei.

Bombardment of nitrogen by alpha particles

In 1919 following his successful scattering experiments with metal foils, Rutherford, now at Cambridge, bombarded gases using alpha particles. His apparatus, Fig. 13.1, consisted of a

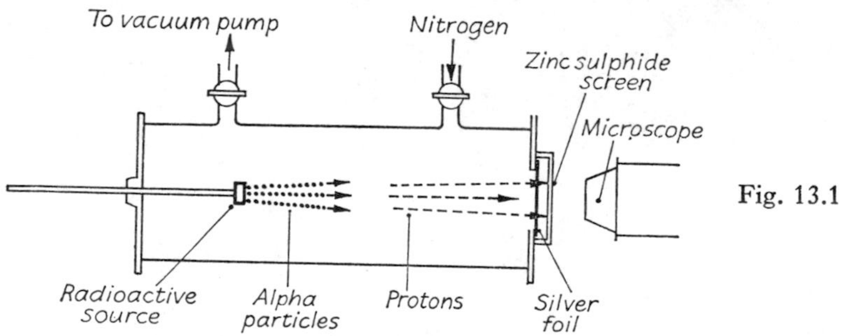

Fig. 13.1

metal cylinder with inlet and outlet tubes for introducing the gas and a support for the alpha particle source. One end of the cylinder was closed by thin silver foil capable of stopping most of the alpha particles, but any which penetrated fell on a zinc sulphide screen and their scintillations were observed through a microscope.

Various gases were admitted; with nitrogen the result was surprising. Instead of a decrease in the number of scintillations due to absorption of alpha particles by the gas, there was a marked increase. Evidently more penetrating particles are produced when alpha particles bombard nitrogen nuclei. Further experiments involving the deflection of these longer range particles in a magnetic field showed that they were positively charged hydrogen atoms, i.e., protons, of high energy.

There are two plausible explanations of this result. Either an alpha particle 'chips' a proton off a nitrogen nucleus, in which case the alpha particle survives the encounter, or the alpha particle actually enters the nitrogen nucleus and the latter immediately ejects a proton. Since only about one alpha particle in a million caused a disintegration the chance of identifying the residual nucleus seemed extremely small. However, in 1925, the compound nucleus interpretation was shown to be correct. In that year P. M. S. Blackett took 20,000 photographs of the tracks of alpha particles passing through nitrogen in a cloud chamber. In eight of these, forked tracks like the one shown in Fig. 13.2 were obtained. The thin track going up to the left is that of a proton, and the short thick track to the right is due to the residual nucleus which becomes charged in the collision and so can create ions in its path. There was nothing to indicate the existence of the alpha particle after the disintegration.

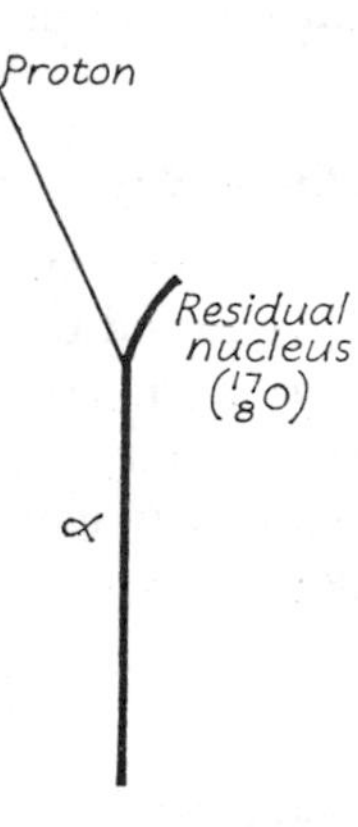

Fig. 13.2

Assuming that protons and neutrons are conserved, the reaction may therefore be represented by the equation

$$\underset{\text{nitrogen nucleus}}{^{14}_{7}N} + \underset{\text{alpha particle}}{^{4}_{2}He} \rightarrow \underset{\text{compound nucleus}}{(^{18}_{9}F)} \rightarrow \underset{\text{residual nucleus}}{^{17}_{8}O} + \underset{\text{proton}}{^{1}_{1}H}$$

$^{18}_{9}F$ is the nucleus of fluorine. The residual nucleus has mass number 17 and atomic number 8 and is an isotope of oxygen. This was the first occasion on which one element, nitrogen, was changed into another, oxygen, although only a few atoms were transformed. In popular language the event is sometimes referred to as the 'splitting of the atom'. One other point requires comment.

If the inverse square law holds right up to the nucleus the repulsive electrostatic force would approach infinity as the distance approaches zero. A charged particle would never enter a nucleus, no matter how large its energy. Nuclear reactions do occur however, as Rutherford demonstrated, and so the repulsive force must be replaced by an extremely powerful attractive force acting over a range of about 10^{-15} m. It is in fact this force which keeps nucleons together in a nucleus and is responsible for the existence of matter; it is called the *nuclear force.*

Discovery of the neutron

After the transmutation of nitrogen many other light elements were found to emit protons when bombarded by alpha particles. Beryllium however behaved unexpectedly. In 1930 W. Bothe and H. Becker, working in Germany, discovered that when this element was exposed to alpha particles a very penetrating radiation capable of passing through several inches of lead was

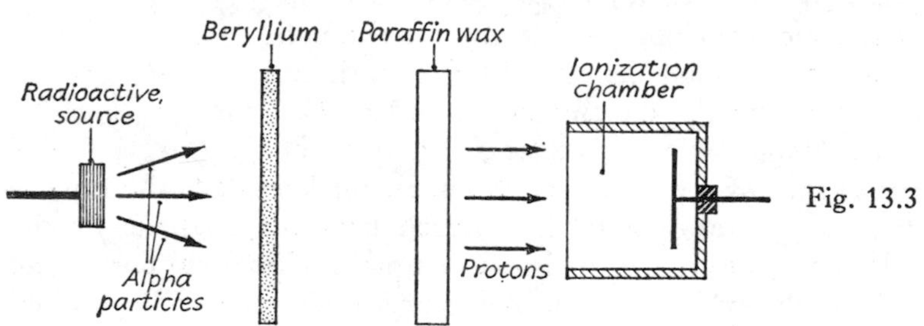

Fig. 13.3

emitted. It was suggested that it might be gamma radiation of high energy.

Two years later F. Joliot and his wife Irene Joliot-Curie observed that the passage of the beryllium radiation through a substance rich in hydrogen, such as paraffin wax, caused the expulsion of fast-moving protons, Fig. 13.3. They calculated the energy of the protons from measurements of their range and by assuming conservation of momentum and energy in the collision process in paraffin they estimated that the suspected gamma ray photons had an energy of about 50 MeV. Since this is much greater than the energies found among gamma rays from any known radioactive substance, doubts were raised about the interpretation of the effect.

Shortly afterwards, James Chadwick showed it was highly improbable that such high-energy gamma rays could be emitted by the action of alpha particles on beryllium. He repeated and extended the work of the Joliots and suggested that the radiation was not gamma rays but consisted of particles of mass about one atomic mass unit (1 a.m.u.), i.e., nearly equal to that of the proton but with no electrical charge. The absence of charge on such particles would account for their weak interaction with matter and great penetrating power. Twelve years previously, in 1920, Rutherford had predicted the existence of a particle with these properties and had proposed it be called the *neutron*. By identifying the beryllium radiation as neutrons, Chadwick was able to account for all the observed effects and established that the action of alpha particles on beryllium was represented by

$$ {}^{9}_{4}\mathrm{Be} + {}^{4}_{2}\mathrm{He} \rightarrow ({}^{13}_{6}\mathrm{C}) \rightarrow {}^{12}_{6}\mathrm{C} + {}^{1}_{0}\mathrm{n} $$

The unstable compound nucleus ${}^{13}_{6}\mathrm{C}$ disintegrates to carbon 12 and a neutron ${}^{1}_{0}\mathrm{n}$. In general, nuclear reactions induced by alpha particles cause the emission of either protons or neutrons depending on the energy of the alpha particles and the nucleus under attack.

The discovery of the neutron was hailed with relief among physicists. Previously it had been thought that the nucleus contained electrons so that the nucleus of an atom such as helium, ${}^{4}_{2}\mathrm{He}$, was supposed to consist of four protons and two electrons giving a net positive nuclear charge of two. However, the successful explanation by wave mechanics of certain nuclear properties, a subject too advanced to be considered here, is based on the supposition that there are no nuclear electrons. Chadwick's work clearly supported this view. Although a neutron decays *outside* the nucleus with a half-life of 13 minutes to a proton and an electron, *inside* it is perfectly stable and an entity in its own right.

Cockcroft and Walton's experiment

Alpha particles from radioactive sources have limitations as atomic projectiles. This is due partly to the fact that, since their energy never exceeds 10 MeV, they cannot overcome the powerful repulsion of the large positive charge on the nucleus of a heavy atom. In addition only a very small proportion of particles are generally able to cause disintegration, and so radioactive sources of high activity which emit a large number of particles per second would be necessary. These are both difficult to obtain and to manipulate. Accordingly, in the early 1930's attention was devoted to the problem of building devices, called *particle accelerators*, which accelerated charged particles such as protons,

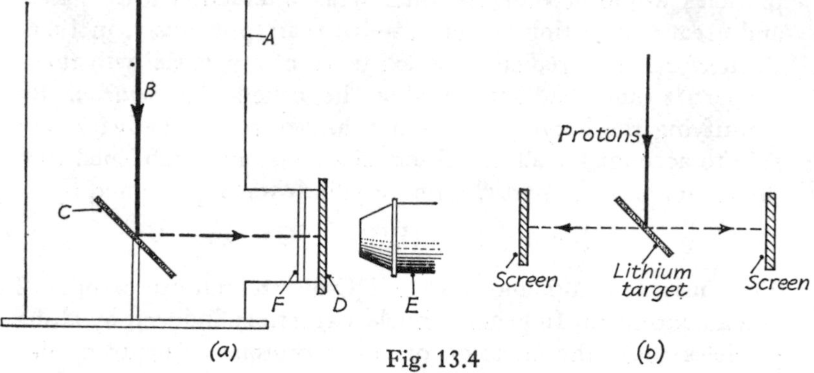

Fig. 13.4

to high velocities by means of potentials of hundreds of thousands of volts.

The first nuclear reaction to be induced by artificially accelerated particles (protons) was achieved in 1932 by J. D. Cockcroft and E. T. S. Walton who were working under Lord Rutherford at Cambridge. The essential features of their experimental arrangement are shown in Fig. 13.4*a*. Protons, i.e., hydrogen ions, from a hydrogen discharge tube were accelerated down an evacuated tube *A*, about 2 metres long, by a potential difference of up to 300 kV supplied from a special voltage multiplier circuit. The beam *B* of fast protons hit a lithium target *C*, inclined at 45°, and any particles emitted at right angles to the beam fell on a zinc sulphide screen *D* which was viewed using a microscope *E*.

The sheet of mica *F* absorbed the many protons scattered from the target and prevented them reaching the screen. Nonetheless bright scintillations were still observed.

Cockcroft and Walton believed that the scintillations were caused by alpha particles produced in the disintegration of a lithium nucleus when a proton made a direct hit and was absorbed. They represented the reaction by the equation

$$^{7}_{3}\text{Li} + ^{1}_{1}\text{H} \rightarrow (^{8}_{4}\text{Be}) \rightarrow ^{4}_{2}\text{He} + ^{4}_{2}\text{He}$$

Their conclusion was based on various observations. First, to the trained observer, the scintillations resembled those of alpha particles and not protons. Second, when the zinc sulphide screen was replaced by a thin window leading to a cloud chamber the tracks were characteristic of alpha particles and were of constant length. Third, assuming the principle of conservation of momentum holds, the two fragments should be shot out in opposite directions with equal velocities (since the momentum of the bombarding proton was small by comparison). This was verified by having a second screen opposite the first, as in Fig. 13.4*b*, when two simultaneous scintillations were obtained, one on each screen.

Einstein's mass-energy relation

In 1905, while developing his special theory of relativity, Einstein made the startling suggestion that energy, as well as matter, has mass. He stated that the mass *m* of a certain amount of energy *E*, whatever its form, is given by

$$E = mc^2$$

where *c* is the velocity of light. In view of the large value of *c*, a very small mass has a huge energy equivalent; 1 g of mass is equivalent to 9×10^{13} joules. In nuclear physics mass is measured in atomic mass units (a.m.u.) on the carbon 12 scale (see p. 150) and energy is generally expressed in MeV. Using these units it can be shown that

931 MeV of energy has mass 1 a.m.u.

A unit of energy may therefore be considered to be a unit of mass, and in tables of physical constants the masses of various atomic particles are often given in MeV as well as in grams (or kilograms) and a.m.u. For example, the electron has a rest mass of about 0·5 MeV.

The first experimental confirmation of $E = mc^2$ was obtained from the results of the Cockcroft and Walton experiment. Consider the masses of the particles involved:

	Initial particles		*Final particles*
$^{7}_{3}Li$	7·0160 a.m.u.	$^{4}_{2}He$	4·0026 a.m.u.
$^{1}_{1}H$	1·0078 a.m.u.	$^{4}_{2}He$	4·0026 a.m.u.
Total	8·0238 a.m.u.	*Total*	8·0052 a.m.u.

The total mass of the two alpha particles produced in the disintegration is *less* than the total initial mass by (8·0238 − 8·0052) = 0·0186 a.m.u. Since 1 a.m.u. = 931 MeV, this is the mass of 17·3 MeV of energy and if we add the kinetic energy of the bombarding proton, 300 keV if it is accelerated through a p.d. of 300 kV, the total energy released in the reaction should be 17·6 MeV. The liberated energy appears as kinetic energy of the alpha particles and Cockcroft and Walton estimated from measurements of the range of the alpha particles in air that each had an energy of 8·6 MeV. The total observed energy was thus 17·2 MeV which, allowing for experimental error, was in substantial agreement with the calculated value of 17·6 MeV. Clearly, if conservation of mass is to hold for nuclear reactions, energy must be considered to have mass. In chemical reactions the mass and energy changes are small compared with those of nuclear reactions and the conservation of mass is substantially true without Einstein's modification.

It should be noted that, for convenience, the masses given above for the initial and final particles are atomic mass values. They include the mass of the extranuclear electrons, but since the number of these is the same for both totals, their mass cancels and the nuclear mass change is not affected.

Einstein's equation is now used to make forecasts of the energy liberated (or in some cases absorbed) in nuclear reactions. For this purpose an accurate knowledge of atomic masses, such as is obtained from mass spectroscopy determinations, is essential.

Nuclear reactions and conservation laws

Certain important principles of classical physics also apply to nuclear physics.

(*i*) CONSERVATION OF ENERGY. This states that in a nuclear reaction energy is conserved. The energy may be in the form of kinetic energy of moving particles (given by $E = \frac{1}{2}mv^2$) or radiation (given by $E = hf$). Where mass changes are involved the energy equivalent (given by $E = mc^2$) must be taken into account. In view of the equivalence of mass and energy, the principle is sometimes referred to as the conservation of mass or the conservation of mass-energy.

If kinetic energy is also conserved in a nuclear reaction, the collision is elastic. In an inelastic collision a nucleus may be left in an excited state and subsequently emits as nuclear radiation (gamma) the energy it gained in the encounter. Alternatively, a bombarding particle may enter a nucleus and cause a nuclear reaction in which the nucleons are rearranged to form new nuclei with a consequent mass (and therefore energy) change.

(*ii*) CONSERVATION OF MOMENTUM. This states that in any kind of nuclear collision (or radioactive disintegration) involving nuclei, protons, neutrons, electrons, or photons of radiation, the momentum gained equals the momentum lost. It holds for both elastic and inelastic collisions.

(*iii*) CONSERVATION OF CHARGE. This principle requires the sum of the atomic numbers to be equal before and after the reaction.

(*iv*) CONSERVATION OF NUCLEONS. This principle has emerged from nuclear physics itself and requires the sum of the mass numbers after the reaction to be equal to the sum before the reaction.

Our belief in the validity of the conservation laws in nuclear physics is based on their ability to analyse nuclear reactions and to make verifiable predictions. From time to time cases have arisen in which they appeared to be violated; the emission of beta particles by radioactive decay is a case in point. However, rather than discard such well-established principles, the existence of another particle, the ***neutrino*** (p. 249) was postulated. So far this faith and boldness has always been justified by the eventual discovery of the particle.

Information concerning the energies and velocities of particles may be obtained from absorption experiments or from the lengths of tracks in cloud chambers etc. (p. 251, question 6). A particle such as the neutron, which does not leave a visible track, can be investigated if it produces, as a result of a collision, an ionizing particle.

Worked example

A particle of mass m and velocity v has a head-on collision with a stationary particle of mass M. Assuming the collision is elastic, derive an expression for the velocity of each particle after impact.

Hence determine what happens if the moving particle is an alpha particle and the stationary particle is (a) an electron, (b) a helium atom, (c) a gold atom.

Under what conditions is there maximum energy transfer?

The collision is head-on and so all velocities are in the same straight line. Let v_1 and v_2 be the velocities after impact of the moving and stationary particles respectively.

In an elastic collision momentum and energy are conserved.

Hence
$$mv = mv_1 + Mv_2 \tag{1}$$
and
$$\tfrac{1}{2}mv^2 = \tfrac{1}{2}mv_1^2 + \tfrac{1}{2}Mv_2^2 \tag{2}$$

From (1)
$$v_2 = \frac{m}{M}(v - v_1) \tag{3}$$

Substituting for v_2 in (2) and rearranging we get
$$v_1 = \frac{m - M}{m + M}\cdot v \tag{4}$$

Substitution for v_1 in (3)
$$v_2 = \frac{2m}{m + M}\cdot v \tag{5}$$

Expressions (4) and (5) give the required velocities.

(*a*) When the stationary particle is an electron, M is small compared with the mass m of the alpha particle. Hence from (4) and (5) $v_1 = v$ and $v_2 = 2v$. The alpha particle retains its original velocity and the electron moves off with twice that velocity.

(*b*) When the stationary particle is a helium atom, $M = m$. Hence $v_1 = 0$ and $v_2 = v$. The alpha particle is stopped and the helium atom acquires the original velocity of the alpha particle.

(*c*) When the stationary particle is a gold atom. M is large compared with m. Hence $v_1 = -v$ and $v_2 = 0$. The alpha particle rebounds with the same velocity and the gold atom remains at rest.

From (*b*) we see that the bombarding particle transfers all its kinetic energy when it has a head-on elastic collision with a stationary particle of equal mass.

Binding energy

The mass of a nucleus is found to be less than the sum of the masses of the constituent protons and neutrons. This is explained as being due to the binding of the nucleons together into a nucleus and the mass deficiency represents the mass of the energy which would be released in forming the nucleus from its component particles. The energy equivalent is called the *binding energy* of the nucleus; it would also be the energy needed to split the nucleus into its individual nucleons, if this were possible.

Consider an example. The helium atom, ${}^4_2He$, has an atomic mass of 4·0026 a.m.u.; this includes the mass of its two extranuclear electrons. Its constituents comprise two neutrons each of mass 1·0087 a.m.u. and two hydrogen atoms (i.e., two protons and two extranuclear electrons) each of mass 1·0078 a.m.u.; the total mass of the nucleons is thus $(2 \times 1{\cdot}0087 + 2 \times 1{\cdot}0078) =$

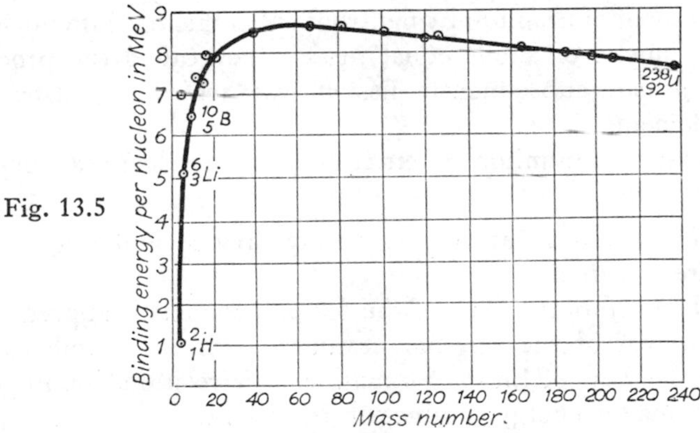

Fig. 13.5

4·0330 a.m.u. The mass deficiency is (4·0330 − 4·0026) = 0·0304 a.m.u. and since 1 a.m.u. = 931 MeV, it follows that the binding energy of helium is 28·3 MeV.

The binding energy is derived in a similar manner for other nuclides and is found to increase as the mass number increases. For neon, $^{20}_{10}Ne$, it is 160 MeV. If the binding energy of a nuclide is divided by its mass number (i.e., the number of nucleons), the *binding energy per nucleon* is obtained. The graph of Fig. 13.5 shows how this quantity varies with mass number; in most cases it is about 8 MeV. Nuclides in the middle of the graph have the highest binding energy per nucleon and are thus the most stable since they need most energy to disintegrate. The smaller values for lower and higher mass numbers imply that potential sources of nuclear energy are reactions involving the fusing of particles to form a nucleus of higher mass number and the disintegration of a heavy nucleus. In both cases nuclei are produced having a greater binding energy per nucleon and there is consequently a mass loss during their formation.

Nuclear fission

The discovery of the neutron provided nuclear physicists with an important new atomic missile. Being uncharged it does not suffer the electrostatic force of repulsion which is experienced by protons and alpha particles when they approach a nucleus. In 1939, following some work done by Fermi in Italy and Hahn and Strassmann in Germany, Meitner and Frisch suggested that the bombardment of uranium by neutrons splits the uranium nucleus into two nuclei of about equal mass. They called the process *nuclear fission*; subsequently fission was achieved with other heavy elements.

The fission of uranium differs from earlier nuclear reactions in certain respects.

(*i*) The uranium nucleus is deeply divided and large fragments are obtained.

(*ii*) The combined mass of the fission products is appreciably less than that of the original uranium atom and bombarding neutron. In view of Einstein's mass-energy relation, the importance of this for energy production is evident.

(*iii*) The disintegration of a single nucleus causes the emission of other neutrons, called *fission neutrons*. Under suitable conditions these can produce further fission and a self-maintaining or *chain reaction* occurs.

Natural uranium is a mixture chiefly of two nuclides, ${}^{235}_{92}U$ (0·7 per cent) and ${}^{238}_{92}U$ (99·3 per cent) and each behaves differently under neutron bombardment. Uranium 235 gives fission with both fast and slow neutrons but much prefers slow neutrons having thermal energies, i.e., energies equal to the average kinetic energy of the surrounding atoms; at 20°C this is about 0·03 eV. Uranium 238 undergoes fission only with fast neutrons of energy greater than about 1 MeV; medium-speed neutrons, particularly those having certain energies between 5 and 500 eV, are captured without causing fission, while thermal neutrons tend to be ignored by uranium 238. Thus ${}^{235}_{92}U$ gives both fast and slow fission, ${}^{238}_{92}U$ suffers only very fast fission.

The fission of uranium 235, the most useful of the uranium nuclides, may be represented by the equation

$$ {}^{235}_{92}U + {}^{1}_{0}n \rightarrow ({}^{236}_{92}U) \rightarrow {}^{141}_{56}Ba + {}^{92}_{36}Kr + 3\,{}^{1}_{0}n $$

The compound nucleus ${}^{236}_{92}U$ is shown as splitting into barium and krypton but other pairs of nuclides can be formed. Whilst three fission neutrons are emitted in this case, on the average 2·5 are produced. Consideration of the masses of the atoms involved shows that the mass loss which occurs as a result of the reaction has an energy equivalent of about 200 MeV per fission. This may not seem to be a very large yield, but in chemical reactions energy changes amount to no more than a few electron-volts per atom. If all the 6×10^{23} atoms in a mole (i.e., 235 g) of uranium 235 are fissioned, $1{\cdot}9 \times 10^{13}$ joules is released. The same amount of energy would require the combustion of about 8×10^{5} kg of coal. The fission energy appears mostly as kinetic energy of the fission fragments (e.g., barium and krypton nuclei) which fly apart at great speed. The kinetic energy of the fission neutrons also makes a slight contribution. In addition one or both of the large fragments are always highly radioactive and a small amount of energy takes the form of beta and gamma radiation.

When uranium 238 captures a neutron without undergoing fission it forms uranium 239 which decays by the emission of a beta particle to the first transuranic element, *neptunium.*

$$^{238}_{92}U + ^{1}_{0}n \rightarrow ^{239}_{92}U \rightarrow ^{239}_{93}Np + ^{0}_{-1}e$$

Neptunium decays, also by beta emission to *plutonium.*

$$^{239}_{93}Np \rightarrow ^{239}_{94}Pu + ^{0}_{-1}e$$

Plutonium is not found in nature but, like uranium 235, it can suffer fission with slow neutrons.

Chain reactions in uranium

If one of the neutrons emitted in each fission of a uranium 235 nucleus produces a new fission, a *steady* chain reaction occurs at

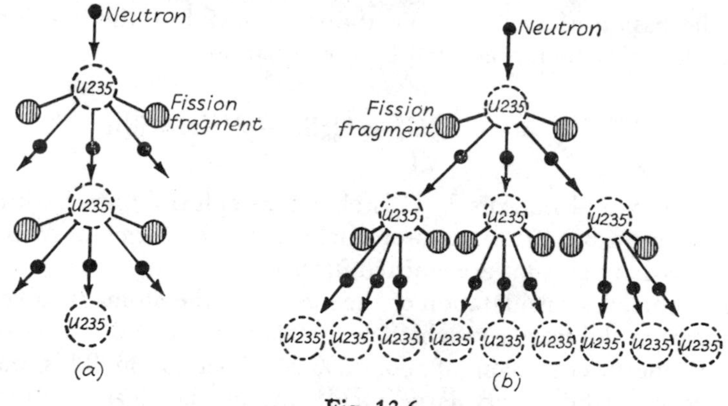

Fig. 13.6

a constant rate, Fig. 13.6*a*. An *increasing* chain reaction is represented in Fig. 13.6*b* in which all three neutrons cause fission at each stage.

In practice only a fraction of the fission neutrons is available for new fissions. Some are lost either by escaping from the surface of the fissionable material or as a result of capture by a nucleus without inducing fission. The proportion of neutrons escaping compared with those causing fission decreases as the size of the system comprising the fissionable material increases. For every system there is a *critical size* which must be attained before a chain reaction can start.

Normally a chain reaction will not occur in natural uranium because any neutrons produced by an initial fission have, on the average, an energy less than the 1 MeV required for the fast fission of uranium 238. Also, the proportion of uranium 235 is so small that the supply of neutrons from the fast fission of this nuclide is insufficient to make good the losses. The more highly favoured slow fission of uranium 235 would occur if uranium 238 did not capture the fission neutrons when their energy is reduced by collisions to values between 5 and 500 eV. Hence, in natural uranium, the chance of a neutron being captured by uranium 238 greatly exceeds the chance of it causing fission in uranium 235.

Two methods are employed to induce chain reactions. In the first, natural uranium is used which has been 'enriched' so that it contains a greater percentage of uranium 235. The probability of a neutron producing fission rather than being captured is thereby increased. In the 'atomic bomb' an increasing uncontrolled chain reaction occurs in an exceedingly short time when two or more pieces of almost pure fissionable material, such as uranium 235 (or plutonium 239), are suddenly brought together to form a mass greater than the critical size. The reaction is started either by having a small neutron source in the bomb or relying on the fission neutrons from the occasional spontaneous disintegration of a uranium 235 nucleus. The second method of causing a chain reaction uses natural uranium along with a 'moderator'. The latter has light atoms and slows (without absorbing) the fission neutrons very quickly to energies less than 5 eV so that a high proportion escape capture by $^{238}_{92}U$. It will be recalled that a bombarding particle gives up most energy when it has an elastic collision with a particle of similar mass (p. 237). For neutrons, hydrogen atoms would be most effective but unfortunately absorption occurs. However, deuterium (in heavy water) and carbon (as graphite) are both suitable.

Nuclear power

In a nuclear power station a nuclear reactor provides the heat required to produce steam instead of a coal-burning furnace. It was stated earlier that most of the energy of a nuclear fission, about 85 per cent, appears as kinetic energy of the two large fragments, e.g., barium and krypton nuclei, which separate at high speed. This kinetic energy is shared with surrounding atoms as a result of collisions, and thereby causes an increase in the average kinetic energy of the system. Heat, which is kinetic energy of atoms and molecules, is thus generated.

A simplified diagram of a graphite-moderated nuclear reactor is shown in Fig. 13.7. It consists of a strong steel pressure vessel enclosing a graphite core having a series of vertical channels

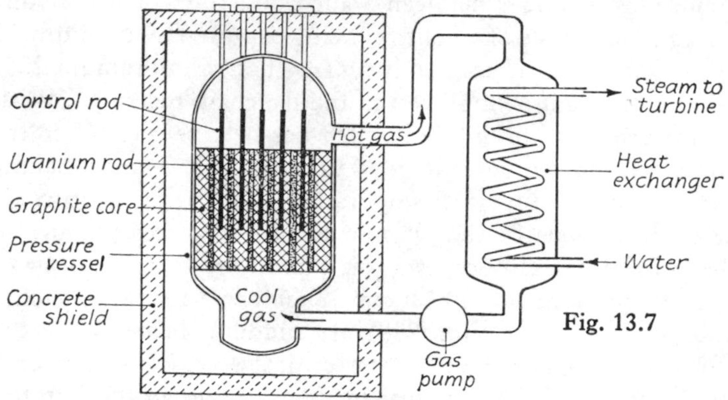

Fig. 13.7

containing sufficient natural uranium fuel rods to make the reactor critical. The chain reaction can be stopped or slowed down by lowering into the core, rods of cadmium or boron steel which are strong neutron absorbers; these are called control rods. A current of high-pressure carbon dioxide is pumped through the pressure vessel and carries away the heat generated in the reactor to a special boiler known as the heat exchanger, where water is converted to steam. The steam is then used as in a conventional power station to drive a turbo-alternator. A thick concrete shield gives protection from neutrons and gamma rays and in the latest type it also acts as the pressure vessel.

Nuclear reactors like the one just described are called *thermal reactors* because fission is caused by slow neutrons with thermal energies. Other types of reactors are being developed including the *fast breeder reactor*. This has a core made almost entirely of uranium 235 surrounded by a blanket of uranium 238 which is converted to plutonium by fission neutrons that would otherwise be lost. New fissionable material is thus 'bred' at the same time as uranium 235 is consumed.

Important by-products of nuclear reactors are artificial radio-isotopes. They are formed when stable nuclides, inserted in the core of the reactor, are bombarded by neutrons.

Thermonuclear fusion

The union of light nuclei into heavier nuclei can also lead to a loss of mass and a consequent liberation of energy. Such a reaction has been achieved in the 'hydrogen bomb' and it is believed to be the source of the sun's energy.

A reaction with heavy hydrogen or deuterium which yields 3·3 MeV per fusion is

$$^{2}_{1}H + ^{2}_{1}H \rightarrow ^{3}_{2}He + ^{1}_{0}n$$

By comparison with the 200 MeV per fission of uranium 235 this seems small, but per unit mass of material it is not. Combination of the two deuterium nuclei, i.e., deuterons, will only occur if they overcome their mutual electrical repulsion. This may happen when they are heated to a temperature of several million degrees Centigrade and collide at a very high speed. If fusion occurs, enough energy is released to keep the reaction going, and since heat is required the process is called *thermonuclear fusion.* Attempts have been made to reach the temperatures necessary by passing large electric currents through deuterium gas. Under these conditions the gas is ionized and can conveniently be concentrated in the centre of the containing vessel, away from the walls, by a suitable magnetic field. The hot ionized gas consists of equal numbers of positive and negative ions and is called a *plasma.* There were hopes in 1958 that thermonuclear fusion had occurred at Harwell in an apparatus called ZETA but they were subsequently shown to be unfounded and research work continues into this difficult problem.

In the hydrogen bomb an uncontrolled thermonuclear reaction occurs, the high initial temperature being obtained by using an atomic fission bomb to trigger the fusion process. If a controlled reaction can be achieved an almost unlimited supply of energy will become available, since it is estimated there is enough deuterium in the water of the oceans to meet the world's needs for millions of years.

Particle accelerators

Particle accelerators are designed to accelerate charged particles to high velocities by means of a large potential difference. By their aid, a copious supply of a variety of particles, electrons, protons, deuterons, alpha particles and nuclei of heavier atoms, of a desired energy, can be obtained. The particles may be used to bombard a target and cause nuclear reactions designed to provide further insight into the structure of the nucleus. They are also used to produce artificial radioisotopes from stable atoms (p. 165), and since 1945 they have led to the discovery and production of traces of the transuranic elements (Appendix 1). Since the construction of the first accelerator by Cockcroft and Walton, a large number have been built; only two types will be briefly described here.

(*a*) *Van de Graaff accelerator*

This machine employs an electrostatic generator, invented by Van de Graaff in 1931, for producing a high accelerating voltage. The essential features are shown in Fig. 13.8. A discharge comb *B* is connected to a source of high potential (e.g. a 50-kV rectifier circuit) and positive electric charge is 'sprayed' by action at points on to the belt of insulating material *C*. The belt is driven by an electric motor and another discharge comb *D* draws off the positive charge from the belt when it reaches the hollow conductor *E* supported on the insulating stand *F*. The potential of *E* rises as charge collects on its outside surface and if the whole apparatus is enclosed in a steel chamber (not shown) containing a good insulating gas such as freon under pressure, a p.d. of about 7 million volts may be reached without breakdown. This p.d. is then used to accelerate ions, from an appropriate source, down an evacuated tube *G*. At the bottom of *G* a magnetic field bends the particles by amounts depending on their velocities so that only those with a particular energy pass through a fine slit and enter the tube leading to the target to be bombarded.

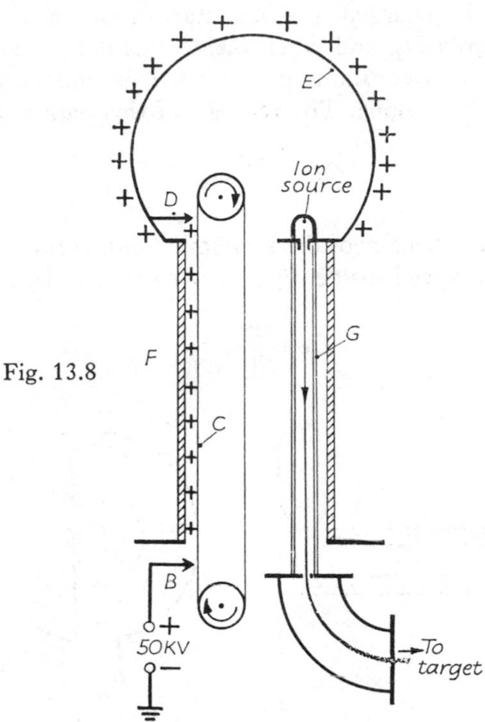

Fig. 13.8

(b) *Cyclotron*

The cyclotron, first built by E. O. Lawrence in America in 1931, accelerates charged particles to high energies by making them traverse a spiral of increasing radius rather than a straight path. The machine consists of two semi-circular boxes, D_1 and D_2 in Fig. 13.9*a*, called 'dees' because of their shape, enclosed in a chamber C containing gas at low pressure. C is arranged between the poles of an electromagnet so that a uniform magnetic field acts at right angles to the plane of the dees. A hot filament F emits electrons which ionize the gas present, producing protons from hydrogen, deuterons from deuterium, etc. An alternating electric field is created in the *gap* between the dees by using the dees as electrodes to apply a high-frequency alternating potential. Inside the dees there is no electric field, only the magnetic field.

Suppose that at a certain instant D_1 is positive and D_2 negative. A positively charged particle starting from F will be accelerated towards D_2, and when inside this dee it describes a semi-circular path at constant speed since it is under the action of the magnetic field alone. The radius r of this path is given by

$$BQv = \frac{mv^2}{r}$$

where B is the flux density of the magnetic field, Q the charge on the particle, v its speed inside D_2 and m its mass. Hence

$$r = \frac{mv}{BQ} \tag{1}$$

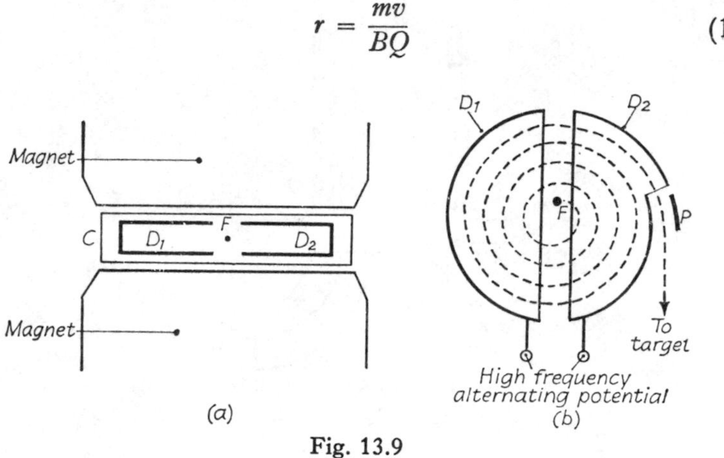

Fig. 13.9

If the frequency of the alternating potential is correct, the particle reaches the gap again when D_1 is negative and D_2 positive. It accelerates across the gap and then describes another half-circle inside D_1 but of increased radius since the speed is now greater. The particle thus gains kinetic energy and moves in a spiral of increasing radius, Fig. 13.9*b*, provided that the time for one half-cycle of alternating potential equals the time for the particle to make one half-revolution. We shall now show that this condition generally holds.

Let T be the time for the particle to describe a semicircle of radius r with speed v then

$$T = \frac{\pi r}{v}$$

Substituting the value of r from equation (1) gives

$$T = \frac{\pi m}{BQ}$$

T is therefore independent of v and r and constant if B, m and Q do not alter. Hence, for paths of larger radius the increased distance to be covered is exactly compensated by the increased speed of the particle. A plate P, at a high negative potential, draws the particle out of the dees before it bombards the target under study.

It is not possible to obtain protons with energies greater than about 20 MeV using a cyclotron. The limit arises when the speed of the particle is sufficiently great for its relativistic increase of mass to increase the time of revolution and upset the synchronization. This difficulty has been overcome in many of the giant accelerators now in use. One of these, a proton *synchrotron* costing £20 million, is installed in the laboratories of the European Organization for Nuclear Research (CERN) at Geneva and can produce protons with energies of nearly 30,000 MeV, i.e., 30 GeV, where G stands for giga (from the Latin *gigas* meaning giant).

Cosmic rays: antiparticles

Ionizing radiations from outer space, now called *cosmic rays*, were first postulated to explain the gradual loss of charge from a well-insulated, charged electroscope. The rays have been a source of great interest to physicists, not only because of the mystery of their origin but also on account of their energies which are far in excess of any that present-day accelerators can produce. Their use as projectiles for bombarding nuclei has led to the discovery of the positron and of various types of mesons.

Those rays arriving at the outer limit of the earth's atmosphere are called *primary cosmic rays* and consist mostly of protons, but alpha particles and heavier nuclei are also present. Their mean energy is about 10 GeV but some particles may have energies greater than 10^{10} GeV. Information about the primary rays has been obtained by sending stacks of special photographic plates (p. 191) to heights of 30,000 m using balloons, and more recently investigations have been made with instruments in rockets and artificial satellites. The high-energy primary rays react with atomic nuclei in the earth's upper atmosphere, causing nuclear reactions in which the nucleons themselves change and are not just rearranged within the nucleus as in lower energy reactions. As a result *secondary cosmic rays* are produced and these are responsible for most of our 'background' radiation; they comprise gamma rays, electrons, protons, positrons and mesons.

The *positron*, or positive electron, has the same mass as the electron and a charge of equal size but positive sign. It was discovered from cloud chamber studies of cosmic rays by C. D. Anderson in 1932; its average life is about 10^{-9} s. A positron is produced with an electron as an electron-positron pair when sufficiently energetic gamma radiation approaches a nucleus. Some of the energy of a gamma ray photon appears as the mass of the electron and positron, in accordance with $E = mc^2$. Conversely, when a positron meets an electron, pair annihilation occurs and gamma radiation is created. Positrons also occur in the decay of certain artificial radionuclides.

The positron is said to be the *antiparticle* of the electron. Most elementary particles have such counterparts but they are not easy to find because annihilation occurs when they encounter the ordinary particle. Antiparticles were predicted in 1928 by Dirac from considerations involving wave mechanics and relativity. The *antiproton*, which was not detected until 1955 when the 6 GeV accelerator at Berkeley, California, went into full operation, has the same mass as the proton but carries a unit negative charge. Prior to this, close scrutiny of cosmic ray tracks in cloud chambers had failed to provide conclusive evidence for its existence. Like other antiparticles, the antiproton is created in pair production; in this case a proton-antiproton pair is formed but a large amount of energy is required on account of the comparatively large mass of the particles.

Mesons are also very short-lived particles and most types have a mass intermediate in value between the mass of the electron and the proton. Thus a π-meson or *pion* is 270 times heavier than the electron and can have charge of $+e$, 0 and $-e$. K-mesons or kaons have masses 966 times the electron mass.

'Elementary' particles

By 1957 about thirty 'elementary' particles were known. Since then, the bombardment of targets by beams of protons from high-energy accelerators has led to the unexpected discovery of at least another 60 short-lived sub-atomic bodies whose nature and role is one of the exciting mysteries of nuclear physics at the present time. Many physicists believe that these new particles may be composite bodies not qualifying for the term 'elementary'.

The 90 or so particles have been arranged into groups and may be broadly classified as *baryons*, *mesons* and *leptons* (or their anti-particles), as shown in Table 13.1. These terms denote heavy, medium and light particles respectively and it is now usual in nuclear physics to express masses in terms of energy equivalents, i.e., in MeV. Thus the electron has mass 0·511 MeV and the proton 938 MeV.

The *neutrino* is (along with the photon) the lightest of all particles and was postulated by Pauli in 1933 to account for the continuous-energy spectrum of beta particles (p. 158). When a beta particle is emitted with energy E, where E is less than the maximum observed value E_{max}, the difference $(E_{max} - E)$ is carried off by a neutrino. In beta decay an electron and a neutrino are thus emitted simultaneously. Conservation of charge requires the neutrino to have zero charge. It must also have zero rest mass but can have energy except on those occasions when it is all taken by a beta particle. (Compare the photon which likewise has zero rest mass but has energy.) A particle with neither rest mass nor charge is not readily observed but the feat was accomplished in 1956 by allowing the neutrino to induce a reaction whose products were detected.

The nuclear particles have been fitted into a pattern and from this pattern a previously unknown particle named *omega-minus* ($\Omega-$) was predicted. In 1964, amidst great excitement, omega-minus was discovered using the large accelerator at Brookhaven, U.S.A. The present situation in nuclear physics is analogous to that which existed in chemistry after the elements were arranged in the periodic table, but before sufficient was known about atomic structure to explain the arrangement. It seems likely that an explanation of the nuclear physics pattern will not emerge

TABLE 13.1

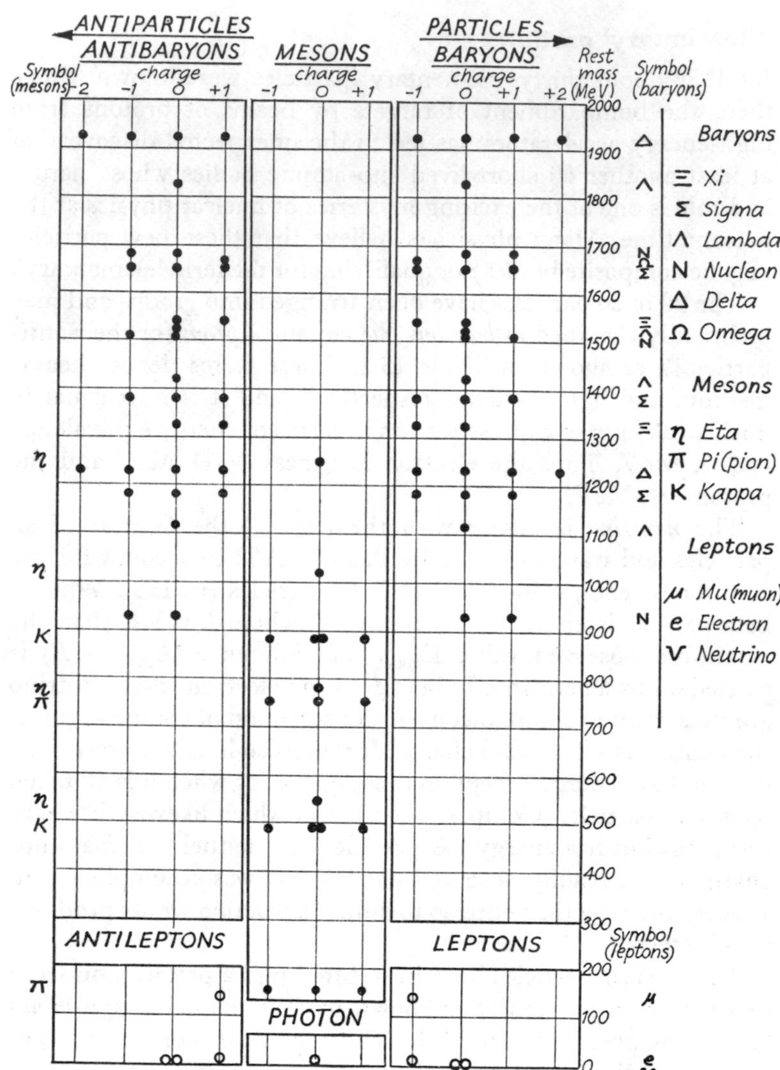

This table of 'elementary' particles is adapted, by permission, from *Scientific American* Vol. 210, No. 2 of February 1964 and includes only particles with a rest mass below 2000 MeV. Where the same symbol is used for particles of different masses, those of higher mass are thought to be excited states of those having the smallest mass. In the study of mesons rapid developments are taking place.

until the 'atoms' of the nuclear particles themselves, the so-called 'quarks', have been found. This will require the construction of larger and much more expensive accelerators.

QUESTIONS

1. Discuss the reaction represented by $^{14}_{7}N + ^{4}_{2}He = ^{17}_{8}O + ^{1}_{1}H$ explaining the meaning of the subscript and superscript numbers.
[*L. part qn.*]

2. An alpha particle (4·0026 a.m.u.) is formed along with a lithium nucleus (7·0160 a.m.u.) when a neutron (1·0087 a.m.u.) enters the nucleus of boron $^{10}_{5}B$ (10·0129 a.m.u.). Write the symbolic equation for this reaction and calculate the energy change in MeV which occurs.
(1 a.m.u. = 931 MeV.)

3. A stationary radioactive nucleus of mass 210 units disintegrates into an alpha particle of mass 4 units and a residual nucleus of mass 206 units. If the kinetic energy of the alpha particle is E, calculate the kinetic energy of the residual nucleus. [*J. part qn.*]

4. 'The helium nucleus has a mass number 4 but its mass is only 3·9715 times that of the hydrogen nucleus.' Comment on the significance of this statement. [*L. part qn.*]

5. What is the velocity of (*a*) a hydrogen atom and (*b*) a nitrogen atom, which suffers a head-on collision with an alpha particle whose velocity is $1 \cdot 5 \times 10^7$ m s^{-1}? Assume the collisions are elastic, that the atoms are at rest when hit and derive any formulae used. (The atomic masses of the hydrogen atom, the alpha particle and the nitrogen atom are 1, 4 and 14 a.m.u. respectively.)

6. In an experiment leading to the discovery of the neutron Chadwick measured the velocity of protons (previously at rest), which had been knocked-on by 'beryllium radiation', by finding the range of the protons in aluminium. In another experiment he allowed the 'beryllium radiation' to enter a cloud chamber containing nitrogen and obtained the velocity of the nitrogen atoms after they had been hit by measuring the lengths of their tracks.

The protons were found to have a velocity about 7·5 times greater than the nitrogen atoms. If the 'beryllium radiation' consists of particles, calculate their mass. State the assumptions on which your calculation is based. (Atomic masses of the proton and the nitrogen atom are 1 a.m.u. and 14 a.m.u. respectively.)

7. Compare nuclear fission and nuclear fusion. How many fissions must occur per second to generate a power of 1 megawatt if each fission of uranium 235 liberates 200 MeV?
(1 eV = $1{\cdot}60 \times 10^{-19}$ joule.)

8. A particle A of mass m has an oblique elastic collision with a stationary particle B in a cloud chamber. The tracks of the two particles after the impact are at right angles to each other. What is the mass of particle B?

9. A neutron collides with a carbon nucleus which is initially at rest. Assuming the neutron and the nucleus to behave like two perfectly elastic spheres, colliding on a line joining their centres, find as a fraction of its initial kinetic energy the kinetic energy lost by the neutron. Assume the mass of the carbon nucleus to be twelve times that of the neutron.

Protection from a source of neutrons may be obtained by enclosing it in a block of paraffin wax, which is a mixture of hydrocarbons. Discuss the efficacy of paraffin wax for this purpose. [*L. Special part qn.*]

14 Semiconductor devices

The striking advances in electronics during recent years have been due to the development of semiconductor devices such as crystal diodes, transistors and integrated circuits. On account of their small size, low power requirements and almost infinite life they are now replacing thermionic valves and it seems likely that before very long technical advances will enable them to take over completely.

Energy bands, conductors and insulators

Modern solid-state theory explains the difference between electrical conductors and insulators in terms of energy levels (p. 208). When atoms are closely packed, as in a solid, the fields due to their positive nuclear charges overlap and the *higher* energy levels are slightly altered by mutual interaction. As a result the individual levels of the various atoms are replaced by *energy bands* shared by all the atoms in the solid. Each band consists of a series of very closely spaced energy levels which electrons can occupy, there being as many levels in a band as there are atoms present. Fig. 14.1 shows how the distinct energy levels of single atoms are modified when atoms come closer together.

Conductors are characterized either by having a partly filled band, Fig. 14.2*a*, or by having a filled band overlapping an empty one so that there is in effect one continuous, partly filled band, Fig. 14.2*b*. In both cases the upper energy levels are empty and

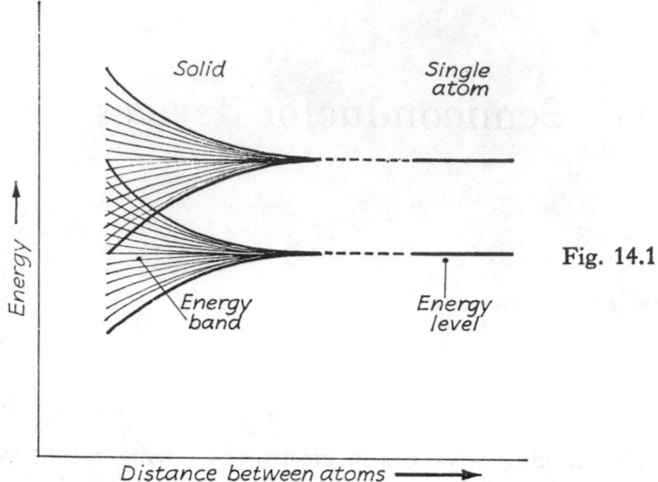

Fig. 14.1

electrons in the highest occupied levels can readily accept from an electric field applied to the conductor the small amounts of energy which enable them to move to empty, slightly higher levels where they are so loosely held that they can drift through the solid as 'free' electrons and form an electric current.

In an insulator there are neither partly filled bands nor overlapping bands. The highest occupied band, called the ***valence band***, is full but the band above it, ***the conduction band***, is empty, Fig. 14.2*c*. To reach the conduction band an electron must gain a certain minimum amount of energy, of the order of several electron-volts. Once in this band it can accept small amounts of energy from an electric field and participate in conduction in the same way as in conductors. However, to bridge the so-called

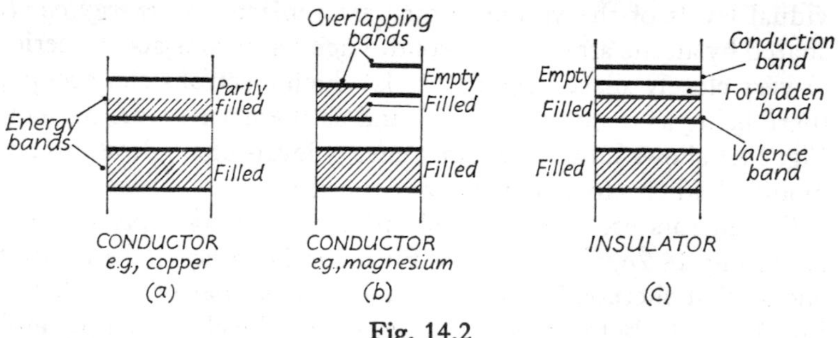

Fig. 14.2

forbidden band between the valence and conduction bands, the energy required is more than can be supplied by electric fields from ordinary sources of potential difference.

Semiconductors

Semiconductors, such as germanium and silicon, resemble insulators but have narrower forbidden bands between the valence band and the conduction band. For germanium an energy of 0·66 eV is required to bridge the forbidden band and for silicon 1·08 eV (both at 27°C).

Consider germanium, atomic number 32. The atom has 32 extranuclear electrons distributed so that the *K*-, *L*- and *M*-levels are complete with 2, 8 and 18 electrons respectively while the *N*-level, with four valence electrons, is incomplete. In a pure germanium crystal each germanium atom shares its four valence electrons with four neighbouring atoms so that each atom has eight *N*-level electrons and the stable configuration of the inert gas krypton. The bonds so formed link the atoms together to form a regular crystal lattice, Fig. 14.3, and are called covalent bonds.

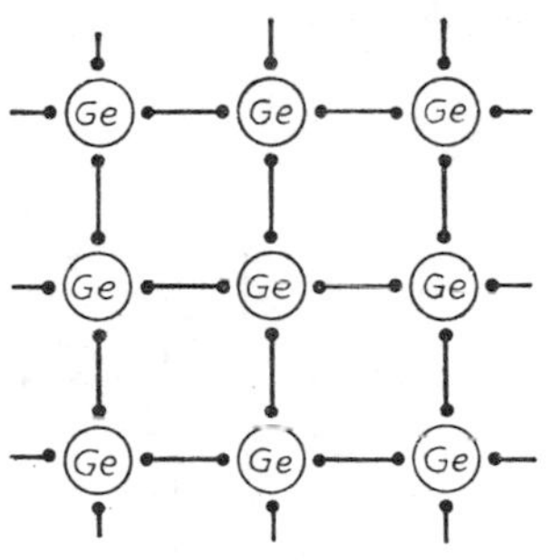

Fig. 14.3

At very low temperatures the valence band in germanium is filled, the conduction band is empty and pure germanium under these conditions is an insulator. At room temperatures a few valence electrons gain sufficient energy from the thermal vibration of surrounding atoms in the crystal to reach the conduction band. When an electric field is applied these thermally energized electrons create a very small current, enough to make germanium slightly conducting. Above 100°C many valence electrons are able to reach the conduction band, and although the conductivity increases sharply it cannot be controlled because the crystal lattice disintegrates. This *intrinsic conductivity* in pure germanium (and pure silicon) is undesirable, and in practice precautions have to be taken to limit the working temperature. Decrease of resistance with increasing temperature is a feature which distinguishes semiconductors from metals.

Silicon, atomic number 14, has complete K- and L-levels and an incomplete M-level with four valence electrons. Its behaviour is similar to that of germanium but it has the advantage of a maximum working temperature of 150°C. However, in the past purification was more difficult and the earliest semiconductor devices were made from germanium.

n-type and p-type germanium

Pure germanium (and pure silicon) can be made semiconducting without destroying the crystal lattice by adding tiny amounts of certain 'impurities'. The impurity introduces a controlled number

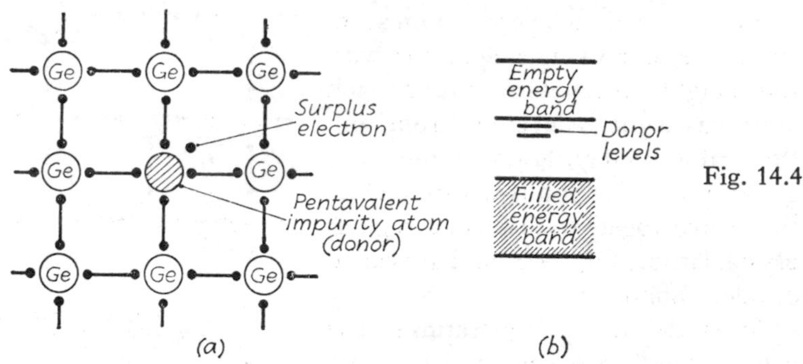

Fig. 14.4

of charge carriers and must be an element which is either pentavalent or trivalent.

Suppose a pentavalent atom, such as phosphorus, arsenic or antimony, is introduced into the lattice of a pure germanium crystal. The impurity atom has five valence electrons but only four are required to form covalent bonds with adjacent tetravalent germanium atoms. One electron from the pentavalent atom is spare, Fig. 14.4*a*, and being loosely held it can take part in conduction when an electric field is applied. The impurity atom is called a *donor* and by donating an electron it becomes positively charged. The 'impure' germanium is called an *n-type* semiconductor because the charge carriers are *negative* electrons.

Every donor atom introduced in the crystal contributes a free electron but the crystal as a whole is electrically neutral.

In terms of energy bands, the donor atom provides *filled* energy levels in the forbidden band of germanium, just below the conduction band, Fig. 14.4*b*. An impurity electron in one of these donor levels can easily acquire from an electric field or incident photons, the small quantity of energy it needs to reach the empty conduction band in germanium.

A trivalent impurity, such as aluminium, gallium or indium, also enables conduction to occur but in a different way. In this case the impurity atom in the crystal has three valence electrons and can only form covalent bonds with three of the four surrounding germanium atoms, Fig. 14.5*a*. One bond is incomplete and

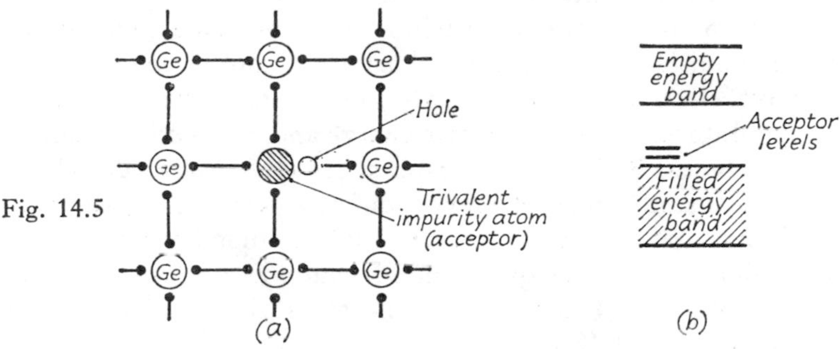

Fig. 14.5

the position of the missing electron is called a ***hole***. If a valence electron in an adjacent germanium atom gains just a small amount of energy it can move and fill the hole. A new hole is then created in the germanium atom and it is as if the hole has moved in the opposite direction to the electron. The germanium atom is left with a positive charge and so it is convenient to think of the hole as an actual positive charge which can take part in conduction and form a 'hole current' when an electric field is applied. The impurity atoms are called *acceptors* because they accept electrons from germanium atoms; as a result they become negatively charged. This type of germanium is called a *p-type* semiconductor since the charge carriers are considered to be *positive* holes. As with n-type material, the total charge in p-type germanium is zero. The notion that moving holes constitute an electric current may seem strange for in fact the current is due to electrons moving from hole to hole. However, the idea makes it easier to understand how transistors work. A hole is rather like one vacant seat in a row of otherwise occupied chairs. If the vacancy is at one end of the row and everyone moves one place towards it, the vacancy appears at the other end. The vacancy (hole) seems to have moved along the row but the motion has really been of the occupants (electrons) of the chairs in the opposite direction.

In the energy band diagram of Fig. 14.5*b*, the acceptor atom is shown as supplying *empty* energy levels in the forbidden band of germanium just above the filled valence band. A valence electron can easily occupy one of these slightly higher levels and create a vacancy in the valence band which makes conduction possible in p-type material.

To sum up, n-type germanium contains fixed pentavalent donor atoms having a positive charge and conduction is due to negative electrons. p-type germanium contains fixed trivalent acceptor atoms having a negative charge and conduction is due to positive holes. Both types of material are electrically neutral.

In the manufacture of semiconducting germanium, the germanium is first purified to 1 part in 10^{10} and then impurity atoms are added to produce the required conductivity. An impurity concentration of 1 part in 10^8 increases the conductivity of germanium about 12 times at 27°C.

Hall effect

This effect depends on the fact that charges moving at right angles to a magnetic field experience a force. It can be used to show that the charge carriers are negative (electrons) in n-type semiconductors and positive (holes) in p-type.

In Fig. 14.6*a* a piece of n-type germanium has a p.d. applied across its ends A, B and a magnetic field acts perpendicular to AB into the plane of the paper. Electrons are moving from B to A and by Fleming's left-hand rule (taking conventional current to be in the direction A to B), they experience a force acting towards the edge X which leaves edge Y with a positive charge. An e.m.f. is thus created between X and Y, X being negative with respect to Y. In p-type material, Fig. 14.6*b*, the force on the positive holes is also towards X but in this case the Hall effect e.m.f. makes X positive with respect to Y. The e.m.f. and its direction may be detected by connecting a sensitive galvanometer between X and Y.

The Hall effect occurs in all metals but in most cases the

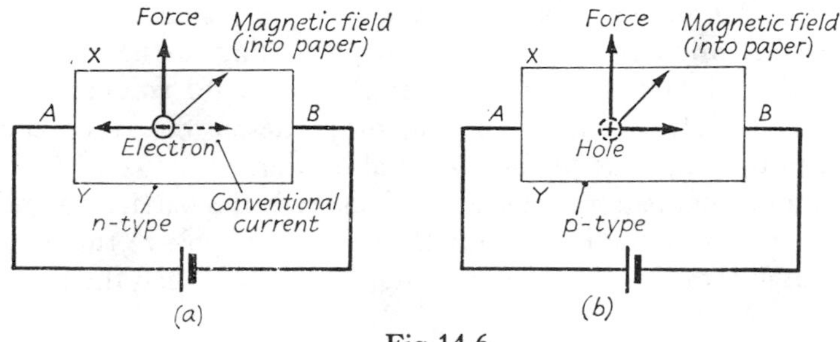

Fig 14.6

e.m.f. is very small and a strong magnetic field is necessary to obtain a measurable indication. Semiconductors show the effect more easily.

The effect also provides a method of measuring magnetic flux.

p–n junction diode

A crystal of germanium (or silicon) with a junction of p- and n-type materials can act as a rectifier. The junction must be grown

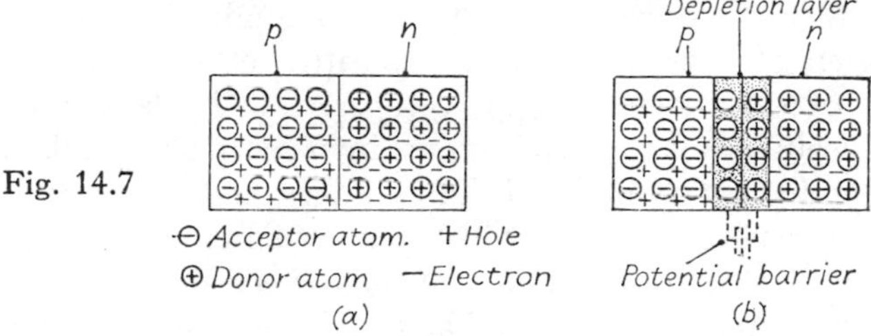

Fig. 14.7

as one crystal so that the lattice is continuous across it; merely having p- and n-type materials in contact is not enough. The action is as follows.

As soon as the p–n junction is formed, electrons from the n-type material diffuse into the p-type to fill its holes and holes from the p-type diffuse into the n-type to be filled by its electrons, Fig. 14.7*a*. The exchange is only momentary since, due to both materials being initially neutral, a narrow region on either side of the junction loses its charge carriers, and static negative acceptor atoms are left in the p-type and static positive donor atoms remain in the n-type. The p-type region of this so-called *depletion layer* becomes negative and the n-type region positive. A *potential barrier* is thus established preventing further flow and behaving like a battery with an e.m.f. of about 0·1 volt connected as in Fig. 14.7*b*. The rectifying properties of the junction are due to the existence of the potential barrier.

If an actual battery whose e.m.f. exceeds the barrier potential is joined across the junction with the positive pole to the p-type material, then the p-type is at a higher potential than the n-type.

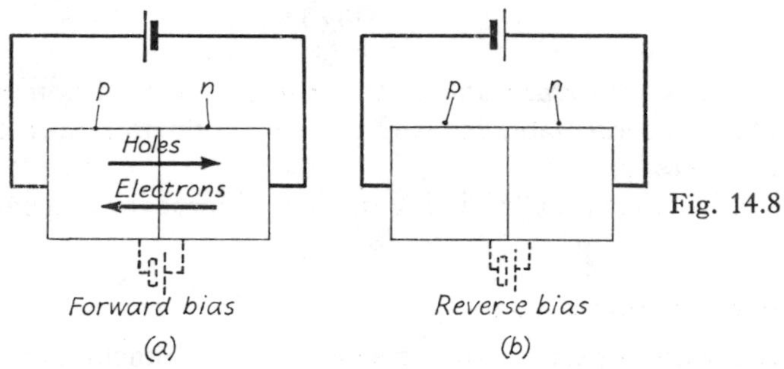

Fig. 14.8

Positive holes again cross the junction from p-type to n-type and electrons pass in the opposite direction, i.e., conduction occurs by the motion of both positive and negative charge carriers, Fig. 14.8*a*. (The process can be compared with electrolysis where both positive and negative ions are involved.) This method of connecting the battery is called 'forward bias' and a current of several milliamperes is obtained with a battery e.m.f. of no more than 0·2 volt. Reversing the polarity of the battery gives 'reverse bias' connection and increases the barrier potential so that very few charge carriers cross the junction, Fig. 14.8*b*. The reverse current may be a few microamperes and is due to intrinsic conductivity.

The characteristic curve for a typical p–n junction diode, Fig. 14.9, shows that it is a non-linear device which can be used as a rectifier on account of its low forward resistance and high reverse resistance. If the reverse voltage exceeds a certain value, the *turn-over voltage*, the crystal structure is destroyed and rectification no longer possible. In this respect silicon diodes are

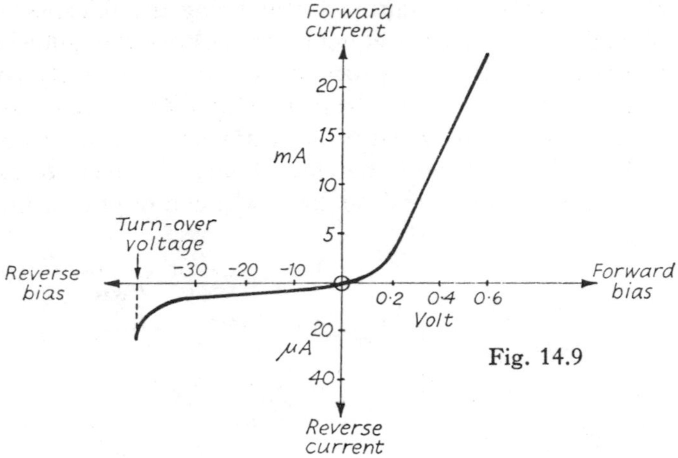

Fig. 14.9

preferable to those made from germanium because of their ability to withstand higher reverse voltages.

The construction of a p–n junction diode is shown in Fig. 14.10. The p–n junction is formed by melting a pellet of a trivalent impurity into a thin slice of n-type germanium (or silicon) in an inert atmosphere. Connections are made to the pellet and to the germanium and the diode is then sealed in a small metal can packed with grease to protect it from moisture.

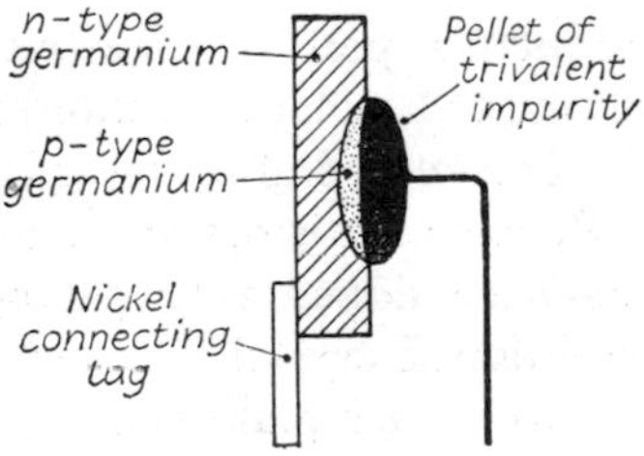

Fig. 14.10

Transistors

The transistor, first made in 1948 by Shockley, Brattain and Bardeen of the Bell Telephone Laboratories, New York, may be regarded as a semiconductor triode. The p–n–p transistor is a sandwich with a very thin wafer of n-type semiconductor called the *base*, between two layers of p-type material, one of which is called the *emitter* and the other the *collector*. In effect it consists of two p–n diodes with a common n-type region. Another arrangement, known as the n–p–n transistor, is also used.

Various techniques are used to manufacture semiconductor devices. *Alloy-junction* transistors are unsuitable for frequencies above about 1 MHz, the limiting factor being the thickness of the base region. For high frequency transistors the diffusion technique is used. Diffusion processes occur more slowly and for this reason can be better controlled. *Alloy-diffused* transistors can be used up to 800 MHz and *planar* transistors which are now mass produced from silicon in batches of several thousand, can be made extremely small and so have a much improved high

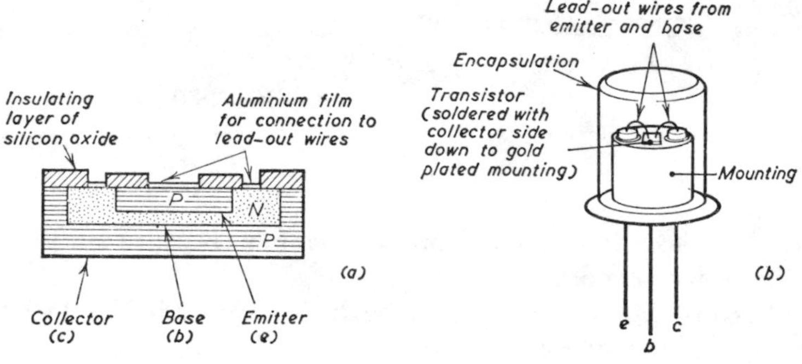

Fig. 14.11

frequency performance (well above 1000 MHz, i.e., 1 GHz). Because the planar technique cannot be used with germanium, the present trend is towards using silicon planar transistors.

Planar transistors are made from a crystal of pure silicon that has been doped with p-type impurity, for a p–n–p transistor. The doped crystal is sliced into thin plates of diameter 2–3 cm and from each plate as many as 6000 transistors can be made. The plate acts as the collectors. Bases are formed for all transistors on the plate by a photographic etching process (using a mask and ultraviolet light) followed by baking in an oven with a little of the required n-type doping impurity. The latter diffuses into the plate to a depth of 3 to 5 micrometres to provide the bases. A similar procedure is followed to form the emitters. A simplified section of one p–n–p transistor is shown in Fig. 14.11(*a*), in practice there are no well-defined demarcation lines between areas and the lines are not straight. After testing, the plate is cut into small squares each having a single transistor and leads attached before encapsulation, Fig. 14.11(*b*).

Transistors can be used for amplification and oscillation and, apart from their applications in radio, television and audio equipment, they are ideally suited for computers, artificial satellites, submarine telephone repeaters, etc., due to their small size and low voltage supply, often less than 9 volts being required. Their disadvantages arise from the risk of breakdown above a certain temperature and the possibility of permanent damage if voltages are exceeded or connected with the wrong polarity.

Action of a transistor

A p–n–p transistor is represented in Fig. 14.12*a* and its symbol in Fig. 14.12*b*. Typical bias potentials are also shown; with respect to the emitter *e*, the base *b* is 0·2 volt negative and the collector *c*, 2 volt negative. The base-emitter p–n boundary is therefore forward biased and positive holes, the charge carriers present in

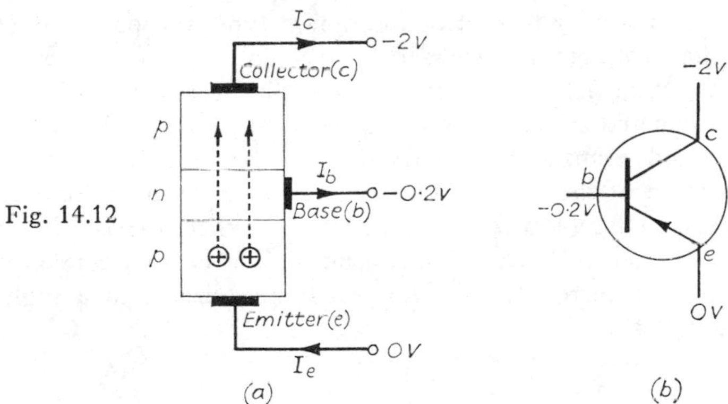

Fig. 14.12

the p-type material of the emitter, are able to cross this boundary into the base because the applied electric field overcomes the barrier potential. At the same time there is a flow of electrons from base to emitter, but since the transistor materials used are such that the concentration of holes in the p-type regions is much greater than the concentration of electrons in the n-type base, only hole flow need be considered. In the base, which is very thin, only a few holes combine with electrons of the n-type material; most cross the base-collector boundary because the collector is negative with respect to the base. Although the collector-base p–n boundary is reverse biased and prevents holes passing from collector to base it allows them to move in the opposite direction.

Holes reaching the collector combine with circuit electrons at the collector terminal and cause a collector current I_c in the external circuit. At the emitter terminal, holes are injected into the emitter by electrons entering the external circuit by the action of the applied voltage. This emitter current I_e is only slightly greater than I_c on account of the small hole-electron recombination in the base. The little recombination which does occur gives rise to a small base current I_b, in the form of electrons flowing into the base from the external circuit. Thus $I_e = I_b + I_c$; if $I_e = 1$ mA, I_c may be 0·98 mA and $I_b = 0{\cdot}02$ mA. In Fig. 14.12*a* the current directions for I_e, I_b and I_c refer to conventional current flow; electrons flow in the opposite directions.

The reason for the terms emitter and collector is evident from the action in the transistor. In the n–p–n transistor, whose behaviour is similar to that of the p–n–p type, the polarities of the applied voltages are reversed, i.e. the collector and base are positive with respect to the emitter, and it is electrons, not holes, that are injected at the emitter and received by the collector.

The word 'transistor' is derived from the 'transfer of resistance' action of the device. The emitter-base circuit is forward biased and so has a low resistance, while the collector-base circuit is reverse biased and has a high resistance. The emitter current is therefore transferred from a low-resistance circuit to a high-resistance circuit.

Transistor as an amplifier

The commonest method of connecting the transistor is known as the *common-* or *grounded-emitter* circuit. In this arrangement the emitter is common to both base and collector circuits, Fig. 14.13*a*, and is sometimes connected to earth, i.e., grounded.

The action of the transistor is as previously described. The collector current I_c is regarded as the output current and the base current I_b as the input current. If the base current is reduced, by increasing R_1 for example, there are fewer replacements for the electrons lost in the base by recombination with holes. As a result the base becomes positively charged and reduces hole current flow. I_c is therefore reduced. In a typical transistor a change in I_b can produce a change 50 times as great in I_c; the *current amplification factor* is said to be 50. A small input *current* to the base thus controls a comparatively large output collector current and an alternating base current would create a large alternating collector current. To obtain an amplified output *voltage*, a suitable load R has to be included in the collector circuit.

The common-emitter transistor circuit can be compared with a simple triode valve circuit, Fig. 14.13*b*. Certain points may be noted.

(*i*) The emitter, base and collector are analogous to the cathode, grid and anode respectively. The emitter, like the

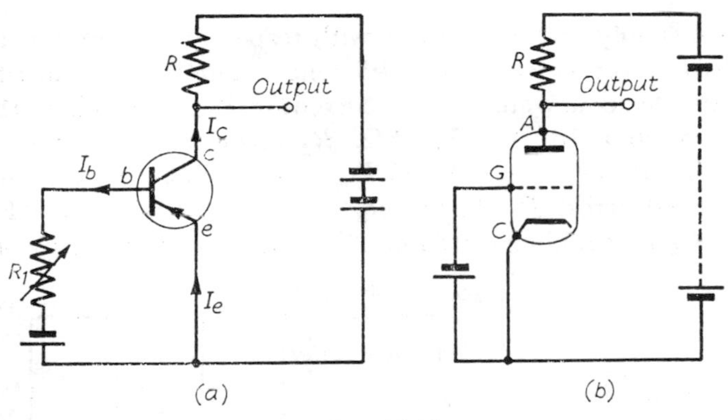

Fig. 14.13

cathode, emits charge carriers and the collector receives them, as does the anode.

(*ii*) Whereas the grid *voltage* controls the anode current in a valve, the base *current* controls the collector current in a transistor. The valve is therefore said to be a voltage-operated device and the transistor a current-operated device.

(*iii*) The supply voltage to the collector of a transistor is only a few volts compared with the 100 volts or more required by the anode of a valve and for the commoner p–n–p transistor it is of the opposite polarity.

In practice it is possible to obtain bias for both the base and the collector from one battery by connecting a resistor R_1 as shown in Fig. 14.14. If the battery supplies 4·5 volts then since

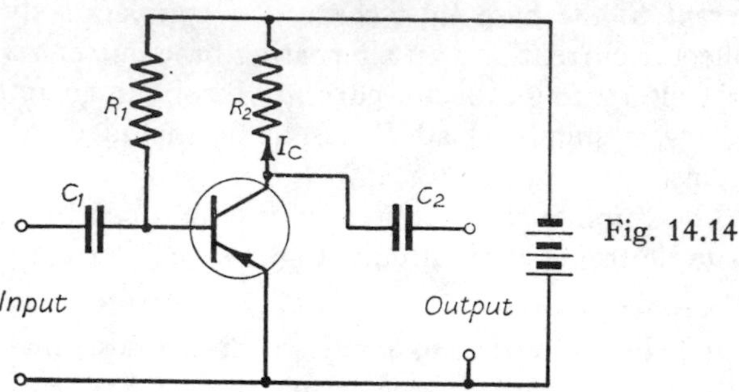

Fig. 14.14

the base is only slightly negative with respect to the emitter, the voltage drop across R_1 is nearly 4·5 volts. Assuming the transistor is to operate about a steady base current of 20 μA, it follows that $R_1 = 4{\cdot}5/(20 \times 10^{-6}) \simeq 220$ kΩ. R_2 forms the load for the amplifier and if $I_c \simeq 1$ mA and $V_{ce} = -2$ volts, 2·5 volts must be dropped across R_2. Hence $R_2 = 2{\cdot}5/(1 \times 10^{-3}) = 2{\cdot}5$ kΩ. C_1 and C_2 are coupling capacitors. This method of obtaining bias

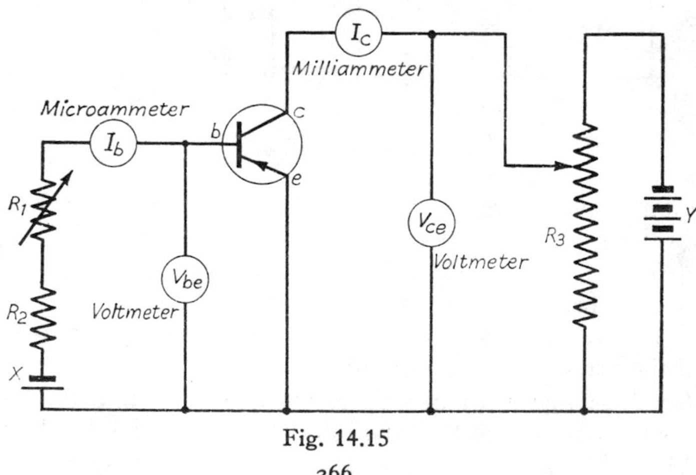

Fig. 14.15

has disadvantages if the temperature varies and other self-stabilizing circuits have been developed.

Transistor characteristics in common-emitter connection

A triode valve has three variables, the grid voltage, the anode voltage and the anode current, and the relationships between these quantities are given by the anode characteristics and the mutual characteristics. Static characteristic curves can also be obtained for a transistor but in this case there are four variables, which, in the common-emitter connection, are the base-emitter voltage V_{be}, the base current I_b, the collector-emitter voltage V_{ce} and the collector current I_c.

A circuit for studying a p–n–p transistor in common-emitter connection is given in Fig. 14.15. Variable resistor R_1 controls I_b and the fixed resistor R_2 is such that when R_1 is zero, I_b has its maximum permissible value for the transistor being used. Both voltmeters are high-resistance types and the batteries X and Y have low voltages. R_3 acts as a potential divider and enables small values of V_{ce} to be applied. Three characteristics are of interest.

1. INPUT CHARACTERISTIC. The collector-emitter voltage (V_{ce}) is kept constant and V_{be} measured for different values of I_b, obtained by varying R_1. A typical curve is shown in Fig. 14.16. The input resistance is obtained from the reciprocal of the slope of the tangent at any point in volt/amp, i.e., $\Delta V_{be}/\Delta I_b$. For a transistor such as the Mullard OC 71, the input resistance has a value between 500 and 1000 ohms. By comparison with a valve, this is very low and is due, as mentioned previously, to the forward bias of the emitter-base.

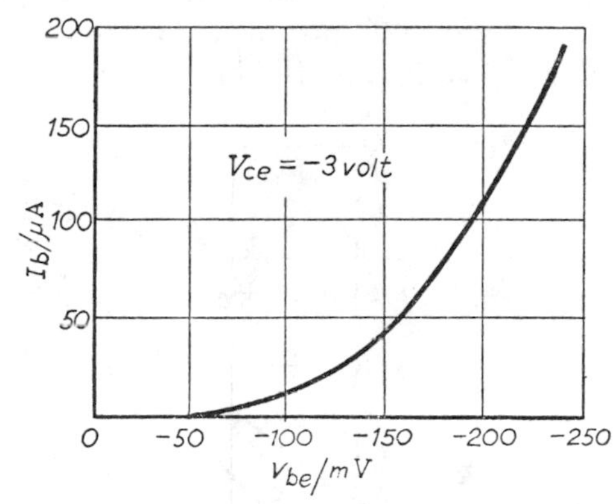

Fig. 14.16

2. OUTPUT CHARACTERISTIC. The base current I_b is fixed at a low value and I_c is measured as V_{ce} is increased by steps, small at first and then greater. This is repeated for different base currents to give a series of curves, Fig. 14.17. If V_{ce} is initially too large the sharp bend or 'knee' in each curve is missed. Normally a transistor is operated beyond the knee where the output

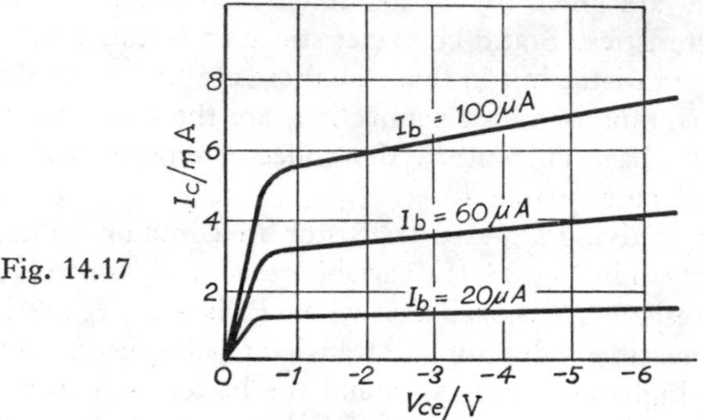

Fig. 14.17

resistance, given by $\Delta V_{ce}/\Delta I_c$ in volt/amp, is high and of the order of 0·5 MΩ. The high value is explained by the reverse bias condition of the collector-base.

3. TRANSFER CHARACTERISTIC. This gives the relationship between the output current I_c and the input current I_b for a fixed value of V_{ce}, Fig. 14.18. The graph is almost a straight line whose

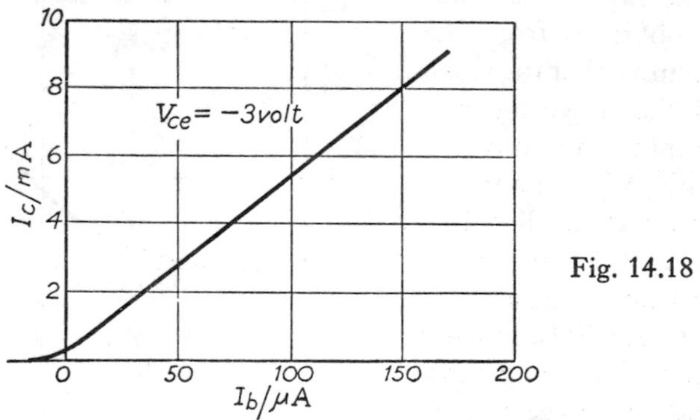

Fig. 14.18

slope, $\Delta I_c/\Delta I_b$, is the current amplification factor in grounded-emitter connection; a value of about 50 is common.

Other semiconductor devices

Many semiconductor devices have been developed in recent years apart from the crystal diode and the transistor. A few will be considered.

1. PHOTOTRANSISTOR. This is a transistor with a light-sensitive base. Its ability to amplify as well gives it an advantage over an ordinary photocell and permits it to be used directly in a circuit to operate a counting or warning mechanism (p. 121).

2. TUNNEL DIODE. Discovered in 1957 by the young Japanese physicist, Leo Esaki, this device consists of a p–n junction made from semiconducting materials heavily doped with impurities. It can amplify or oscillate at frequencies as high as 30,000 MHz and seems likely to replace the transistor for many purposes. It is also much less affected by temperature variations; one tunnel diode can perform the work of several conventional components. A proper explanation of its action requires a knowledge of wave mechanics, but the fact that it does work reveals in a striking manner that electrons do not always behave in a predictable way. In this respect nothing is impossible but some events are more likely than others.

3. SOLAR CELL. A solar cell converts solar energy into electricity directly and consists of a layer, 0·00025 cm thick, of p-type silicon on a slice of n-type silicon. The p-type layer is so thin that light is able to penetrate to the p–n junction and cause the generation of electricity. Silicon solar cells are much more efficient than photovoltaic cells (p. 120) and are used to power the electronic equipment in artificial satellites.

4. SOLID-STATE DETECTOR. The detection of ionizing radiation by this type of detector was mentioned previously (p. 193).

5. THERMISTOR. This is made from semiconducting oxides of iron, nickel and cobalt with small amounts of other substances added. The resistance of one kind of thermistor decreases as the temperature increases, i.e., it has a negative temperature coefficient of resistance. Applications include (*a*) temperature measurement if the resistance of the thermistor is known at

various temperatures, and (*b*) stabilization of the resistance of a circuit by compensation for a resistance increase in other components due to a temperature rise. Compensation is sometimes used in television receiver and transistor radio circuits.

Microelectronics: integrated circuits

Computers and space vehicles both require miniaturization and reliability in their electronic circuits and are responsible for much of the progress in these respects in recent years. In microelectronics a complete circuit is 'engraved' on a crystal of very pure silicon 1 to 2 mm square and 1 mm thick. Silicon has several advantages for use in such 'micro-integrated' circuits, among them the fact that it readily forms a strong insulating skin of oxide.

The manufacturing process is not very different from that used for planar transistors (see p. 262) involving photographic masking, etching and diffusion into the surface of the silicon wafer of n-type and p-type impurities. A network of tiny resistors, capacitors, diodes and transistors is thus created. The resistance of the silicon itself provides resistors and capacitance is provided by layers of silicon sandwiching a film of oxide. On a wafer of silicon, 2–3 cm in diameter, thousands of circuits, e.g. logic gates for a computer, can be made simultaneously.

The step from individual components soldered to connecting wires or to the copper strips of printed circuits, to the integrated circuit, was a tremendous advance in electronics. There appears however, to be yet another step, stated recently by two physicists of the Bell Telephone Laboratories, New York, writing in the *Scientific American*—'For the rather more distant future one may hope to find a new conception that will drastically reduce the numbers of devices now needed to perform a given function. One has the feeling that present circuit theory, tied as it is to the familiar circuit elements, fails to provide system functions directly and simply as possible. It should be possible to develop a new class of functional devices that use basic properties of matter to obtain results now achieved by sheer multiplication of devices.'[1]

[1] *Scientific American*, Vol. 213, No. 5, 1965.

Appendix 1

TABLE OF THE ELEMENTS

Atomic number	*Element*	*Symbol*	*Atomic number*	*Element*	*Symbol*
1	Hydrogen	H	25	Manganese	Mn
2	Helium	He	26	Iron	Fe
3	Lithium	Li	27	Cobalt	Co
4	Beryllium	Be	28	Nickel	Ni
5	Boron	B	29	Copper	Cu
6	Carbon	C	30	Zinc	Zn
7	Nitrogen	N	31	Gallium	Ga
8	Oxygen	O	32	Germanium	Ge
9	Fluorine	F	33	Arsenic	As
10	Neon	Ne	34	Selenium	Se
11	Sodium	Na	35	Bromine	Br
12	Magnesium	Mg	36	Krypton	Kr
13	Aluminium	Al	37	Rubidium	Rb
14	Silicon	Si	38	Strontium	Sr
15	Phosphorus	P	39	Yttrium	Y
16	Sulphur	S	40	Zirconium	Zr
17	Chlorine	Cl	41	Niobium	Nb
18	Argon	A	42	Molybdenum	Mo
19	Potassium	K	43	*Technetium*	Tc
20	Calcium	Ca	44	Ruthenium	Ru
21	Scandium	Sc	45	Rhodium	Rh
22	Titanium	Ti	46	Palladium	Pd
23	Vanadium	V	47	Silver	Ag
24	Chromium	Cr	48	Cadmium	Cd

APPENDIX 1

Atomic number	*Element*	*Symbol*	*Atomic number*	*Element*	*Symbol*
49	Indium	In	77	Iridium	Ir
50	Tin	Sn	78	Platinum	Pt
51	Antimony	Sb	79	Gold	Au
52	Tellurium	Te	80	Mercury	Hg
53	Iodine	I	81	Thallium	Tl
54	Xenon	Xe	82	Lead	Pb
55	Caesium	Cs	83	Bismuth	Bi
56	Barium	Ba	84	Polonium	Po
57	Lanthanum	La	85	*Astatine*	At
58	Cerium	Ce	86	Radon	Rn
59	Praseodymium	Pr	87	*Francium*	Fr
60	Neodymium	Nd	88	Radium	Ra
61	Promethium	Pm	89	Actinium	Ac
62	Samarium	Sm	90	Thorium	Th
63	Europium	Eu	91	Protactinium	Pa
64	Gadolinium	Gd	92	Uranium	U
65	Terbium	Tb	93	*Neptunium*	Np
66	Dysprosium	Dy	94	*Plutonium*	Pu
67	Holmium	Ho	95	*Americium*	Am
68	Erbium	Er	96	*Curium*	Cm
69	Thulium	Tm	97	*Berkelium*	Bk
70	Ytterbium	Yb	98	*Californium*	Cf
71	Lutetium	Lu	99	*Einsteinium*	E
72	Hafnium	Hf	100	*Fermium*	Fm
73	Tantalum	Ta	101	*Mendelevium*	Mv
74	Tungsten	W	102	*Nobelium*	No
75	Rhenium	Re	103	*Lawrencium*	Lw
76	Osmium	Os			

Elements shown in italic are made artificially and do not occur naturally. Those with atomic numbers greater than 92 are the *transuranic* elements.

Appendix 2

SOME PHYSICAL CONSTANTS
(to three figures)

N_A	The Avogadro constant	$6{\cdot}02 \times 10^{23}$ mol^{-1}
F	The Faraday constant	$9{\cdot}65 \times 10^{4}$ C mol^{-1}
e	Electronic charge	$1{\cdot}60 \times 10^{-19}$ C
e/m	Electron charge to mass ratio	$1{\cdot}76 \times 10^{11}$ C kg^{-1}
m	Electron rest mass	$9{\cdot}11 \times 10^{-31}$ kg 0·000549 a.m.u. 0·511 MeV
c	Velocity of light	$3{\cdot}00 \times 10^{8}$ m s^{-1}
h	Planck's constant	$6{\cdot}63 \times 10^{-34}$ J s
R_h	Rydberg's constant	$1{\cdot}10 \times 10^{7}$ m^{-1}

Appendix 3

FURTHER READING

Only a short reading list is given but it provides a representative selection of modern books. The student will find extensive and detailed bibliographies in the works marked with an asterisk; many of the others supply references. Most of the textbooks are more advanced.

1. Textbooks

Agger, L. T., *Principles of Electronics* (Macmillan, 1958)

Buckingham, H., and Price, E. M., *Principles of Electronics* (Cleaver-Hume, 1958)

*Caro, D. E., McDonell, J. A., and Spicer, B. M., *Modern Physics* (Arnold, 1962)

Glasstone, S., *Sourcebook of Atomic Energy* (Van Nostrand, 1958)

Physical Science Study Committee (P.S.S.C.), *Physics* (Harrap, 1960)

Rogers, E. M., *Physics for the Inquiring Mind* (Oxford, 1960)

*Smith, M. S., *Modern Physics* (Longmans, 1960)

Tolansky, S., *Introduction to Atomic Physics* (Longmans, 1964)

2. Other useful books and articles

Anderson, D. L., *The Discovery of the Electron* (Van Nostrand, 1964)

Andrade, E. N. da C., *An Approach to Modern Physics* (Bell, 1960)
Rutherford and the Nature of the Atom (Heinemann, 1965)—Science Study Series

Bairsto, A., 'Lasers' (*School Science Review*, June 1965, No. 160)

Carter, H., *An Introduction to the Cathode Ray Oscilloscope* (Philips Technical Library, 1960)

Chew, G. F., Gell-Mann, M., and Rosenfeld, A. H., 'Strongly Interacting Particles' (*Scientific American*, Vol. 210, February 1964)

Duquesne, M., *Matter and Antimatter* (Arrow Books, Ltd, Hutchinson, 1960)

Fink, D. G., and Lutyens, D. M., *The Physics of Television* (Heinemann, 1961)—Science Study Series

Fishlock, D., *The New Materials* (Murray, 1967)

Frisch, D. H., and Thorndike, A. M., *Elementary Particles* (Van Nostrand, 1964)

Hoffmann, B., *The Strange Story of the Quantum* (Dover Publications, 1959)

Hughes, D. J., *The Neutron Story* (Heinemann, 1960)—Science Study Series

Mann, M., *Revolution in Electricity* (Murray, 1962)

Massey, H., *The New Age in Physics* (Elek Books, 1960)

Messell, H. (editor), *Selected Lectures in Modern Physics* (Macmillan, 1960)

Müller, E. W., 'Atoms Visualized' (*Scientific American*, Vol. 196, June 1957)

Pierce, J. R., *Electrons and Waves* (Heinemann, 1965)—Science Study Series

Redman, L. A., *Nuclear Energy* (Oxford, 1963)

Wright, S. (editor), *Classical Scientific Papers* (Mills and Boon, 1964)

Annual Reports of the United Kingdom Atomic Energy Authority. These contain interesting information and can be obtained from the Public Relations Branch, U.K.A.E.A., 11 Charles II St., London, S.W.1

Mullard Minibooks number 3—*Semiconductor Devices* (Mullard Educational Service)

Basic Electronics (six parts) (The Technical Press, 1962)

Scientific American. Many interesting articles appear in this magazine and a list of offprints can be obtained from W. H. Freeman & Co., 48 Upper Thames St., London, E.C.4

Answers

Chapter 1. Atomic nature of matter and electricity

2. 11×10^{-10} m
3. $6{\cdot}1 \times 10^{23}$ mol^{-1}
4. **(a)** 3×10^{-23} g **(b)** $3{\cdot}9 \times 10^{-10}$ m
7. 2006 V
8. $1{\cdot}32 \times 10^{-5}$ m; $\pm 1{\cdot}6 \times 10^{-16}$ C
9. $1{\cdot}01 \times 10^{-19}$ C
10. 3; $19{\cdot}62$ m s^{-2}

Chapter 2. The electron

2. **(a)** 20 kΩ (b) 250 V
3. $1{\cdot}60 \times 10^{-19}$ J $3{\cdot}2 \times 10^{-14}$ J; $6{\cdot}19 \times 10^{6}$ m s^{-1}
4. **(a)** $0{\cdot}385 \times 10^{-15}$ N
(b) $4{\cdot}22 \times 10^{14}$ m s^{-2} **(c)** $5{\cdot}63 \times 10^{6}$ m s^{-1}
5. $2{\cdot}65 \times 10^{7}$ m s^{-1}; $3{\cdot}2 \times 10^{-4}$ W
6. **(a)** $1{\cdot}88 \times 10^{7}$ m s^{-1} (b) $7{\cdot}1 \times 10^{-3}$ T
7. $f = Be/2\pi m$; 0·11 m
8. $1{\cdot}76 \times 10^{11}$ C kg^{-1}
9. $3{\cdot}75 \times 10^{7}$ m s^{-1}; circle of radius 0·213 m; $3{\cdot}75 \times 10^{4}$ V m^{-1}
10. $5{\cdot}2 \times 10^{-4}$ m

Chapter 3. Cathode ray oscilloscope

3. **(i)** 5 waves **(ii)** $\frac{1}{2}$ wave
5. Deflection of 2·2 cm

Chapter 4. Rectification

4. Step-up 1:2

Chapter 5. Amplification

3. (a) 24 (b) $R_a = 30$ kΩ; $\mu = 40$; $g_m = 1{\cdot}33$ mA per volt
4. 5·4 V
6. 500/Ω; 10/πΩ
7. 300

Chapter 6. Radio: oscillation: detection

4. (c) 2·25 MHz; 711·5 kHz

Chapter 7. Photoelectric emission

2. (a) 200 kHz (b) $1{\cdot}32 \times 10^{-28}$ J (c) 3×10^{33} photons/s
3. $1{\cdot}5 \times 10^{20}$ photons/s
4. $4{\cdot}125 \times 10^{-7}$ m
5. (a) 1·5 eV (b) $3{\cdot}5 \times 10^{14}$ Hz
6. $8{\cdot}8 \times 10^{5}$ m s^{-1}
7. $5{\cdot}1 \times 10^{14}$ Hz
8. $0{\cdot}44 \times 10^{-19}$ J
9. (a) 4×10^{-15} V s (b) $6{\cdot}4 \times 10^{-34}$ J (c) 1·5 eV
10. $6{\cdot}64 \times 10^{-34}$ J s

Chapter 8. X-rays

1. $8{\cdot}5 \times 10^{7}$ m s^{-1}
2. (a) $6{\cdot}25 \times 10^{15}$ electrons/s (b) $2{\cdot}4 \times 10^{-16}$ J
3. 5·04 mA; $1{\cdot}6 \times 10^{-14}$ J; $1{\cdot}88 \times 10^{8}$ m s^{-1}
6. $1{\cdot}2 \times 10^{-10}$ m
7. $3{\cdot}9 \times 10^{18}$ Hz; X-rays
8. 777 kV

Chapter 9. Conduction in gases: positive rays: isotopes

3. $^{35}Cl : ^{37}Cl = 3{\cdot}35 : 1$
4. (a) $3{\cdot}27 \times 10^{27}$ electrons (b) $2{\cdot}13 \times 10^{-18}$

Chapter 10. Radioactivity

2. Mass number changes by 4, atomic number unaltered
3. (a) 3 (b) $\frac{1}{8}$ (c) $\frac{63}{64}$
4. (a) 4866 years (b) $12\frac{1}{2}$ hours
5. (a) 2:1 (b) 1:1 (c) 1:16
6. $3{\cdot}36 \times 10^{22}$ atoms
7. $5{\cdot}7 \times 10^{15}$ particles/s
10. 33 days
11. 10,150 years

Chapter 11. Radioactivity measurements

1. $2{\cdot}3 \times 10^{-14}$ A
7. 0·11 cm^{-1}

Chapter 12. Structure of the atom

1. $2{\cdot}4 \times 10^{35}$:1

3. A—0·648 μm; B—0·480 μm; C—0·428 μm; D—0·405 μm

4. **(a)** 4·9 eV; 6·7 eV; 8·8 eV; 10·4 eV
(b) 10·4 eV
(c) **(i)** 5 eV, $(5-4{\cdot}9) = 0{\cdot}1$ eV
(ii) 10 eV, $(10-4{\cdot}9) = 5{\cdot}1$ eV, $(10-6{\cdot}7) = 3{\cdot}3$ eV, $(10-8{\cdot}8) = 1{\cdot}2$ eV, $(10-2 \times 4{\cdot}9) = 0{\cdot}2$ eV
(d) **(i)** absorbed and disappears
(ii) passes through atom

5. **(i)** 5 eV, 3 eV, 2 eV
(ii) 6 eV, 5 eV, 4 eV, 3 eV, 2 eV, 1 eV

6. If E eV is energy of ground level, another two levels of energies $(E + 1{\cdot}66)$ eV and $(E + 3{\cdot}66)$ eV account for spectral lines.

7. **(a)** $6{\cdot}6 \times 10^{-38}$ m **(b)** $1{\cdot}2 \times 10^{-10}$ m

Chapter 13. Nuclear reactions

2. 2·79 MeV released

3. $2E/103$

5. **(a)** $2{\cdot}4 \times 10^{7}$ m s^{-1} **(b)** $0{\cdot}67 \times 10^{7}$ m s^{-1}

6. 1 a.m.u.

7. $3{\cdot}1 \times 10^{16}$

8. m

9. $\frac{48}{169}$

Index

INDEX

INDEX

INDEX

INDEX

INDEX